CW00665729

WARSHIP 2002-2003

WARSHIP 2002-2003

Edited by Antony Preston

CONWAY MARITIME PRESS

Frontispiece:
The destroyer HMS Oracle *at sea during the First World War.* Oracle *was one of the very numerous 'M' class, of which over a hundred were built in a number of variations on the basic design, and which formed the backbone of the British destroyer fleet during the conflict. Early in the morning of 12 August 1917 she rammed the Germand minelaying submarine U-44 near Utsire, an effective anti-submarine tactic that claimed over 20 of the 187 U-boats sunk during the war.* Oracle's *bows were severely damaged, but the U-boat was sunk with all hands.*

© Conway Maritime Press 2003

All rights reserved. No part of this book may be produced, stored in a retrieval system, or transmitted in any form, without the prior permission of the publisher.

First published in Great Britain in 2003 by
Conway Maritime Press,
64, Brewery Road,
London, N7 9NT.
www.conway maritime.com

member of **Chrysalis** Books plc

9 8 7 6 5 4 3 2 1

Cataloguing in Publication
A catalogue record of this title is available on request from the British Library.

ISBN 0 85177 926 3

Set in 9^1/$_2$ on 10^1/$_2$ Goudy.

All illustrations Chrysalis Images except where indicated.
The assistance of Rachel Silverson and John Fletcher of the Isle of Wight museum for help with photographs of the Argentine destroyer *Mendoza* is gratefully acknowledged.

Typesetting and layout by Stephen Dent
Printed and bound in Spain.

CONTENTS

EDITORIAL

This twenty-fifth volume of *Warship* appears at a time when new technology is transforming the major navies and some of that technology is likely to be tested in war all too soon. It is salutary to look back at some of the prophecies which were so confidently promoted. (Something that journalists and historians need to do at least every five years.) In 1982 it was widely predicted that the large surface warship was obsolescent, yet only two decades later six European navies are building large air defence ships, and the Royal Navy has begun the process of acquiring two 60,000-tonne aircraft carriers. In the second half of the 19th Century it was the ram, based on sloppy interpretation of the Battle of Lissa in 1866, followed closely by the 'torpedo boat scare', which committed the sin of crediting new technology with much more than it could deliver. It is hard to believe that the existence of these frail craft would transform both sides of the English Channel, as stone and concrete breakwaters enclosed harbours to allow the mounting of searchlights and guns to protect shipping taking refuge.

This does not exempt *Warship* from looking at abandoned projects. More often than not, they shed light on contemporary preoccupations. It is not enough to ask 'What idiot thought this one up?'. As the decades pass it becomes harder to get into the minds of contemporary administrators and designers, and it is part of *Warship*'s remit to present the reasons for starting design projects. What is not built is often as revealing as ships that get built.

Another trap for the unwary is ostensibly authoritative 'horse's mouth' information. I was once assured by someone who had been a stoker in the old carrier *Ark Royal* that she and her half-sister *Eagle* had started life as suspended Lion-class battleships. His explanation was that the 'Ark' was 'much more a battleship than a carrier below the waterline'. Across the Atlantic similar myths attached themselves like barnacles to the design-history of the Midway-class carriers. Large ships like carriers often had similar powerplants to contemporary capital ships, but that is where the similarity ends.

Although this volume has been delayed, not least by the Editor's spell in hospital, we hope that *Warship* readers will regard the wait as worthwhile. The contributors, on whom *Warship*'s quality depends, have done us proud. We rely for the large part on long-serving contributors, but *Warship* is not a 'closed shop', and we welcome both comment and new contributors.

Iain McCallum looks at the origins of the 'shell scandal' which has caused endless controversy since the Battle of Jutland in 1916. This first part traces the Royal Navy's hunt for effective fuzing for its heavy shells after the Bombardment of Alexandria in 1882. This is the first searching analysis of the subject, with no over-simplified offer of scapegoats. Readers must contain their curiosity until Part 2 appears in *Warship 2003-2004*.

John Jordan continues his look at the French Navy 'between the Wars', with his usual detailed examination. This time he has chosen the unusual seaplane carrier/aircraft transport *Commandant Teste*, a vessel which embodied many advanced ideas but sadly never fulfilled her designed function in wartime. The author's drawings as always add to the quality of his writing.

To many of us the 'Battle'-class destroyers were among the finest of the Royal Navy's post-1945 flotillas, but George Moore shows how much opposition there was to the design. Many senior officers, notably the Navy's leading 'destroyer man', Admiral Cunningham, thought they were too big and underarmed, a classic example of how difficult it is to discern changes in technology if they are taking place around you. Today we know (or ought to) that the powerful anti-aircraft armament of the 'Battles' could only be achieved on a hull much larger than the wartime 'Emergency' designs. Although in one sense an interim design, they were an important step towards the Daring class and the multi-role fleet escort which eventually replaced the classic destroyer.

Pierre Hervieux continues his exhaustive series on Kriegsmarine minor warships with a detailed study of the activities of the *Raumboote* or 'R-boats'. Although often overshadowed by the reputation of the *schnellboote* or E-boats, these much more numerous craft provided doughty opponents for the Royal Navy's Coastal Forces in many bitterly fought encounters. At times the actions resembled those of Nelson's day, with small craft closing to point-blank range. The contribution of 'Costly Farces' to the Allied victory at sea may be disputed in some quarters, but with opponents such as these no-one can doubt their bravery.

John Brooks gives another unusual insight into the evolution of the Admiralty fire control tables, a vital element in the improvement of long-range gunnery which began in the Edwardian Royal Navy and continued to the end of the battleship era after 1945. Understanding of such arcane matters is vital to any student of battlefleet tactics, and this lucid account will help many to comprehend what went into the effort to 'hit first and hit fast'. The great advances in Royal Navy gunnery up to 1916 were, of course, largely frustrated by the fuzing problems discussed earlier in this issue. The feature also draws attention to the drawbacks of the celebrated 'partnership' between the Admiralty and the British armaments industry. While such a link can yield spectacular results, there is always a risk that industry will skew procurement to suit its own priorities. One cannot help but recall that the role of the Principal Naval Overseer in shipyards has always been to ensure that the customer's requirements were not overlooked!

The great Tyneside armament and shipbuilding company Armstrongs was in the vanguard of Britain's commanding lead in the design and construction of warships for export in the later years of the 19th Century. Peter Brook looks at the work done for the Italian Navy, both in direct construction and support of local shipbuilding. In fact the Italian Navy had a very British look about it until the end of the First World War, and there was a lively dialogue between the two countries' armament manufacturers. Although Armstrongs' works at Pozzuoli, near Naples, did not last the course, Vickers' investment in the Oder-Terni-Orlando works is commemorated by the very progressive modern firm Oto Melara, based at La Spezia.

In a rare incursion into the realm of Latin American naval policy, Guillermo J Montenegro looks at Argentinean efforts to create a powerful navy in the 1920s. The rivalry of the 'ABC' navies (Argentina, Brazil, and Chile) generated many unorthodox warships, but the three countries can be grateful that their expensive fleets never fought one another in the twentieth century. The rivalry does, however, provide wargamers with endless harmless amusement.

In his exhaustive study of anti-submarine warfare in the First World War, David K Brown shows convincingly that there is no justification for claims that the U-boat was beaten by the narrowest of margins in November 1918, or that a renewed onslaught on shipping was likely if the war had continued into 1919. The 'crunch' was in the spring of 1917, and it is hard for today's students of naval history to understand the appalling destruction of lives and ships before the introduction of convoy. As in the Second World War, the victors owed an incalculable debt to those merchant seamen, nationals and neutrals, who never refused to sail no matter how terrifying the odds.

Warship concludes by following its traditional format, with 'Warship Notes', book reviews, and 'Navies in Review'. The latter cannot claim to be exhaustive, but it shows how navies across the world are changing. There is a frenzy of new construction, some of it reflecting the emergence of new maritime states after the breakup of old power blocs, and some it replacement of obsolete tonnage. There is also a brisk trade in second-hand ships, particularly to small nations needing to conserve offshore fisheries and other natural resources.

General Guidelines for Contributors

Feature Articles
Warship welcomes articles and documents on naval subjects in the period since 1860 covering such topics as: warship development and construction, modern refurbishment and reconstruction, gunnery technology, maritime strategy, naval battles and campaigns, fighting tactics, naval infrastructure, maritime art and nautical archaeology.

Text is preferably supplied as a double-spaced typescript on single sides of paper and be accompanied by an electronic version on disc in a text-only format. Accompanying illustrations, plans, maps and photographs are most welcome.

The ideal size of an article is between 3,500 and 10,000 words. Both longer and shorter articles are welcome, but articles must be submitted complete: publication of articles proposed as multiple instalments will not begin until all the parts are complete and in the hands of the Editor.

Warship Notes and Naval Books of the Year
Notes between a few hundred words in length up to two thousand are welcome as are book reviews of three hundred to a thousand words. We are also interested in receiving information related to naval research facilities and new or modified permanent exhibitions.

All submissions, queries and correspondence should be sent by mail to

The Managing Editor,
Warship,
Conway Maritime Press,
64 Brewery Road,
London   N7 9NT,
England.

Antony Preston

THE RIDDLE OF THE SHELLS, 1914-18

The Approach to War, 1882-1914

Rivers of ink have been spilt in explaining the failure of British heavy shells at Jutland in 1916. Here, for the first time, **Iain McCallum** that shows the origin and history of that failure, analysing the interaction of chemistry, ballistics, industrial capability and human shortcomings in the story. He begins a three-part series with the story of the pre-war developments in shell-types and explosives.

During the halcyon years of the Pax Britannica the Royal Navy was rarely put to the test of battle, and minor engagements were welcomed as a diversion from the routine of exercises and 'showing the flag'. One such took place in 1882, when Colonel Arabi Pasha led a nationalist insurrection in Egypt against colonial rule. Europeans were attacked, and British and French fleets were despatched to Alexandria to protect them. As the riots continued, Arabi's soldiers set about strengthening the seaward fortifications of the city, which were defended by an assortment of Armstrong rifled muzzle-loading (RML) weapons with some more modern rifled breech-loading (RBL) guns from Krupp. Since these presented a clear threat to the allied ships lying offshore, the British Admiral Seymour sought and obtained approval to destroy the guns and earthworks, and, the French having departed, the British squadron proceeded to subject the forts to a ten-hour bombardment.

It was the navy's first action of any significance since the Crimean War and the last fought with muzzle-loading guns. Although in the end successful, it raised disturbing questions about the effectiveness of the fleet's gunfire. At such close range it was hardly possible for the ships to miss, despite the clouds of gunsmoke which obscured their aim, and the forts were engulfed in spectacular shell bursts. The impact of the bombardment, however, was surprisingly small. 'The fleet,' recalled Captain Percy Scott, 'fired in all 3000 rounds at the forts and as far as the enemy's guns were concerned made ten hits.' Captains J A Fisher and A K Wilson found that although 'our fire was accurate…the batteries appear to have been silenced more because the men were driven from their guns than because the guns were actually disabled or the earthworks demolished.' According to a more recent account: '…over fifty per cent of shells either failed to burst, burst prematurely or split on striking… only about one-third of the squadron ammunition was suitable for fortress attack, the bulk being armour-piercing Palliser shells with a small

bursting charge. Such common shell with a heavy bursting charge as could be served out had the Pettman percussion fuze of War Office design, and this failed to function in a lamentable way…' [1]

These results confirmed the reservations of many naval officers about the guns and ammunition being supplied to the fleet by the royal ordnance factories. Since the Crimean War, Woolwich Arsenal had been under the control of the Ordnance Committee of the War Office, and between 1863 and 1880 the navy, like the army, had remained wedded to the muzzle-loading system of artillery. Thereafter, researchers in France, Britain and Germany introduced revolutionary changes affecting each component of the artillery round, viz the shell with its bursting charge, the propellant to send the shell on its way and the fuze and primer to explode the shell in the right manner and at the right time. These brought to an end the long reign of gunpowder as the sole propellant and bursting charge in artillery ammunition, and in its place a new explosives industry came into being, dependent on dynamite-related technology.

In 1886 Paul Vieille of the Ecole Polytechnique produced his *Poudre Blanche Nouvelle*, a propellant based on nitrocellulose which produced significantly less smoke than gunpowder while imparting up to five times more energy to the projectile. Shortly afterwards the inventor of dynamite, Alfred Nobel, patented a smokeless powder based on a combination of nitrocellulose and nitroglycerine which he called 'ballistite'. At Woolwich Frederick Abel and George Dewar collaborated on a propellant of similar composition to which they gave the name 'cordite', and after a legal battle with Nobel over patents this was duly adopted for British service shells. By gradually increasing the pressure behind the projectile as it travelled up the barrel of the gun, the new propellants enabled higher velocities to be achieved, but they also required gun barrels to be long and tapering, and so led to the abandonment of the muzzle-loader.

As the so-called smokeless propellants were matched by stronger shell casings, the authorities redoubled their efforts to supplant the old black powder bursting charge with some form of high explosive carrying the destructive power of dynamite. The difficulty was that shells filled with high explosive could not be subjected to the stress of firing from a gun without incurring the risk of a premature explosion. From the United States came a possible solution in the shape of the Zalinski dynamite gun, which used compressed air as the propelling medium to minimise the shock of discharge, but this was cumbersome and inaccurate and soon given up when a more practical alternative presented itself.

Again the critical discovery was made in France, where the chemist Eugene Turpin came up with the idea of heating phenol or picric acid, a substance widely used in the dyeing industry, and pouring the resultant yellow treacle directly into the shell. Turpin claimed not only that his explosive was much more powerful than gunpowder, but that by employing a 'retarded fuze' a shell filled with it could be made to carry through armour plate before detonating. The relevance of this for naval purposes was obvious, and when in 1885 Turpin submitted

his findings to the French ministry of war they were taken up with such alacrity that by the year's end projectiles filled with the new explosive (dubbed 'melinite' after the Greek for honey, 'meli', which it was thought to resemble) were being put into production.

Turpin was made a Chevalier of the Legion of Honour and paid 250,000 francs on the understanding that until the French arsenals had achieved a clear lead in the manufacture of melinite he was not to divulge its secret to foreigners. However, in May 1888, tempted by the opportunities presented by legislation liberalising the export of munitions, he demonstrated his shells filled with melinite at the siege artillery range at Lydd, on Romney Marsh, in the presence of Andrew Noble of Armstrongs, Frederick Abel and Captain Fisher of the Admiralty; later that year Armstrongs sought and obtained the approval of the War Office to pay Turpin royalties for the use of his patents.

At the bombardment of Alexandria Captain Fisher had commanded the battleship *Inflexible*, which carried four of the latest Armstrong 80-ton RML guns firing 1800lb projectiles, but over the next few years the advantages of breech-loading in terms of efficiency and ease of

The aftermath of the bombardment of Alexandria in 1882, showing RMLs blown from their mountings. While this photograph suggests an effective bombardment, the Royal Navy was in fact disappointed with the results of their ten-hour bombardment.

working became increasingly apparent. Aware that the French and Russian navies were going over to breech-loading, Fisher chafed at the conservatism of the War Office : 'If,' he grumbled, 'the Navy had been free to buy in the market and had not been under the heel of Woolwich, we should long ago have had steel breech-loaders...' Never one to let the grass grow under his feet, the thrusting young officer was soon in a position to put his ideas into practice.

During the next thirty years Fisher was to exert an influence over the Royal Navy few individuals have exerted before or since. His reforms affected every aspect of the naval scene, but were calculated above all to improve the fleet's firepower. Appointed to command the gunnery training ship *Excellent*, he was shocked to find practice still being carried out with smooth-bore guns which he replaced with modern weapons. Subsequently, he kept abreast of the latest research in ordnance, as in submarines, torpedoes and mines. Fisher was a relentless critic of government establishments, resentful of what he saw as the over-dominant influence of the army at Woolwich and conscious of the fact that more often than not new ideas originated with commercial initiatives outside the services. For this reason he maintained cordial relations with Sir William Armstrong and his colleagues at the Elswick Ordnance Company, who were constantly breaking new ground in warship design and the development of guns and projectiles.

In 1886 Fisher became DNO (director of naval ordnance) and embarked on a campaign to take over from the War Office responsibility for the supply of naval guns and ammunition. He believed the gunnery needs of the navy to be essentially different from those of the army, and thought those needs more likely to be met by Armstrongs than by Woolwich. It was at his behest that the Admiralty turned to Elswick for the supply of 4.7in and 6in quick-firing guns (utilising the new smokeless propellants), and in 1891 a Naval Ordnance Department was established at the Admiralty through which the navy asserted its right to make its own arrangements, relying on the private companies rather than Woolwich Arsenal for weapons and munitions. The activities of this department and its dealings with the trade were to influence strongly the development of naval gunnery before and during the First World War.

During the 1890s the hegemony of Armstrongs in the production of ordnance and armour plate for warships was challenged by other armament concerns, notably Vickers, where responsibility for the design of guns and projectiles lay with the firm's youngest director, Lieutenant Trevor Dawson. An outstanding naval officer, Dawson had graduated with distinction from HMS *Excellent*, where he was appointed instructor in gunnery before being selected for special duty at Woolwich Arsenal. In 1896, while in charge of gun trials at the firing range at Shoeburyness, he was approached by the company's technical director, T E (Tom) Vickers, who offered him the job of superintendent of ordnance. He thereupon resigned from the service, and within a few months of his arrival at the River Don works in Sheffield he registered his first patent jointly with the engineer

John Fisher, as Vice-Admiral.

George Buckham for 'Improvements in Breech-Loading Ordnance and their Mountings'.

The building of heavy naval artillery continued to be Dawson's main preoccupation, and when in 1897 Vickers, Sons and Maxim took over the Naval Construction and Armaments Company at Barrow-in-Furness, he supervised the installation of the pits and other plant for turning out the great guns and their huge and complex mountings. It was a profitable speciality, for within a few years the private companies had supplanted Woolwich as the main supplier of guns and mountings to the Admiralty as well as in warships produced for foreign powers. The proud boast of Vickers was that it was able 'to supply ships with their engines complete and equipped with Guns and Armour Plate, entirely manufactured by the Company in its own Works', and this capability was enhanced by collaboration with Armstrongs, especially after the latter's amalgamation with Whitworth. While ostensibly in competition, Armstrong-Whitworth and Vickers-Maxim were to draw ever closer in the coming years, sharing out contracts and profits, benefiting from membership of cartels controlling the supply of raw materials, and joining forces with firms such as the German-owned Chilworth Powder Company and the shipbuilder William Beardmore of Glasgow.

In the course of this general extension of activities a series of patent and other agreements was entered into with companies abroad, enabling armament concerns world-wide to take advantage of new inventions and incorporate in their products the latest components and mechanisms. Until about 1907 no serious objection appears to have been raised to the principle of free trade in weaponry. Thus in 1890, even as Armstrongs were supplying their quick-firing guns to the Admiralty for use against French torpedo boats, they were also selling them to the French government, which was charged at the higher rate 'as they were taken to be copied, with the understanding that private firms should not make them'. In the years before 1914 the Patent Office in London published lists of hundreds of inventions, naval and military, registered by British and foreign companies. Admiralty regulations provided that serving officers were 'at liberty to apply for permission to patent any invention which they may originate', and although subject to obli-

gations of secrecy such inventions frequently found their way into foreign hands.

After 1897 Vickers, led by a vigorous management team headed by their German chief executive Sigmund Loewe, was increasingly dominant. Advised by the Paris-based Basil Zaharoff, broker to the European armament industry, they profited from a network of overseas business associations, particularly with Krupps of Essen and the Deutsche Waffen und Maschinenfabrik (or DWM) of Berlin. For some years Krupp had been concentrating on the development of heavy artillery, tested on their range at Meppen in Lower Saxony. Vickers also made use of the Meppen range before acquiring their own at Eskmeals in Cumberland, and so were aware of the progress being made by their German colleagues in evolving new projectiles and adapting their expertise to the demands of large naval guns. At this time political and commercial relations between Britain and Germany were healthy. With the help of Lord Rothschild, whose German connections were strong and whose guiding hand frequently pointed the way in such matters, mutually advantageous arrangements were made between Vickers, Krupp and DWM with regard to Maxim machine-gun patents. In return Krupp licensed the manufacture in Great Britain of their cemented armour plate, which Vickers, Armstrongs and Cammells of Birkenhead were producing in large quantities for the building of warships.

By the end of the century, the world's navies were

The bombardment and capture of Fort Fisher, North Carolina, 15 January 1865, from a painting by J Davidson. In a bloody battle lasting several hours the Federal forces under Rear-Admiral Porter and General Terry captured the fort, together with some 2000 of its defenders and over seventy large calibre guns. (CPL)

devoting much effort to improving the armour-piercing projectiles without which the heavy guns of the battleships could not be fully effective. In 1899 the position was described by Sir Andrew Noble, soon to become chairman of Armstrongs, in a lecture to the Institution of Naval Architects on 'The rise and progress of rifled naval artillery' :

> Firing against unarmed structures, shell charged with gunpowder do not generally explode until they are some short distance within the side of a vessel. But with gun-cotton and lyddite…the shell may either be fired with a fuze and detonator so arranged that (it) will burst immediately on impact, or it may be so arranged as to give rise to a slight delay. In the first alternative…a hole of very large dimensions will be made in the side of the ship. In the second alternative the shell will probably burst inside, making only a small hole in the side of the vessel, but the full effects of the explosion, and the destruction of the crew, would undoubtedly be serious…from the explosion taking place within the vessel. Where an attack is made against thin armour, shell charged with gunpowder are more effective than high explosive shell…as the former can be got to pass through the armour and burst inside. I doubt if shell charged with any explosives can be got to pass through thick armour before exploding.

At a time when capital ships were protected by ever tougher layers of iron and steel plate this last consideration was of the first importance. The development of armour had been pressed forward during the 1880s by the naval rivalry between Britain and France, with the French steel industry leading the way. Other countries then entered the field, with compound armours being replaced by a hardened steel plate produced by the American Harvey process, and this in turn being superseded by Krupp cemented (KC) armour, which offered even greater resistance to penetration by gunfire. These developments stimulated a closer collaboration between the forgemaster and the shipbuilder, and for a while it seemed possible to think in terms of unsinkable battleships, but the gunmakers were equal to the challenge. Whereas at the close of the century armour seemed set to defeat the gun, within a few years the gun had regained the ascendancy thanks mainly to improvements in the design of projectiles.

There were many contenders in the race to produce more effective explosive and armour-piercing (AP) shells. Navies had always been wary of combustible shells, partly because of the risk of spontaneous explosion and also because it was difficult to devise fuzes at once reliable and safe. Many believed such shells to be more dangerous to the gunners who fired them than to the enemy. 'There was,' recalled Sir Andrew Noble, 'some ground for this contention, as several catastrophes resulted from the first attempts to use fuzed shells. Perhaps the most serious was that which occurred on board HMS *Theseus*, when…shells captured from a French store ship…exploded in quick succession, one of the fuzes having by some accident been ignited. The ship was instant-

ly in flames, the vessel saved from destruction with the greatest difficulty, and 42 men were killed.' Premature explosions were all too common, cast-iron guns being especially vulnerable, and Sir Andrew related how during the bombardment of Fort Fisher during the American Civil War 'all the Parrott guns in the [Federal] fleet burst…45 men being killed and wounded, while only 11 men were killed and wounded by the enemy's fire.'

As for the armour-piercing projectile, this first took the form of a steel shot designed simply to punch a hole in the hull of the opposing ship, attempts to develop an AP shell with even a small charge of gunpowder meeting with only limited success because of the difficulty of carrying the charge through the armour. The French, having pioneered explosive shells, were making good progress, as were their Russian allies, although the Germans, transferring their expertise from land service to naval artillery, were soon to take the lead. By contrast, the British had fallen behind in their gunnery and the quality of their projectiles. In the Royal Navy priority was given to polished brasswork and snowy decks, and captains were notoriously reluctant to besmirch their gleaming vessels with the residue of cordite and black powder. Nor were the authorities overly concerned with firing exercises, which were costly both in projectiles and in wear and tear on the guns. As Admiral Sir Reginald Tyrrwhitt remembered: 'Gunnery was merely a necessary evil. Gunnery *had* to be carried out once in each quarter of the year, [but] no one except the Gunnery Lieutenant took much interest in the results.'

Not until the Boer war, when Great Britain found herself alone in a hostile world, was pressure to improve the standard of naval gunnery exerted from without by public opinion (spurred on by the press and the Navy League), and from within by reforms initiated by the charismatic, now Rear-Admiral, Sir John Fisher. At the turn of the century British warships still carried more muzzle-loading guns than any of their main rivals, together with a bewildering variety of shells and fuzes. Although specialist firms such as Hadfields of Sheffield were trying to come up with more advanced projectiles, most of the shells and fuzes for the service continued to be produced at Woolwich. While the navies of other countries experimented with improved armour-piercing projectiles and high explosives in place of gunpowder, the Royal Navy carried only powder-filled common shell for attacking thinly armoured ships, blunt-nosed Palliser type shells (virtually useless against the latest armour plate), shrapnel for shore targets and forged steel shot imported from France.

Meanwhile the British armament companies concentrated their energies on the lucrative business of constructing and equipping warships for foreign navies. The reputation of British yards was second to none and orders were not far to seek. Much effort was directed to more efficient gun mountings, barrels built up from steel wire wound round a central core and improved systems of aiming and fire control. For experimental research the Admiralty looked mainly to Vickers and Armstrongs, both of whom, as the historian of Vickers points out, 'were gun-makers before they were battleship builders…

a battleship was to them only a means of bringing guns within range, just as her armour was a means of protecting guns and gunners.'[2] The two companies were now reaping the benefit of membership of associations such as the Harvey Steel Syndicate and the Nobel Dynamite Trust, the latter in particular enabling them to collaborate with German colleagues in the manufacture and marketing of propellants, explosives and fuzes developed at the Central Scientific and Technical Testing Centre[3] established in 1897 at Potsdam, near Berlin.

The period from 1902 to 1912 was one of constant innovation and trial affecting all the component parts of ammunition for heavy naval guns. During the 1890s, as we have seen, the Admiralty adopted cordite as the propellant and turned towards lyddite as the high explosive in naval projectiles. Neither turned out to be altogether satisfactory. While effective as a propellant, Mark I cordite generated hot gases which eroded the inner lining of the gun barrels, so shortening their operational life. Shells filled with lyddite detonated with much greater force than black powder but were liable to break up on impact or go off at half cock, 'fizzling' in a cloud of yellow-green smoke, which was unfortunate since the purpose of an armour-piercing shell was to carry its charge *through* the plate before exploding and scattering a hail of steel fragments inside the hull. Further disadvantages were that since such shells were expensive they could only be used sparingly, while since lyddite tended to form dangerous salts when in contact with lead it acquired the reputation of being unsafe to handle and store.

The task of producing an efficient armour-piercing shell proved in fact to be as demanding as producing the guns themselves, with their complicated hydraulic mountings, ammunition hoists, ramming gear and clearing mechanisms. Apart from snags with the propellant and the explosive filling there were constant problems with the fuze, that tiny, intricate device on which the whole exercise ultimately depended. During the Boer war cordite Mark I was supplemented by cordite MD (i.e. modified) which reduced wear and tear on the gun barrels, but in 1903 the vice-president of the Ordnance Committee, Rear-Admiral Chase-Parr, was still noting that 'neither at home nor abroad has the question of a propellant been finally settled…experiments in so important a matter should be exhaustive.' At the same time he described the problems involved in designing an AP shell at once safe from the threat of premature explosion and sufficiently resilient to pass through thicker armour without bursting. The fuze, he declared, 'created the main difficulty', for 'sensitiveness and safety are not easy to combine' and this factor 'might almost be considered insuperable'.

So indeed for many years it proved. The naval 'gungineers' faced an even greater dilemma than their army colleagues. Projectiles designed to penetrate armour plate had to be base-fuzed, but base fuzes, activated by the shock of discharge, carried with them the risk of premature explosions. While with black powder charges prematures were rare and limited in their effect, prematures with lyddite were all too frequent and in a heavy naval gun could be catastrophic. For this reason the Admiralty

refused at first to approve the use of lyddite in shells over 6in calibre. Technicians at Elswick and at Vickers grappled with the problem, consulting their associates at Krupp and carrying out tests on base-fuzed shells with powder and lyddite charges. It was, however, another Sheffield company, Thomas Firth, which in 1903 came up with a shell 'capable of perforating KC armour a calibre in thickness, with a suitable striking velocity, without breaking up, and consequently capable of carrying a powder bursting charge through this thickness of armour and bursting behind….These results are so far superior to anything that has yet been attained in this country with AP projectiles that it should be at once introduced into the Service.'[4]

The Firth 'Rendable' was the first base-fuzed heavy armour-piercing shell to be carried by the fleet, supplementing existing stocks of common shell. Like the latter it was filled with black powder, not lyddite, both on grounds of safety and because no fuze existed which would enable lyddite to carry through armour plate. The 'Rendable' was adopted for its ability to penetrate an opponent's hull at quite short range. Weight-for-weight, powder had little destructive effect compared with lyddite and, as the DNO remarked, the new shell 'is not much use except against armoured ships at moderate ranges. Nevertheless… every ship should have *some* projectiles capable of perforating the thickest armour of their probable opponents.'

By this time, the world's navies were devoting much attention to the evolution of a new, fast, all big-gun battleship. For some years Armstrongs at Elswick and Vickers at Barrow had been supplementing the productive capacity of the dockyards at Portsmouth, Devonport and Chatham, and Sir John Fisher was confident that by drawing on their combined expertise the Royal Navy could keep one step ahead of the field in terms of guns and gunnery. An attempt having been made to persuade him to take over the management of Armstrongs from the ailing Sir Andrew Noble, a lifelong friend, he wrote with characteristic glee: 'it's a place I should revel in, and I should immediately set to work to revolutionise the naval fighting by building on speculation a battleship, cruiser and destroyer on revolutionary principles—oil fuel, turbine propulsion, equal gunfire all round, greater speed than any vessels of their class—and put up the Elswick shares fifty per cent!' Instead, he was appointed Second Sea Lord, and under his guidance the tendency of the Admiralty to collaborate with the Armstrongs/Vickers consortium in the supply of naval ordnance was openly acknowledged. Although the regulations required that contracts be put out to tender by any firm on the approved list of contractors, officials considered that 'Elswick, Woolwich and Vickers between them will be easily able to meet all requirements, and will furnish sufficient competition to keep prices down to reasonable figures…'

Operating as they did in the commercial market-place, Vickers were unable to resist the temptation to turn the situation to their advantage. In 1902 they published details of test firings of projectiles despite an Admiralty instruction that such information should not be publicly revealed. When rebuked, Trevor Dawson replied that the instruction had referred to trials of plate for the Admiralty, whereas these had been private trials 'conducted only to enable us to represent relative superiority, in order to compete in foreign business with such firms as Messrs Krupp, Schneider-Creusot and Skoda of Pilsen'. There were complaints in *The Times* that reports of gunnery trials 'savour more of an advertisement for the contractors than of interesting reading for the general public...the communication of all these details by Messrs Vickers is so like an advertisement that it is impossible for the ordinary observer to detect any difference at all'. Again a letter was sent to Vickers requiring that such reports be vetted before publication, but mere admonition had little effect. The identity of interest between the companies and the Admiralty meant that the latter was prepared to overlook minor infractions of the rules. As the DNO acknowledged: 'it is easier to enter into partnership with Elswick and Vickers (for that is what it amounts to) than to enforce the principle of open competition'.

For their part Vickers and Armstrongs were conscious that sales of warships and naval ordnance to foreign countries were led by the reputation of the Royal Navy. The introduction of a new class of battleship incorporating all the latest technical advances could be expected to open up substantial commercial opportunities, and in August 1904 Sir Andrew Noble wrote to Fisher: 'I only last week completed a variety of designs [for a battleship] in which your principles are perfectly followed'. A few weeks later Albert Vickers, the firm's managing director, declared in a speech at Barrow that 'the time had come when only two calibres of guns, the 12in and the 9.2in, would be used. There should be the biggest possible artillery for fleet actions, and quick-firing guns for repelling destroyers and torpedo boat attacks. What he should like to see...was a battleship with, say, a dozen 12in guns...strongly protected by thick armour plate, and with a good twenty knots speed...' These were the attributes already being considered by the experts appointed by Fisher to design the battleship *Dreadnought*, which was indeed to 'revolutionise the naval fighting', but even as the Committee of Designs set about its task events in the Far East gave pause for thought.

By the terms of the Anglo-Japanese treaty of 1902 the British were obliged to adopt a neutral stance during the war between Russia and Japan which broke out in February 1904 and continued until the summer of 1905. Nonetheless public sympathy was firmly on the side of the Japanese, who, following their victory over China in 1895, had used the indemnity paid to them to place orders in Britain for the latest warships. By 1904, having benefited from British financial and technical assistance on a generous scale, they possessed twelve modern battleships and armoured cruisers, all but two built in British yards. The Japanese navy was modelled on the Royal Navy. British instructors were seconded to the Tokyo Naval College and stayed on as advisers. Japanese personnel travelled to England to be trained in the use of British methods and equipment, and Japanese sailors were a familiar sight on the streets of Newcastle. The

commander-in-chief of the Imperial Navy, Admiral Togo, had served his apprenticeship on the training ship *Worcester* and supervised the building of warships on the Tyne. He and his staff were kept abreast of developments by the Japanese naval attaché in London and an agent based permanently at Elswick.

The naval fighting in the Russo-Japanese war provided a welcome opportunity to see the latest materiel tested in action, and the Admiralty lost no time in arranging for observers to be attached to the Japanese fleet. British firms, and particularly the Armstrong/Vickers consortium, were well placed to take advantage of the conflict. As well as their warships, the Japanese primary armament of 12in guns was largely of British manufacture since the Imperial arsenals were unable to turn out naval guns over 10in calibre. Both sides launched torpedoes supplied by the Whitehead factory at Fiume, which was effectively part of the consortium, and the Japanese quick-firing guns, rangefinders and gun-laying equipment had their origin with British companies. In its projectiles, the Imperial navy used cordite propellant together with explosives and fuzes as developed by Elswick and the researchers of the Nobel Dynamite Trust. For the first time, high explosives were fired in action at sea. During the 1890s the Japanese had adopted lyddite as the filling of common and AP shell under manufacture at the Kure arsenal. The new explosive they called 'Shimose' after the official responsible for its introduction, and the base fuze in their AP shell they dubbed the 'Ijuin' after an admiral on the naval staff.

Despite the careful preparations made by the Japanese, initial results were disappointing. At the battle of the Yellow Sea in August 1904 Admiral Togo's fleet failed to win a clear-cut victory despite being at least equal in gunpower to the Russian Pacific Squadron, which was able to return intact to Port Arthur. In the Official History[5] Julian Corbett notes that although the Japanese fired 1200 heavy shells and scored many hits 'not a single [Russian] ship had been taken [or even] rendered incapable of proceeding under her own steam, and...a feeling of dissatisfaction arose...' Many of the Japanese projectiles failed to burst or detonated on the Russian armour, creating 'a large volume of thick yellowish smoke'. A British observer reported that the Russian ships came through the action 'without serious injury...hardly any of the numerous shell that had penetrated the upper deck seemed to have passed through the main deck...' Another described how 'the bursting of a 12in shell against a hull at first gave the impression of some catastrophe in which the whole ship seemed to be involved, but when the smoke passed away all seemed as before'. Worst of all, the Imperial battleships lost three out of sixteen 12in guns from shells charged with shimose exploding prematurely in the barrel.

During the following months, therefore, the Japanese took steps to improve the performance of their projectiles, deciding in particular to follow the practice of the Royal Navy and replace shimose/lyddite by black powder in the high-capacity common shell. The fuze having been adapted accordingly, the large powder charge ensured a more complete and reliable explosion while

The Russian battleship Tsessarevitch *in Kiaochow Bay (modern Jianzhou) after the battle of the Yellow Sea in August 1904.*

The Russian battleship Orel *in Japanese hands after the battle of Tsushima in May 1905. Shell damage is more evident.*

increasing the incendiary effect, which in the case of shi-mose was minimal. At the same time the Ijuin fuze of the shimose-filled AP shell was replaced by a new base fuze, probably of Krupp design, which gave a better delay and reduced the likelihood of prematures.[6]

While in Manchuria the land war raged on and the protracted siege of Port Arthur ground along to its con-clusion, the ships of the Russian Pacific Squadron trapped in the harbour were bombarded at their moorings by 11in BL howitzers originally designed by Armstrongs but built by the Japanese for purposes of coastal defence. Eighteen of these formidable weapons were brought into action following the capture of 203 Metre Hill, from where the Japanese gunners were able to rain 480lb pro-jectiles on to the thinly protected decks of the ships below, leading to the sinking of four battleships, two cruisers and several destroyers.

This success, hastening the end of the siege, enabled the Imperial Navy to return to base for repairs and pre-pare a suitable reception for the Russian Baltic fleet, which, renamed the Second Pacific Squadron, was pro-ceeding on its epic but ill-fated journey half-way round the world. In the spring of 1905 Commander Jackson RN observed the re-fuzing of the Japanese 12in projectiles; also that officers were agreed on 'the necessity for a real armour-piercing shell in place of their present high-explosive one, which detonates outside the armour'. In May he reported that in anticipation of the coming bat-tle the guns of the Japanese ships had been extensively overhauled and refitted. Fresh cordite propellant was received from Armstrongs, and British-made powder-filled common shell were served out in addition to AP shell charged with shimose. At fleet exercises the Japanese gunlayers improved their aim by using the 'dot-ter' system developed earlier by Captain Percy Scott in HMS *Excellent*. Everything was ready for the showdown.

The decisive encounter in the Strait of Tsushima (27 May 1905) fully vindicated these measures, and especial-ly the action taken to improve the effectiveness of the Japanese projectiles. It was always going to be an unequal contest, for the Second Pacific Squadron was in poor shape after its long voyage, but few were prepared for the completeness of the Japanese success. After the Yellow Sea battle Captain Pakenham had noted that 'no ship has yet been sunk unless her magazines were affected'. At Tsushima no fewer than six Russian capital ships were sunk or disabled by gunfire, and Pakenham commented that the Japanese victory 'was in the first place a triumph of the gunner and the gun'. As to their heavy shell, its achievements 'exceeded all that its fondest admirers had formerly predicted... a suitable fuze...had rendered the effect of each projectile that penetrated greater than it had formerly been...' However, the damage had been done not so much by the armour-piercing as by the com-mon shell with its large bursting charge of black powder. All observers commented on the inflammatory effect of these shells, the Russian Admiral Rozhdestvensky declar-ing that 'the very paint would take fire and wrap the ships with a sheet of flame'. By comparison the Russian shells filled with pyroxylin, or wet gun cotton, inflicted only superficial wounds. The quality of the Russian shooting

was not that much inferior to that of their opponents, but their projectiles did little harm and many failed to explode. While the Second Pacific Squadron was almost totally destroyed, no Japanese ship was more than tem-porarily put out of action, and only 115 men were lost compared with 5000 on the Russian side.

Detailed accounts of the gunnery exchanges were later published by Russian survivors of the battle.[7] While acknowledging that the Japanese ships had been better handled, Commander Semenoff, who was present at the Yellow Sea and at Tsushima, thought that 'their chief superiority lay in their new shells, of which we had no inkling'. According to Novikoff-Priboy, the enemy pro-jectiles 'did not perforate the armour of our ironclads, but wrought havoc in the upper works, put guns out of action, destroyed our means of communication, started fires, scattered wounds and death... our missiles on the other hand were armour-piercing shells. Before explod-ing, they had to penetrate the cuirass to a considerable depth. This meant that they were only effective at com-paratively short range. When fired from a great distance, they rebounded from the armour plate or broke into frag-ments...' He believed the bursters of the Russian shell to be defective because the Ministry of Marine had

Admiral Sir Percy Scott made several important contributions to Royal Navy gunnery during this career.

11

12-inch guns on board the battlecruiser HMS Indomitable. *The 12-inch weapon was the standard for Royal Navy pre-dreadnoughts and dreadnoughts until the development of the 13.5in gun and its introduction in the Orion class.*

increased the proportion of moisture in the pyroxylin to guard against the drying effect of passing through hot climates and the consequent risk of explosions. 'A year later, in 1906, when the fortress of Sveaborg was in revolt, it was bombarded by the ironclad Slava which had not been ready in time to sail with the Second Pacific Squadron, but had been supplied with the same shells. When the fortress surrendered, the naval gunners found that hardly any of their shells had exploded....'

At Barrow and on the Tyne there was much rejoicing. By making effective use of British technology, the Imperial Navy had won the most crushing victory in the annals of modem naval warfare. The armament companies had been able to try out their latest guns and projectiles under battle conditions and useful lessons had been learned. While the fact that so many Japanese heavy guns had been disabled by premature explosions confirmed the Admiralty in its doubts about the safety of lyddite in heavy projectiles, the general effect was to encourage a somewhat uncritical belief in the power of the 12in naval gun and the high-capacity common shell. According to Charles Repington of *The Times*, the battle of Tsushima persuaded the naval authorities that British guns and gunnery as reflected in the success of the Japanese were second to none: 'the havoc wrought by guns made in England appears to justify us in the belief that we can hold our own with the best'. It was also seen as justifying decisions already taken to press ahead with the first all big-gun battleship, the *Dreadnought*.

As today, the ultimate symbol of power is the nuclear weapons system, so before 1914 (and until well into the Second World War) it was the heavily armed battleship. These awesome vessels represented the state of the art in contemporary engineering and in hitting power, being in essence floating batteries of long-range guns. After he became First Sea Lord in October 1904, Fisher's authority was such that the Admiralty was at last able to arrange for the supply of ordnance independently of the War Office. In theory, the latter was supposed to share out contracts between the ordnance factories and the trade. In practice the navy contracted more and more of the work to Armstrongs and Vickers and their associates. Guns and mountings were turned out by Vickers at Barrow, by Armstrongs at Elswick and the Openshaw works at Manchester. Projectiles were designed and manufactured by Elswick, Vickers, Hadfields and Firth as well as by the Royal Arsenal. In 1906 this process was taken a step further when, despite opposition from the War Office, the Admiralty formed its own naval ordnance inspection branch charged with carrying out 'the entire inspection and proof of guns and ammunition for the naval service'. Henceforward the Admiralty made its own dispositions in matters of procurement, a position it was resolutely to defend up to 1914 and throughout the war.

Soon after his appointment Fisher was again approached by Sir Andrew Noble, who offered him the

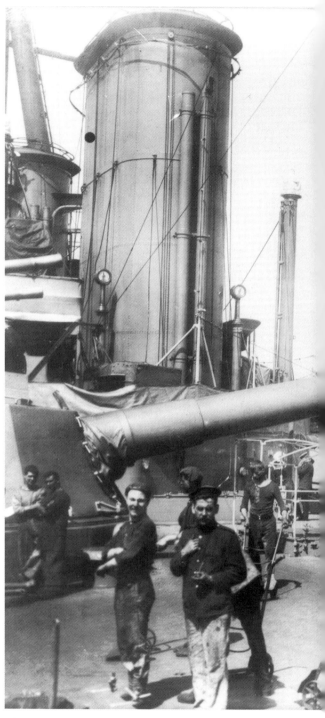

chairmanship of the Armstrong/Vickers consortium. 'I may explain SECRETLY', he wrote to the King's private secretary, Viscount Knollys, 'that an immense combination of the greatest ship-building, armour-plate and gunmaking firms in the Country are willing to unite under my presidency (and practical dictatorship!), and I fancy I should have about £20,000 a year, as I see my way to double all their dividends. *This may sound big, but it's true!* Directly peace comes, Russia and Japan will want to spend about fifty millions sterling on new ships, and I know how

to get the orders….' The King, however, did not approve, and in any case the First Sea Lord's energies were fully engaged by the building of *Dreadnought*. There are indications that Armstrongs and Vickers pressed hard for the contract, and that Fisher would have liked them to have it, but in terms of experience, resources and capital investment the royal dockyards still led the way in ship construction. The new battleship was built at Portsmouth, which claimed with good reason to be able to complete more rapidly than any of its competitors, public or private.

But there continued to be friction over the allocation of orders for naval guns. While the building of *Dreadnought* was the responsibility of the Admiralty and its constructors, guns and ammunition were still charged to the army estimates, and problems were created by the Admiralty's wish to rely on the trade. In 1904 the DNO confirmed that Armstrongs and Vickers had agreed not only to produce gun mountings to each other's designs but to share the designs with the ordnance factories, waiving royalties in expectation of the exclusive right to manufacture. Although this had practical advantages in terms of the standardisation and interchangeability of components, official suspicions were aroused. While it suited Fisher to work with a caucus based on Armstrongs, Vickers and Woolwich, the War Office remained determined to diversify the source of supply. When in May 1905 the Admiralty proposed to extend the same arrangement to the manufacture of the guns themselves, the War Office objected that it was departing from agreed procedures and seeking to establish the private companies as exclusive suppliers of artillery to the navy. Since Fisher refused to give way, both sides appealed to the Treasury for a ruling.

In its submission the Army Council took a strong line, declaring that: 'there is evidence that Messrs Armstrongs and Vickers have for some time past been more in friendly co-operation than in a state of rivalry as regards supplies to His Majesty's Government.' It was, therefore, 'doubtful whether a Government Department is at liberty to enter into such an arrangement as that proposed by the Admiralty, the practical effect of which is to secure to the firms in question a monopoly, perhaps for many years, against all outside enterprise as regards the manufacture of ordnance.' Since the Lords Commissioner of the Treasury shared this view, the Admiralty had no alternative but to back down, agreeing 'to continue the principle of open competition for the supply of guns'. It was confirmed that all orders for guns should be routed through the War Office, and that the list of firms authorised to tender for their manufacture be extended to other concerns, notably the Coventry Ordnance Works, now an affiliate of the John Brown group of companies.

It is doubtful whether this ruling succeeded either in broadening the manufacturing base or of saving money by encouraging more competition. The fact was that the Department of Naval Ordnance depended largely on the engineering expertise of Armstrongs and Vickers, which alone commanded the resources to develop and supervise the production of the great guns with their elaborate mechanisms and mountings. The dispute rumbled on, with the Army Council complaining a few months later that the Admiralty was still ordering guns direct from Armstrongs. Whereas the War Office doled out contracts to Woolwich and a number of small firms on the approved list, the Admiralty continued to rely mainly on Armstrongs and Vickers, which resisted any attempt by competitors such as the Coventry Ordnance Works to infringe their patents. Since the value of orders from the Admiralty exceeded those from the War Office by a considerable margin, the consortium prospered by comparison with Woolwich and their lesser commercial rivals, who struggled to keep their heads above water.

As for the ammunition for the heavy guns of the battleships and battle cruisers, naval opinion continued to favour black powder rather than lyddite as the filling for large projectiles, as it favoured common rather than armour-piercing shell. This preference was strengthened by the experience of the Russo-Japanese war, during which Fisher observed that 'something like four-fifths of the best-protected ship is unprotected by armour. The chances then of hitting the unprotected portion is 5 to 1!

Now, if you fire armour-piercing projectiles, they will go clean through any of this four-fifths of the hull just making a round hole as big as your head, which you can stuff up with a hammock… But supposing instead it is a common shell that pierces this thin armour, then the whole structure in the vicinity is wrecked.' This was why in the Far East, 'many officers are insistent on using common shell largely in action, as they maintain the enemy would be so wrecked, demoralised and put out of trim by the effect of these large explosions, as not to necessitate any attack on his thick armour, which forms so small a target and is so small a proportion of the visible hull.'[8]

With this consideration in mind, Fisher agreed with Reginald Bacon, his adviser on ordnance and the first captain of *Dreadnought*, that the new vessel be equipped with a uniform armament of 12in guns firing mainly powder-filled common shell. Within the fleet, Fisher's preference for speed and big guns at the expense of thicker armour and a varied armament aroused fierce controversy. In 1904 competitive trials were conducted by Admirals Sir Reginald Custance in the *Venerable* and Sir Hedworth Lambton in the *Victorious*. The results were contradictory, highlighting the division between those who like Custance advocated a mixed armament of heavy guns and lighter, quick-firing guns, and those who supported Fisher in favouring big guns only. 'It is on the number of hits,' Fisher maintained, 'not the number of shots fired, that the action depends.' To which Custance retorted that: 'A small shell on the right spot is more effective than a large shell in the wrong one.' The lessons to be drawn from the fighting in the Far East were hotly debated. After the Yellow Sea battle, Captain Pakenham observed that 'the effect of every gun is so much less than that of the next larger size, that when 12in guns are firing, shots from 10in pass unnoticed….' It is true that he was referring to their 'moral' rather than their destructive effect, and he also noted that no shell on either side had succeeded in penetrating main belt armour, but the impression given was that the heaviest gun was likely to prove decisive.

For some years after the Russo-Japanese War the Admiralty continued to rely on the ability of powder-filled common shell to disable enemy vessels at fighting ranges still expected to be in the region of 6000 to 8000 yards. In 1904 Fisher wrote of *Dreadnought* : 'Absolutely nothing has been allowed to stand in the way of the most nearly perfect power and scope of the guns….The result of all long-range shooting has gone to prove that…the guns must be fired slowly and deliberately….Hence the advantage of a few well-aimed guns with large bursting charge is overwhelming. Suppose a 12in gun to fire one aimed round each minute. Six guns would allow a deliberately aimed shell with a huge bursting charge every ten seconds. Fifty per cent of these should be hits at 6000 yards. Three 12in shells bursting on board every minute would be HELL!' This view he subsequently modified in the light of experience which showed that when all the guns fired simultaneously, straddling the target, this gave better results than trying to spot the fall of single shot, and after 1906 salvo firing came to be generally adopted.

After Tsushima the predilection for common shell was confirmed by an evaluation of the battle by the DNO,

John Jellicoe, which showed that the Japanese victory owed more to such shell than to armour-piercing projectiles, the effect of which had been 'slight'. Nonetheless it was thought important to develop projectiles capable of reaching the vitals of an opposing vessel and *sinking* it rather than merely inflicting damage. With the attention of the leading companies concentrated on the building of warships, guns and mountings, the tendency was to leave research on heavy ammunition to the specialist firms Hadfield and Firth, and it was the former which in 1906 came up with the 'Heclon' range of capped armour-piercing (APC) shells. These featured a mild steel cap designed to pre-stress the area of impact before the hardened point entered the plate, and a base fuze similar to that adopted by the Japanese at Tsushima. Tests showed the new projectile to be capable of perforating nine inches of Krupp cemented armour at 10000 yards and twelve inches at 6000 yards, and Fisher was delighted. Such results, he declared, 'cleared the ground of untrustworthy deductions from the late war'. At these ranges, 'no armour at present on any ship in the world can protect the vitals of a ship from the direct blow of a projectile from our latest 12in gun....Effective armour penetration is an essential qualification of the hit. In this attribute the

John Jellicoe, as Rear-Admiral.

12in gun is supreme. Up to 9500 yards the thickest armour afloat is open to effective attack....'

A year later, in May 1907, Jellicoe reported to the Ordnance Board that Hadfields had succeeded in producing a common pointed capped (CPC) shell combining greater penetrative power with a large bursting charge of black powder. This, the 'Eron', also featured a soft-metal cap and was adopted despite its high cost. The shell casing was made of Hadfield's 'Era' chrome-nickel steel, and the 'Eron', like the 'Heclon', was fitted with the No 15 base fuze produced (probably to a Krupp design) by the Royal Laboratory, Woolwich. Wherever manufactured, all heavy shell were filled, assembled and inspected at the Royal Arsenal before being issued to the Fleet. As between 1909 and 1911 supplies of the new APC and CPC projectiles became available, stocks of the old, blunt-nosed AP and common shell were withdrawn from service, leaving the navy with three main categories of ammunition, namely APC and CPC, both base-fuzed and filled with black powder, and HE common shell, nose-fuzed and charged with lyddite for purposes of 'bombardment'.

Already, however, perspectives were being altered by improvements in the efficiency of the torpedo, whereby the range of this weapon was increasing to 6000 yards and beyond, and the Admiralty responded by calling for the longer reach of more powerful guns. Following the precept of Sir Andrew Noble that in a given gun with a given charge the ballistic advantage lies with the heavier shot, Fisher looked for a weightier shell to achieve distance with accuracy. Both Reginald Bacon, now director of naval ordnance, and Frederic Dreyer, the navy's leading gunnery expert, had discovered that the performance of some of the 12in guns was suspect, erosion in the barrels giving rise to excessive spreads in range and direction. This fault it was thought would be eased by a larger shell with a lower muzzle velocity, which would also be more destructive in its effect. 'To attack a ship successfully,' wrote Dreyer, 'we must pierce the gun positions and break down the armour deck; therefore the heavier the shell and the larger the burster that we use the better.' In October 1908, Commander Trevor Dawson of Vickers, restored to the Navy List during the Boer War, was asked what he could do, and 'soon returned with the design of a 13.5in gun with a muzzle velocity of some 2400 feet per second weighing about 75 tons. The projectile weighed 1250lb [compared with 850lb for the 12in].'[9]

By November 1909 the new 13.5in gun was ready for testing together with representative samples of CPC and APC shell. Since Woolwich was unable to guarantee that stocks of the latter would be ready by the specified date, Hadfields were authorised to manufacture them to their own designs, and naturally sought to incorporate the latest chrome-nickel steel, high explosives and ballistic caps. Until this time it had been assumed that to fill large base-fuzed shell with any explosive other than black powder was unacceptably risky, but attitudes were changing following the development of higher quality steel casings and the adoption of a protected fuze designed to eliminate the possibility of prematures. Accordingly, Ordnance Board trials indicated that there was no longer any reason why heavy armour-piercing projectiles should not safely be filled with high explosive in place of powder. The question now was whether the high explosive should be lyddite or TNT.

During the Boer War, the Admiralty had observed that other navies were moving ahead in the development of high explosives, and, in the light of difficulties being experienced with lyddite, Sir Henry Brackenbury and Major Nathan of the Royal Arsenal arranged for an Explosives Committee to be formed 'to carry out trials to obtain a safe and reliable high explosive for use in shell'. The Committee, presided over by Lord Rayleigh and including such luminaries as Sir William Crookes, FRS (a well-known chemist), R B Haldane (barrister and Liberal MP) and Sir Andrew Noble (artillerist and physicist), was instrumental in setting up a research department at Woolwich which over the next six years conducted experiments with both propellants and high explosives. Among its first achievements was the introduction of cordite MD, which by lowering the nitroglycerine content effectively reduced the level of erosion in guns. The Committee also examined alternative high explosives including TNT, which the Germans were believed to be trying out as the bursting charge in their heavy projectiles. A derivative of coal tar formed by the action of nitric acid on toluene, TNT was more inert than picric acid and therefore at once safer and potentially more effective when used in armour-piercing shell. However, as tests showed it to be marginally less violent in its effect than lyddite, no further action was taken.

In 1907 the work of the Explosives Committee was taken over by the Ordnance Board, to which Sir William Crookes wrote with dramatic news: 'I hear from Captain Tulloch [of Vickers' associate Chilworth Gunpowder Company] that the German Government have finally adopted trinitrotoluene as their high explosive for shells. The French Government have followed suit and have discarded Melinite... I hope we shall not be left behind...as the advantages [TNT] possesses over picric acid...are sufficiently great for Continental nations to take it up seriously.' This Sir William amplified in further letters pointing out that the German authorities were ordering 150 tons of TNT per month, and that the German firms had got round the safety problem presented by the fulminate cap by using a detonator primed by the explosive tetryl. Doubtless acquired through Vickers' connections with the Nobel Dynamite Trust, this information was circulated to interested departments with the proposal that research into the use of TNT be resumed, and the Ordnance Board decided that 'no time should be lost in taking up the question of the introduction of trinitrotoluene as a high explosive burster for shells.' At the Department of Naval Ordnance an assistant to the director, Frederick Tudor, minuted: 'It appears advisable to continue the experiments as recommended...but serious consideration would be necessary before deciding to adopt any high explosive which required fulminate to detonate it.'

Accordingly, in 1908 the Ordnance Board carried out a series of trial firings with 9.2in shells against armour plate to assess the relative effectiveness of black powder, lyddite and TNT. Its conclusion was that TNT 'would be

The German dreadnought Nassau, *armed with 11in guns that had a higher muzzle velocity than the Royal Navy's 12in guns.*

far more efficient than the present lyddite or common pointed shell', but that 'the effective use of TNT… necessitates employment of a delay action fuze…and such a fuze has yet to be devised.' This being so, lyddite, detonated using a primer of picric acid crystals in place of fulminate, remained the only practicable alternative to black powder. It was reported that: 'The quick, local and extremely violent action of a lyddite shell offers… many great advantages against a large portion of a ship's structure, and…a ship not provided with lyddite shells for its heaviest guns would be at a serious disadvantage…' The Board therefore recommended the adoption of 12in HE shell charged with lyddite provided that great care was taken in its manufacture and that 'a series of trials be instituted to compare their value with powder-filled shells against armoured and unarmoured structures, using an old battleship as a target… it being of great importance and interest that the efficacy of these large-capacity shell be conclusively demonstrated.'[10]

At the same time the superintendent of research, noting continuing problems with lyddite on safety grounds, urged consideration of TNT, which 'according to our information is replacing lyddite in Germany and France'. It was true that TNT required a fulminate cap to ensure detonation, and that a reliable fuze had yet to be worked out, but if these difficulties could be overcome he was in favour of 'pushing on with the investigation of TNT, with the view of displacing lyddite'. Experiments increasingly underlined the advantages of TNT. Being less sensitive it was better able than lyddite to carry through an opponent's armour before bursting. Unlike lyddite it did not react with metals to form dangerous salts, and when filled in shells it was safe to handle and less liable to spontaneous explosion. However, TNT could not be recommended because the advanced type of fuze and gaine needed to detonate it was not available. Until attempts to adapt existing fuzes proved successful there were obvious dangers in using shell charged with TNT, and the Board 'considered the attendant risk of prematures too great to incur in view of the very serious damage to be apprehended in such a contingency'.

This failure to come to terms with the fuzing of TNT remained an insuperable obstacle to its adoption as a burster in service shell. Since the Boer War, many service fuzes had been based on Krupp designs made available to the Armstrong/Vickers consortium by courtesy of the Dynamite Trust, but when after about 1908 Krupps, under pressure from the German government, ceased to keep Vickers informed of details of their latest designs, the British authorities were thrown back on their own resources. Neither at Woolwich nor in the trade did the expertise or the facilities exist to develop new fuzes and especially the combination of fuze, primer and gaine needed to ensure the detonation of TNT. Unlike shells charged with lyddite, TNT-filled shells could not be detonated solely by the shock of discharge, and so could not be activated by the base fuzes currently in use. While, therefore, continuing with experiments to determine the desirability or otherwise of substituting TNT for lyddite as the service high explosive, the Ordnance Board concluded in April 1910 that 'although TNT could probably be used with satisfactory results when a suitable fuze is forthcoming, lyddite is on the whole to be preferred at present.' As regards naval projectiles, it was of the opinion that 'owing to a base fuze not being available that will detonate TNT, the time has not yet arrived to deal with the question of filling [APC and CPC] shell with TNT, but with the production of such a fuze the filling of [shell] with this high explosive…will be further considered.'[11]

Since in the event the fuze was not forthcoming and the whole matter was virtually shelved until 1914, this decision had far reaching consequences for both services. At this time, four of the six members of the Ordnance Board, including the president, were military men and the army saw no reason to change the nature of their explosive charges. One of the two naval members, the Chief Inspector of Naval Ordnance, Lieutenant J A Duncan, was later to be singled out for not taking a stronger line on modernising the design of naval projectiles, but it would seem that he was a convenient scapegoat for more senior officers reluctant to accept the difficulty and expense which such action would have involved. Whoever was responsible, the result was that British naval projectiles continued to be charged only with black powder or lyddite. Since before the war, no shell filled with TNT were approved for either of the services, the fuze technology needed for its detonation was not developed. Nor, since TNT was used only in small quantities as a primer, did plant to manufacture it exist on any significant scale.

On the other hand, much attention was devoted to improved methods of fire control to enable the battle fleet to deliver its projectiles with accuracy at ever-lengthening ranges. In 1905, reacting to the evidence of poor shooting revealed by the Custance and Lambton committees, Fisher appointed the ingenious Captain Percy Scott to be Inspector of Target Practice. Scott had for many years been coming up with ideas to raise the standard of the fleet's gunnery, which met with considerable success, as also did the system of centralised director-firing he was later to evolve. He it was who during the Boer War had improvised carriages to enable naval guns to be deployed on land, and subsequently he worked closely with Trevor Dawson of Vickers, for whom he was virtually a full-time employee and to whom he was contracted to offer first option on his inventions. Since 1903 the annual prize-firing competition had been enhanced by the offer of an extra incentive in the shape of 'a medal (accompanied by a bonus) to be granted to the best shot with each nature of gun….' The scores achieved by the various ships were published in the press, competition was keen and captains were made aware that good gunnery was an essential qualification for promotion.

In 1905 Scott introduced the annual fleet battle practice, first held at 6000 yards and then increased in 1908 to 8000 yards. This provided a more realistic test of gun-laying skills, and the results of each practice were studied with care. At no time, however, does much attention appear to have been paid to the effectiveness of the projectiles on striking the target. The usual method was to train the guns on structures of wood and canvas, at first stationary, later towed at a steady 14 knots. Accuracy was measured by the fall of shot and the number of hits on the target, for according to the regulations: 'The "Hitting System" in gunnery is now regarded as the only efficient test of a practice, whether it be carried out at short or long range'. Practice rounds with low propellant charges were prescribed on grounds of cost saving and to minimise wear on the gun barrels. Rarely was fire directed against armoured vessels, for it was assumed that service projectiles had been tested and inspected for their destructive qualities before being issued to the fleet.

In some quarters the battle practice was thought to be an inadequate substitute for regular gunnery training carried out under conditions likely to be encountered in war. In a booklet, *The Fighting Power of the Capital Ship*, circulated in a limited edition in 1909, Admiral Custance kept up the attack on Fisher's all big-gun policy: 'The "battle practice" as hitherto conducted is so entirely unlike the war condition that the results must be accepted with reserve.' Arguing that poor visibility and the limitations of instruments would oblige fleets to engage at quite moderate ranges, he asked: 'Is it quite certain that the one-calibre big gun armament is the most suitable for action at these short distances?' Admiral de Robeck agreed, commenting that: 'It seems extraordinary that we spend thousands of pounds annually…and yet the only opportunity the Spotting Officer gets of practice, is usually the preliminary Battle Practice and the Battle Practice itself, which take place within a few days of each other….A modern Battle Practice appears to be run entirely for the glorification of the 12in gun, which in the older class of ship fails utterly in bad weather. At the recent Atlantic Fleet's Annual Battle Practice for instance, which took place off the south coast of Ireland, the number of hits obtained by some of the ships was very small…'

Such criticism was brushed aside by Fisher, whose instincts were in the main soundly based. The big gun was indeed to prove decisive, and the tendency was to under- rather than over-estimate fighting ranges. In the years before 1914 all battle practices took place at under 10,000 yards despite clear indications that modern capital ships were unlikely to approach to such a distance without previously engaging. This gave a misleading impression of the success achieved both in terms of fire control and the presumed effect of heavy shells, and in consequence Fisher continued to take an exaggeratedly optimistic view of the fleet's firepower. Writing in 1907 to Lord Esher, he described with pride how during gunnery practice a 'large ironclad' had fifteen times out of eighteen hit a target fourteen time smaller than itself at a distance of five miles [or 8800 yards], the vessel moving at a rate of twenty knots, the target at an unknown speed. And in 1910 he informed A J Balfour that the 'magnificent new 13.5in gun being put in our ships now building before they, the Germans, have any inkling of it has knocked them into a cocked hat! It is as superior to the 12in as the 12in to a peashooter!' So impressed was Winston Churchill with such claims that in 1912 he suggested to Fisher that the time had come to dispense with armour altogether and rely on speed and gunpower alone.

But amid the general euphoria there was some uneasiness about the performance of naval shell. To achieve longer ranges with lower muzzle velocities, gun mountings were allowing for increased elevations so that projectiles followed an ever higher trajectory and reached their target at ever more oblique angles of impact. It was recognised that this further inhibited the capacity of armour-piercing shell to penetrate an opponent's hull. Both capped and uncapped projectiles were breaking up on striking at an oblique angle, and it was evident that action was needed to put matters right. With the decision in 1908 to introduce lyddite as well as black powder in the projectiles of the 13.5in guns, the Department of Naval Ordnance was concerned to try out the new shell against an armoured ship. These trials, specifically to 'determine the effect of thin side armour in keeping out heavy naval shell', took place in 1909-10 using the old battleship *Edinburgh* as a target. The results were disquieting. Although reports confirmed the destructive effect on superstructures of 13.5in HE shell filled with lyddite at a range of 6000 yards, it was shown that armour of rather less than one third calibre thickness was sufficient to keep out the explosion of such shell. It was also confirmed that when striking main belt armour at angles over twenty degrees APC shells charged with lyddite normally broke up and failed to penetrate.

This meant that against a vessel protected with standard armour plate, lyddite-filled common HE and APC shells were unlikely to inflict more than superficial damage. The HE was not of course intended to penetrate armour. However, it was worrying that the problem of how to produce an armour-piercing projectile combining destructive power with the ability to carry through thick armour without exploding remained unsolved. It was also frustrating, especially to those aware of progress being made on the Continent. In an article in the *Royal Artillery Journal* following a visit to the Schneider works in 1910, Colonel Bethell observed that: 'Armour-piercing projectiles are made of nickel-chrome steel…the French Government test all AP and high-explosive shell on the plate; the impact test at 20 degrees from the normal is very severe, and it is stated that no English made AP shell would pass it….'

Reports on the *Edinburgh* trials were circulated to the fleet, and in October 1910 Jellicoe, in his capacity as controller of the navy, requested the Ordnance Board, in the words of Frederic Dreyer, 'to produce designs of AP shell for guns 12in and above which at oblique angle would perforate thick armour plates in a fit state for bursting…'. Thereafter Jellicoe was posted to sea duty, and according to Dreyer: 'Owing to technical blunders in his absence, this requirement of his for armour-piercing shell was not achieved.' This version of events, doubtless calculated to shield Jellicoe from later charges of negligence, has been repeated in all subsequent explanations for the failure of the navy to come up with a satisfactory armour-piercing shell in the years before 1914. Following the same line of reasoning, Jellicoe's successor as controller, Admiral Sir Charles Briggs, is usually held to be responsible on account of his supposed inertia. Referred to by Fisher as 'the old sheep-farmer', Sir Charles has had a bad press. 'It is a mystery,' writes the leading naval historian Arthur J Marder, 'how this incompetent officer

The 'super-dreadnought' Orion, the first battleship to mount the new 13.5 inch guns. She is shown here in 1918, with the full range of wartime alterations: extended bridgework and tops, aircraft and flying-off platform on B turret, deflection scales on B and X turrets, and searchlights re-positioned around the after funnel.

could have been appointed to so exacting a post.'

Another, more likely, explanation is that it was evident to the specialists at the Ordnance Board that given the decision to fill APC shell with lyddite rather than TNT it was *not practicable* to produce them to the specification required. The only realistic means of achieving detonation *after* penetration would have been to use TNT as the burster, but the Ordnance Board had a few months earlier decided after careful consideration to reject TNT and retain lyddite as the high explosive in service shell. Orders for lyddite-filled HE common and APC projectiles for the 13.5in guns had already been placed,[12] and in September 1910 the naval member, Lieutenant Duncan, was informed that fuze No. 16 for APC shell, incorporating the protective shutter device, was to be produced by the Royal Laboratory. Understandably, the Board preferred to meet Jellicoe's request by seeking to improve the APC shell and fuze already approved rather than going to the expense of designing new ones. The trade was, therefore, invited to come up with samples manufactured to the required specification, and Vickers and Elswick, Hadfields and Firth set about producing a variety of lyddite-filled armour-piercing shells capable of penetrating thick armour before bursting at angles of attack up to 15 degrees. To this end Hadfields and Firth devised lightweight hollow caps of hardened steel which lengthened and streamlined the projectile, so achieving greater accuracy and higher striking velocities while equalising the range of CPC and APC. The latter could, it was claimed, 'perforate hard-faced armour plate without becoming broken up, either when striking the plate normally or obliquely...'.

Whether for financial reasons, for armour-piercing shell cost three times more than common shell, or because such claims could not be substantiated, none of these more advanced projectiles was adopted. When Fisher retired in 1910 the War Office made another attempt to introduce a measure of uniformity in the procurement of ordnance for both services, but the

Admiralty was adamant, preferring 'to continue the practice which at present obtains as regards separate Navy specifications'. There was, however, something of a reaction against Fisher's enthusiasm for change and his faith in the ability of the private companies always to come up with something better. Fisher's successor, the conservatively minded Sir Arthur Wilson, was not convinced that fleet actions would take place at very long ranges and disinclined to encourage fire-control systems or projectiles designed with these in mind. The Department of Naval Ordnance, opting for a period of consolidation, cut back on experiments and ceased to publish a record of its activities. In view of the cost involved, trials of new 13.5in projectiles submitted by the trade were discontinued, and it was decided to stay with existing patterns of naval shell as manufactured by the ordnance factories.

The Admiralty continued, therefore, to favour the tactical use of the high-capacity HE shell and, at longer ranges, the powder filled CPC rather than the APC with its small charge of lyddite. Captain Bacon thought that the CPC, besides carrying a heavier bursting charge, had 'practically the same armour-piercing qualities as that of the lighter shell'. His successor as director of naval ordnance, Captain A G H Moore, was of the opinion that 'firing at long range should be carried out by high explosive [i.e. high capacity] shells that would...wreck an opponent's fire control and consequently reduce the effectiveness of his fire at an early stage in the action; armour-piercing shells were to be reserved for close-range work, when trajectories were flat and the impact of the projectiles was thus normal rather than oblique....' Ships were instructed first to use HE common and CPC shells to devastate and disable their foe, and then to change to APC as they closed to finish him off.

After 1912, awareness of the thick armour and strong under-water protection of the hulls of German warships lent support to the view that it made more sense to rely on HE and CPC projectiles than on APC, which had less chance of inflicting significant damage. As one commentator pointed out: 'It is not so much a water-line penetration …that will cause the loss of a vessel. It is the constant pounding, pulverising and splitting of frames and armour backing, the straining and opening of seams, the shattering of bulkheads and the destruction of the watertightness of the whole which eventually sink the ship.' As for the APC shell, Captain Moore thought the introduction of the heavier 13.5in projectile a sufficient answer to the problem raised by the *Edinburgh* trials: 'Existing AP shell on striking armour at an angle have a marked tendency to break up, and this considerably reduces the bursting effect behind armour, more particularly when filled with lyddite. It is therefore intended to utilise the additional weight of the 1400lb AP shell in materially strengthening the walls without reducing the present capacity, and this should considerably augment the effect behind armour….' But this remained unproven, and the limitations of the armour-piercing shell continued to be recognised.

Contrary to the information given to Crookes in 1907, the Germans and French did not at once abandon picric acid in favour of TNT. They did, however, move steadily in this direction, replacing black powder with a variety of high explosives based on admixtures of picric acid, TNT and cresol. The Germans, like the French, used picric acid in their field artillery shells, but they increasingly opted for TNT as the bursting charge in heavy projectiles for both services. This, of course, meant developing the shell bodies and fuzes necessary for the detonation of TNT. In a lavish volume published in 1912 to mark the Krupp centenary celebrations, attention was drawn to the excellence of the firm's heavy projectiles: 'The steel body of explosive shells is thick of metal…fitted either with a percussion or double-acting fuze with a retarding device…so that the bursting charge may be made to act after the projectile has penetrated into the target to a desired depth.' This, the L/34 armour-piercing shell, was not only filled with TNT but incorporated an adaptation of the Hadfield-Firth ballistic cap to help it perforate face-hardened armour at oblique angles of attack.

In Britain the Ordnance Board, observing the use of high-explosive shells during the Balkan Wars of 1912-13, carried on with their researches into TNT as a burster for service shell. Since it could safely be compressed, large charges could be built up of many small blocks, and an Explosives Loading Company was formed to gain experience in the filling of projectiles with blocks of TNT. At Vickers tests were carried out with TNT shells for the battleship *Reshadieh*, under construction for Turkey, but although experiments with such shell continued up to 1914 they produced no positive results. The British authorities placed no orders with the Loading Company, nor were any shell charged with TNT approved for service use. This raises the question why the British, alone among the leading powers, failed to adopt what was by general consent the most effective high explosive then available. Why did both services choose to stay with lyddite in spite of its known disadvantages?

One answer is that the processes and materials employed in the manufacture of TNT (which involved, for example, the treatment of toluene with oleum, a chemical not readily available in Britain) were largely the preserve of German firms, a fact which may account for the reluctance of the British authorities to adopt it. It appears also that the services could see no pressing reason for change. The gunners had become accustomed to lyddite shells, of which a sufficient supply was forthcoming from the trade to meet the peacetime needs of the army and the navy. Owing to their high cost, practice with lyddite shells continued to be severely restricted: only after 1911 was *one* round, for firing against rocks, included in the annual allowance per ship for each 12in gun. More serious, the technology was lacking to produce the fuze and gaine necessary for the detonation of TNT. Since the Boer War the authorities had relied mainly on the trade for artillery fuzes, many of Krupp design: shrapnel fuzes were manufactured by Vickers at Birmingham, howitzer fuzes by Coventry Ordnance and fuzes for naval projectiles by the Royal Laboratory under licence to the Vickers/Armstrong consortium.

The Admiralty's dependence on the consortium had increased when Bacon became director of naval ordnance in 1907. Having worked with Trevor Dawson and his colleagues on 12in guns and the development of the early submarines, Bacon turned naturally to Vickers and Armstrongs for the later 13.5in guns. 'For political reasons,' he wrote, 'a portion of our annual orders for guns was given to the Arsenal', and this provided a yardstick against which to check the prices charged by the private sector. But the cost of manufacture at Woolwich 'almost invariably exceeded that of private firms…the establishment was far too large and costly'. Whether this was really so may be questioned, depending on how the figures are calculated, but the fact is that it was widely believed and cost saving was a crucial consideration. When in 1909 Bacon was obliged as the result of an indiscretion[13] to leave the navy, he was consoled by becoming managing director of the Coventry Ordnance Works. In a paper prepared for his successor, Moore, he referred to continuing difficulties with the 12in guns: 'The Ordnance Board were composed of non-technical members, so far as gun design is concerned….there is little doubt but that it was advantageous to bring the manufacturers of heavy guns more into the actual design of heavy guns, since they have in their offices practical and theoretical gun designers.' And he repeated that: 'At present, broadly speaking, the prices [charged by the Arsenal] are 30 per cent higher than the trade… [Woolwich] is overgrown and far larger than we require.'

Others in the Admiralty, aware that Vickers and Armstrongs were motivated as much by commercial as by patriotic considerations, were less convinced. An increasing proportion of the companies' profits derived from the sale of warships to foreign countries, with whose war departments regular contact was maintained through the agencies operated by Basil Zaharoff. With many friends in high places and backing from powerful financial institutions, Zaharoff could satisfy a growing international demand for munitions of all kinds and especially the latest and most profitable: battleships and battlecruisers. The race was on to follow the example of Britain and Germany, and to maintain some kind of parity in naval armaments. No maritime nation could afford to allow rivals a technical superiority likely to prove decisive, and orders flowed in from Europe, Latin America and Japan. The armaments business had become, as it has remained, essentially cosmopolitan in character, depending on the widest possible spread of demand.

It is as well that this was so, for the British companies could not have flourished on the strength of orders from the War Office and Admiralty alone. Government contracts were notoriously unreliable, being given or withheld according to changing circumstances and with scant regard to investment in plant and trained manpower or the high cost of research and development. In 1906 a Conservative government which had authorised higher levels of spending on the armed services was replaced by a Liberal administration committed to other priorities. This led to a sharp reduction in the Fisher/Cawdor naval building programme and faced the armament companies with the prospect of falling orders and declining profits. Little wonder that Vickers and Armstrongs envied the position of their rival Krupps, which was revered as a national institution, recognised as the primary supplier of weaponry to the Imperial army and navy and assisted in its drive for overseas sales by the German foreign office.

Whereas until about 1908 British and German armament concerns collaborated without hindrance and to their mutual advantage, after that date national politics began to intrude on commercial dealings. With the growing hostility of the German Empire reflected in the Anglo-German naval race, the activities of Krupp were increasingly influenced by its political masters. Although Friedrich Krupp was succeeded as head of the firm by his twenty-year-old daughter Berta, this was not thought to be a satisfactory state of affairs. In any case Grand Admiral von Tirpitz, architect of the German navy, distrusted Krupps, whom he suspected of putting commercial considerations before the national interest. It was partly at his insistence and due to his influence with the Kaiser that the firm was taken in hand and obliged to give certain undertakings. In 1906, following the Kaiser's personal intervention, the career diplomat Gustav Krupp von Bohlen took over the direction of the company. Henceforward its activities were closely monitored by a council of supervision, which ensured that while competing for international business it did nothing likely to work to the detriment of Germany in a future war. Krupp von Bohlen was appointed on the understanding that in return for a virtual monopoly of munitions production for the German armed services he was expected to give absolute priority to furthering the destiny of the German state. So successful was he in pursuing this objective that on the occasion of the Krupp centenary he received the title of envoy extraordinary and minister plenipotentiary of the German Reich.

As the international situation deteriorated so the British and German companies were driven apart in an atmosphere of mutual distrust. This tendency, becoming apparent during the Moroccan crisis of 1906, was accentuated by the Agadir incident of 1911 and the failure of Lord Haldane's mission of 1912, when Great Britain declined to give Germany an assurance that she would remain neutral in the event of a European war. As far as the Royal Navy was concerned, the Entente with France and the destruction of the Russian fleet by the Japanese left the growing German navy as its only likely opponent. Accordingly, the naval race assumed a more critical dimension, being aggravated by not wholly unjustified fears of industrial espionage. It is no accident that this was the period of the German spy scare, of Erskine Childers' *Riddle of the Sands* and the vogue for the thrillers of William le Queux and E Phillips Oppenheim. Although owing more to fiction than reality, these suspicions stimulated the reorganisation and growth of the British Secret Intelligence Service, which originated in the Naval Intelligence Division and had as one of its first priorities the evaluation of the German naval building programme.

To this exercise, Vickers, in the person of Trevor Dawson, made a significant contribution. By virtue of their long-standing contacts with Krupp and other German armament concerns, Vickers' personnel were well placed to keep an eye on developments in the German dockyards and arsenals. Their attitude was not of course disinterested. Within the companies and the Admiralty alike, motives of patriotism mingled with those of personal and commercial advantage. After 1906 Campbell-Bannerman's government was less inclined than its predecessors to favour policies of naval expansion. With spending on warship construction cut back and the 'economists' led by Churchill and Lloyd George seeking further to reduce defence budgets, the Navy League grew worried and the companies felt the chill wind of recession. Clearly it was in the interest of Vickers as well as the Admiralty to persuade the Cabinet that all necessary measures had to be taken to maintain the superiority of the Royal Navy in the face of the threat posed by the build-up of German naval and military might.

Dawson had been active in naval intelligence during the Boer War, and he continued to pass to the Admiralty any information he thought likely to be of value. Having worked closely with successive directors of naval ordnance, he was treated as a colleague by senior figures in the Admiralty, and his knighthood in 1909 may not have been solely for services to the Vickers company—neither Albert nor Tom Vickers was so honoured. Between 1906 and 1914 he took advantage of regular visits to Krupps and other shipyards and arsenals to prepare detailed reports on German battleship construction and armament for submission to Fisher and Churchill at the Admiralty. As early as September 1906, for example, he was noting increased German orders for nickel as 'a practical indication of the great activity in Germany in connection with armaments', giving details of test firings of new 11in guns at Meppen and pointing out that armour plate was being proved 'with 12in capped solid-steel shells—not Krupp, but original Hadfield projectiles with a spherical point under the soft-steel cap'. And in 1908 he was able to give details of an ordnance committee meeting at the Berlin Naval Office on armour and guns for new 'large men-of-war', together with a run-down of shipbuilding production in each of the German yards.

Dawson's dossier on the German naval programme[14] runs to hundreds of pages and contains a mass of technical detail such as could only have come from a number of well-placed informants. Nor is it limited to factual information. Sir Trevor was mainly concerned to emphasise increased activity in the shipyards, but in 1910 he gave it as his opinion that the Germans 'will not allow England to remain superior at sea, as otherwise the commercial and economical development of their country will be compromised, and the natural expansion of their industries will be impaired.' In 1912, commenting on planned increases in the German army, he suggested that: 'Such an army would be thrown into Belgium on the first sign of hostilities, in order to secure the Belgian coast line… with Belgium thus occupied the German Navy…would offer to fight the British Fleet in the North Sea.'

Together with other reports from naval attaches, these revelations helped to convince Asquith's Cabinet that the Germans were, as alleged by the Admiralty and sections of the press, laying down battleships in excess of those announced in the published Navy Laws. The First Lord of the Admiralty, Reginald McKenna, told his young son Stephen of the 'thrilling incidents' which occurred during the critical winter months of 1908-09, 'collecting the evidence about the German navy building programme, how Trevor Dawson skated round the dockyard, I think at Kiel, and actually saw the ships being built, and then the fight in the Cabinet to persuade them of the danger.' All this activity had the desired effect. Opposition from the economists was overcome, steep increases were approved in the Naval Estimates for 1909, and thereafter warship launchings rose year by year.

Apart from vessels supplied to foreign navies (and between them Armstrongs and Vickers controlled two-thirds of the world market for warships and naval ordnance) it has been estimated that: 'The number of capital ships ordered during the four years from 1909-10 to 1912-13…was double that of the four years from 1905-06 to 1908-09, rising from 12 to no less than 24 units. This was accomplished at the same time that spending on fuel, ammunition and the construction of the second class cruisers and destroyers that were required to support the capital units in a fleet action, was also increased substantially.'[15] A contemporary observer noted that: 'So great has been the demand for [post-*Dreadnought* battleships and cruisers] that at the beginning of this year [1911], for Great Britain alone, there were built or building no fewer than twenty-two, and arrangements have been made for laying down five more; while for foreign powers there have been constructed, or were still in the builders' hands…the enormous total of sixty.'

To the extent that what was now known as the British Group of companies was fully stretched to meet this demand, they had less incentive to invest in new projectiles and fuzes for naval guns. While Vickers were doubtless aware of the advances being made by Krupps, their natural inclination was to continue with existing lines of manufacture rather than incur additional expenditure on what from a purely commercial standpoint could be seen as unnecessary commitments to research and development. As it was, their special position enabled them effectively to exclude the products of rival concerns. Vickers' understanding with Krupp in respect of shell

fuzes meant that they were, with the exception of Coventry Ordnance, sole possessors of the manufacturing rights. They had, therefore, an interest in discouraging the development of alternative designs of fuze likely to threaten their monopoly. Although they did on occasion take a firm line, British government departments could not exercise the same control over Vickers and Armstrongs as did the German authorities over Krupp. Provided that the principle of open competition was broadly observed, the British companies were left to get on with a minimum of interference.

Since, moreover, official policies had resulted in the leading British companies becoming dependent for their profits on overseas sales, they tended to be a law unto themselves, jealously guarding an independence in decision-making which did not always accord with national priorities. An allegiance divided between the interests of government departments and shareholders was bound to lead to strains. Despite official remonstrations, Vickers and Armstrongs persisted in regarding trials at their firing ranges as opportunities to demonstrate the latest guns and shells to buyers from abroad. As Trevor Dawson declared in 1906 before a government committee: 'We have projectiles from nearly every market on our range, our own included; we give the foreign officer his choice as to which projectile he wishes to use—Firth's, Armstrongs, sometimes the Government's, and our own.'

The relationship between government departments and the armament companies was, as it has remained, a delicate one. In 1907 an Admiralty official noted that, 'it is impossible to draw a line between what is the outcome of Ordnance Board experiments and what is due to the genius of private firms.' At the same time it had to be recognised that 'the sole object of patenting is to charge a royalty against the manufacture of other firms, which royalty is eventually paid by the Government, and the sole object of publishing is to obtain orders from our foreign rivals'.

With Germany increasingly viewed as a probable future enemy, officials were becoming ever more security conscious. By July 1908 the Department of Naval Ordnance was questioning not only the propriety of Vickers and Armstrongs publishing in their promotional literature information about projectiles and fuzes approved as a result of official trials, but their right to patent them with a view to foreign sales. Was it right that British manufacturers should be selling officially approved shells to foreign powers? By 1908 the answer was obvious. A new Patents Act having tightened up controls, a circular letter was sent to the firms on the Admiralty's list of contractors. Henceforth, participation in Ordnance Board trials was to be on the understanding that information about them was not to be published, patent agreements were not to be entered into without the prior approval of the War Office and the Admiralty, and restrictions were imposed on the sale of projectiles to foreign governments. In 1910 it was laid down that only Admiralty staff and the firms' representatives were allowed to attend trials, and in the following year the Official Secrets Act was extended to cover almost anything that might be considered prejudicial to national security.

The German battleship Helgoland *in 1914. Her laying down in November 1908, armed with new 12in guns, helped persuade the Cabinet to approve increased Naval Estimates the following year.*

Since the Germans were quick to respond in kind, official intervention reinforced the tendency of the great armament conglomerates to polarise along political lines, with Krupps drawing closer to Skoda of Austria-Hungary and the British Group of companies to Schneider-Creusot. In 1909 Dawson reported to Fisher: 'I was well received [at the Hamburg shipbuilders Blohm and Voss], but was informed that it was strictly against the orders of the Ministry of Marine to show foreigners over the yard...', and shortly afterwards the British naval attaché in Berlin was refused permission to attend gun trials or even to visit the shipyards. Such mutual suspicion was bound to affect the exchange of technical information on such matters as the design of projectiles and fuzes. If British firms were prevented from dealing as before with their German colleagues they could hardly expect to benefit from reciprocal arrangements, and Krupps, under the watchful eye of the council of supervision, became increasingly reluctant to make known the results of their cointinuing research.

Limiting the freedom of British companies to sell abroad also meant that the difficult and costly business of developing new projectiles became a less attractive proposition. In time of peace, the volume of demand for gun ammunition was low, and Vickers and Armstrongs preferred to direct their expertise into more profitable channels, leaving the design of new shells to Hadfields and Firth, and their manufacture to the royal ordnance factories. They continued to produce shells which were tested at their firing ranges and to charge royalties on

existing components such as fuzes, but they were not concerned to press for change. In these circumstances few improvements were made in the quality of the Royal Navy's projectiles during the years before 1914. The lack of a fully effective armour-piercing shell was accepted on the assumption that since such shell would be used only at relatively short range, striking at little more than right angles to the armour plate, no improvement was necessary. As to the Ordnance Board's experiments with TNT fillings, the Admiralty's technical history records simply that: 'It was decided not to continue these trials mainly owing to the necessity for employing a gaine and fulminate detonator in conjunction with the fuze...' [16]

Meanwhile firing exercises tended to bear out the Admiralty's faith in the existing provision of heavy shell. In November 1913 trials took place off Portland to try out Percy Scott's central director gear and test the ability of several ships at once to concentrate their fire on an old battleship, *Empress of India*. 'Few officers present,' it was suggested, 'can have taken part in [earlier firings]; few had therefore any clear idea as to the difference between gunnery at a battle-practice target and at a ship.' The *Empress of India* was extensively damaged by common and practice shell and the outcome was thought to be satisfactory, although results with regard to the director gear were inconclusive and none of the projectiles succeeded in sinking the target vessel. Neither APC nor HE lyddite was used because of their high cost, and the old ship eventually foundered after a prolonged pounding, 'so many hits causing innumerable small leaks at rivets etc'.

The battleship Queen Elizabeth *taking on board 15 inch ammunition.*

Early in 1912, responding to reports that the German, American and Japanese navies were moving up to guns of 14in calibre, Churchill and the Department of Naval Ordnance resolved to go one better. Amid much secrecy Armstrongs and Vickers were asked to come up with the design of a new 15in gun which was approved within the year. Trials of projectiles produced by Woolwich and the trade were arranged during 1913, but in view of continuing experiments with TNT there was uncertainty about the choice of burster and fuze to be employed. Until firm decisions could be taken the placing of orders with manufacturers had to be delayed, and so, when the first of the new fast division of 15in gun battleships, the *Queen Elizabeth*, was commissioned early in 1915, only CPC shells filled with black powder were available for her use.

Nor was the unsatisfactory situation with regard to armour-piercing shell improved by the testing and inspection procedures of the Ordnance Board, which continued up to 1914 to prove samples of such shell by firing them at normal impact, that is at right angles to the armour plate. This was no doubt felt to be reasonable given that the APC projectile was expected to be used at relatively short range, but is nonetheless surprising given that the angle of attack was known directly to affect its performance. In general, the proving process did not inspire confidence. A former president of the Board, Vice-Admiral Sir Francis Pridham, explained that: 'The system of proof was more or less determined by the shell makers, and was such that in the opinion of the Board,

the only assumption that could make sense of the procedure was that all shell were good shell and that failures were few and due to the machinations of malignant spirits!' Following firing tests against armour plate, batches of shell were frequently passed into service even though a high proportion were incapable of penetrating the plate whole, and many shell which had failed to pass the standard test were issued to the fleet without even being distinctively marked.

It seems clear that these arrangements were designed to suit the convenience of the shell manufacturers rather than the navy. The technical experts of the firms to which the supply of shell was contracted worked closely with their service colleagues, and all concerned were anxious to avoid the cost and delay resulting from wholesale rejections of projectiles which under normal peacetime conditions (and the Royal Navy had fought no major war for a hundred years) were unlikely to be fired other than in practice. That the manufacturers should have been undemanding in the matter of proof is not surprising, but occasionally they pushed their luck too far. Vickers were reprimanded more than once, and in 1907 Cammell Laird were for a time struck off the list of contractors for attempting to pass faulty work. In 1910 the chief inspector of naval ordnance reported that 'in nearly all cases where ordnance stores of any kind are rejected by the Inspection Department strong pressure is brought by the trade to obtain a reversal of the decision...theoretical reasons are advanced to account for the failure at proof....Applications from firms for re-test or re-proof are frequent and continuous.'

In their dealings with the press, Admiralty spokesmen were concerned to emphasise the weight and the large bursting charge of British naval shell rather than their effect. They pointed out that the German 11in and 12in shell weighed only 700lb and 980lb respectively compared with the 1400lb and 1950lb of the British 13.5in and 15in shell, implying that the destructive effect of the Royal Navy's firepower was that much greater than that of the German High Seas Fleet. But it remained to be demonstrated whether the comparison was justified. The Germans, utilising what was widely acknowledged to be a superior metallurgy, chose to concentrate on smaller-calibre, high-velocity guns, and to put the weight thus saved into better armour and underwater protection. While in theory the heavier British armour-piercing shells were capable of perforating one calibre, or 12-15 inches, of armour plate compared with the German 11-12 inches, the Germans believed their lighter shells to be at least as effective because technically more advanced in terms of steel casing, bursting charge and fuze.

Admiral Bacon, DNO from 1907-09, noted in his memoir *From 1900 Onwards* that when he left the Admiralty 'the armour-piercing qualities of shell were under investigation and trial; and although the Germans in the war...were superior to us in this munition, such advantage was undoubtedly due to their superior technique in steel manufacture, rather than to any lack of foresight on the part of my successor.' There is, however, reason to believe that the Department of Naval Ordnance was ill-prepared to cope with the demands made on it at a time of rapid technological change. It was under-staffed and over-worked, and, since directors were transferred every two years in line with the practice of alternating personnel between shore and sea duty, followed no clear and consistent policy. Nor can the specialist knowledge of senior officers from Fisher and Jellicoe downwards be taken for granted. Fisher, suggests Professor Sumida, 'lacked any understanding of the technical issues, and as a consequence reduced the gunnery question to a matter of changing personnel'. Thus his response to unsatisfactory reports on the battle practice of 1911 was to recommend the replacement of Moore by Frederick Tudor as director of naval ordnance. This lack of expertise did not pass unnoticed. In 1912, A H Pollen, pioneer of fire control systems, wrote to Percy Scott: 'The real truth about the cursedly inept gunnery policy that has prevailed since 1907 is that neither Bacon nor Moore were either of them in the minutest degree Artillerists; by this I mean that there was not a single branch of practical naval artillery technique in which... they were even competent to understanding the leading points.'

Following the Admiralty's taking over responsibility for naval stores, it was announced that Lieutenant John Duncan RN, 'an able and zealous officer', had been seconded to the War Office for special duty as proof and experimental officer at Woolwich Arsenal. After a period in charge of work at the proof butts, he was promoted to lieutenant commander and chief inspector of naval ordnance, in which capacity, as we have seen, he sat as one of the naval members on the Board of Ordnance. Duncan was an obvious candidate when in time to come it was sought to apportion blame for the failure to draw attention to the shortcomings of naval shell. Arthur Marder, on the authority of Frederic Dreyer, at first cited him as 'the person mainly responsible for the shell deficiency', a statement he later withdrew as 'I have only the Admiral's opinion, without supporting facts, and were he alive...he might wish to qualify the charge.' This is indeed likely, for Dreyer must have known that the trouble stemmed from a combination of circumstances rather than negligence on the part of any one individual. Whatever the cause the damage had been done, and in 1914 the Grand Fleet put to sea with the most imposing array of capital ships ever seen and equipped with the most powerful guns ever known, but with its stock of heavy projectiles inadequately proven and of doubtful effectiveness.

Notes

1 Oscar Parkes, *British Battleships, 1860-1950* (1966), p. 315.
2 J D Scott, *Vickers, a History* (1963), p 115
3 Zentralstelle fur Wissentschaftlich-Technische Untersuchungen
4 This and subsequent quotations are taken from the *Record of the Principal Questions dealt with by the Director of Naval Ordnance*, published each year from 1891 onwards.
5 *Maritime Operations in the Russo-Japanese War, 1904-05* (1914), vol I, p 404
6 These and other changes were duly noted by the Admiralty in CB 47 : *The Russo-Japanese war from the point of view of naval gunnery*, issued by the Naval Ordnance Department in 1906.
7 V Semenoff, *The Battle of Tsu-Shima* (1906) and A Novikoff-Priboy, *Tsushima: Grave of a Floating City* (1937)
8 From *Naval Necessities*, a series of dissertations circulated by Fisher to his fellow officers in the autumn of 1904.
9 Admiral Sir Frederic Dreyer, *The Sea Heritage, a Study of Maritime Warfare* (1955), p 60
10 Ordnance Board Report No 2 : *Lyddite shells, designs, strengths and firing trials*, March 1908
11 Ordnance Board Report No 23 : *The filling of high capacity HE common and AP shell*, April 1910
12 Although delivery took time. According to the Admiralty's *Survey of Progress in Gunnery*, 1911, the projectiles supplied for the 13.5in guns of the King George V class battleships 'will probably include AP filled lyddite, instead of AP filled powder'.
13 While serving in the Mediterranean he had written letters critical of his admiral, Sir Charles Beresford, to Fisher, who later chose to make their contents public. The ensuing rumpus led to Bacon's resignation and may have influenced Fisher's decision to retire from the Admiralty.
14 *Secret Reports by Commander Sir A Trevor Dawson to Admiralty, 1906-14, as result of visits made to Continent at request of First Lord of the Admiralty and as collected through special agencies*, Manuscripts Department, Imperial War Museum (Misc 1085).
15 J T Sumida, *In Defence of Naval Supremacy, Finance, Technology and British Naval Policy, 1889-1914* (1989)
16 Admiralty Technical History, *Ammunition for Naval Guns* (TH29), May 1920

THE AIRCRAFT TRANSPORT COMMANDANT TESTE

Following the First World War, the French *Marine Nationale* hesitated between the fleet aircraft-carrier and the mobile aviation base. The conversion of the incomplete hull of the battleship *Béarn* to a fleet carrier in the British mould was followed by the construction of a purpose-built *transport d'aviation*, the *Commandant Teste*. Here, **John Jordan** examines the development of a ship that was to remain unique in conception.

France's first seaplane, the Canard, flew on 28 March 1910. A commission set up in the days which followed concluded, to the surprise of many in the service, that the future of naval aviation lay in the operation of wheeled aircraft from large vessels fitted with a flying-off deck forward, equipped with guide rails to assist launch, and a flying-on deck aft covered in mattresses to assist landing. A certain Captain Daveluy was appointed in 1911 to oversee developments in maritime aviation. He proposed the construction of an naval air base near Fréjus, and the conversion of an elderly cruiser, the *Foudre*, as a mobile base for reconnaissance seaplanes, but received little support from the military establishment for these proposals and resigned in December of the same year.

However, the ever-widening interest in aviation was to result in most of Daveluy's proposals being implemented under his successor, Captain Fatou, and on 12 March 1912 the Naval Air Service, l'Aviation Maritime, was established by presidential decree. The cruiser *Foudre* was duly converted, receiving a short flying-off deck in 1913-14, and was subsequently used for trials with a variety of seaplanes. These trials were effectively cut short by the outbreak of war, and from the end of 1914 *Foudre* would serve as a repair ship for the French Mediterranean Squadron, the hangar being converted into workshops.

The Fleet Carrier Béarn

Trials with both seaplanes and wheeled aircraft were resumed in late 1918 under the aegis of the newly established Aviation d'Escadre, under the direction of the dynamic Lieutenant de Vaisseau Paul Teste. These early trials were beset by problems, particularly in achieving the platform launch of wheeled fighters from ships. There was considerable interest in the developments that had been proceeding on the other side of the Channel, and a commission duly visited the newly completed aircraft-carrier *Argus* in 1920. It was subsequently recommended that a battleship of the *Normandie* class be converted as a fleet carrier. (A virtually identical project was already underway in Great Britain with the conversion of the battleship *Almirante Cochrane*, originally laid down for Chile; she would be renamed *Eagle* and although substantially complete by 1920 would not run full trials until late 1923). *Projet 171* incorporated this proposal alongside the abandonment of battleship construction and a new building programme comprising six cruisers and twelve torpilleurs-éclaireurs.

The Washington Conference then intervened. According to its provisions, France would be allocated 60,000 tons of carrier construction. The Marine Nationale therefore decided to proceed with the proposed conversion of the battleship *Béarn*, the hull of which was virtually complete up to the lower armoured deck, and this decision was formalised in the 1922 tranche of the new Naval Programme. *Béarn* was, however, regarded as essentially an experimental design, the intention being to complete two purpose-built 30,000-ton 'aircraft-carrying cruisers' (*croiseurs porte-avions*) at a later date. In the event the latter project was accorded low priority, since Germany was not permitted to build carriers and Italy did not consider them necessary given her advantageous geostrategic situation astride the Mediterranean. In a period of financial stringency, money spent on these ships would reduce the number of cruisers, flotilla craft and submarines which could be built, and it was only in the late 1930s that the Marine Nationale would again contemplate the construction of fast, purpose-built carriers of new design (Project PA 16 of the 1938 Programme).

The *Béarn* was similar in size and capability to the Royal Navy's *Eagle*. Her primary missions were defined as follows:

scouting for a naval force at sea;

attacks on enemy bases out of range of land-based aviation;

torpedo and bomb attacks on enemy vessels.

However, the Marine Nationale was to experience serious problems in developing torpedo-bombers that could be launched from a flight deck. The design of the ship therefore incorporated a 20m access bay for the embarkation of large bomb-capable seaplanes aft. These could be lowered by crane into the water, from which they would take off to attack enemy ships or shore installations.

There are no indications that such seaplanes were ever embarked on *Béarn*. It was initially envisaged that there would be two squadrons each of twelve reconnaissance aircraft, plus a single squadron of eight fighter aircraft. One of the two recconnaissance squadrons would eventually be replaced by a squadron of torpedo-bombers; this was made possible with the entry into service of the Levasseur PL7 in 1930. However, French thinking during the early 1920s with regard to the possibilities and limitations of heavy maritime bombers was to have a clear impact on the intended purpose and design of the *Commandant Teste*.

Commandant Teste

With the decision to complete the hull of the battleship *Béarn* as an aircraft-carrier, attention turned to the other strand of French naval aviation thinking, the *centre mobile*, or mobile aviation base, which had been under consideration for some time. In 1923 the General Staff requested a second carrier with similar missions to those defined for *Béarn*. Ideally this ship would be a second *porte-avions d'escadre*, but it was accepted that in the absence of a suitable hull for modification this would be an expensive solution.

The General Staff was therefore prepared to accept a *transport d'aviation*, which would be cheaper to build and could be completed more quickly. Such a ship could serve as a mobile base for seaplane squadrons deployed overseas, and in wartime would have an auxiliary function, serving as a repair and replenishment vessel to support other warships equipped with aircraft. Initial requirements were for a ship equipped with two catapults capable of launching a 2500kg aircraft (such a catapult was already under development for the new 10,000-ton cruisers), an air complement of nine scout seaplanes and six float fighters, a speed of 17 knots, and a minimum AA armament of four single 75mm guns. It was thought that an ocean liner might prove suitable for conversion. However, this solution implied a displacement above 10,000 tons, which would then have to be counted as part of the 60,000-ton allowance allocated to France by the terms of the Washington Treaty. Other possibilities were therefore considered, including:

the conversion of a freighter such as the *Jacques Cartier* (judged too slow);

the conversion of an armoured cruiser (a similar study of the *Amiral Aube* had been undertaken in 1919);

a purpose-built ship with a speed of 18-20 knots and nine seaplanes.

Commandant Teste *running sea trials in July 1931, without armament. With her experimental superheated steam propulsion plant she would comfortably attain her designed speed of 21 knots. The alternative coal-firing of the after boilers significantly increased an otherwise limited operational radius.* (Marius Bar)

The limited capacity of contemporary catapults continued to be a problem. The standard land-based bomber of the period was a lumbering biplane built of wood and canvas with a take-off weight of between four and six tons. An early proposal, dated December 1923, was for a transport capable of accommodating twelve Lioré et Olivier (LeO) H 10 scout seaplanes (launch weight: 2400kg) equipped with folding wings, to be stowed in a hold and lowered three at a time into the water by crane from an open section of deck. The ship's armament was to be four 14cm guns in casemates, four 75mm AA and between nine and twelve machine guns.

The *transport d'aviation* as a type was deemed promising, and in September 1924 the General Staff proposed that two such ships should feature in the *Statut Naval*, and that the STCAN (Services Techniques des Construction et Armes Navales) should begin technical studies. In November of the same year, the design team came up with a draft proposal for a 16-knot ship with the armament outlined above, able to accommodate twelve aircraft, of which the three largest would be carried fully-assembled and ready for launch on deck. Operational radius was a mere 2000nm – i.e. sufficient for transit to the French colonies in North Africa and the Middle East. The ship would have a dual role as a mobile seaplane base, providing repair and maintenance facilities together with accommodation for the crews, and as a seaplane transport for a specific attack mission. It was subsequently decided that this would be a new-build ship, and would be ordered with a view to construction being started in late 1925.

As the design evolved, further significant changes were made. The air complement was boosted to six large seaplane bombers of 5.5 tonnes, to be lowered into the water by crane, and 14 float-scouts and fighters, to be launched by catapult. The anti-surface armament was six or eight single 138.6mm guns, while the anti-aircraft armament was set at four 75mm and four 37mm guns, and twelve 8mm machine guns. On a displacement close to the 10,000tW permitted by the Treaty, and with overall dimensions of 154m by 22.5m, the ship would have a maximum speed of 19 knots (17,000shp).

By July 1927 considerable emphasis was being placed on the independent base characteristics of the ship. The aviation complement had by now grown to twenty-four aircraft: eight float planes for reconnaissance and self-defence, launched from four 2500kg catapults and carried on the upper deck; and no fewer than sixteen giant Farman Goliath torpedo bombers, of which ten would be housed in a hangar 100m by 17m, with a further six in crates carried in the hold.

Further studies of the propulsion system led to proposals F and G, presented by the STCAN in November 1925: design F featured a unit propulsion layout with twin funnels outboard and *en echelon*, and a hangar for six 5.5-tonne bombers; design G had a conventional propulsion layout with the boiler rooms adjacent and a single centre-line funnel, and a shorter, broader hangar divided into two by the intakes and uptakes for the machinery rooms, capable of accommodating ten 5.5-tonne bombers. The General Staff opted for an amalgam of these two designs, with the hangar of design G and the

This port quarter view, taken during sea trials, shows clearly the large double doors of the hangar structure which occupied approximately half the ship's length. The low quarterdeck, served by a single 7-tonne crane, was used for the assembly and embarkation of the large Levasseur PL 14/15 torpedo bomber. (Marius Bar)

COMMANDANT TESTE

Name	Builder	Laid down	Launched	In service
1925 Programme				
Commandant Teste	FC de la Gironde	06.09.27	12.04.29	18.04.32

CHARACTERISTICS (as completed)

Displacement:	10,000 tons standard
	11,500 tonnes normal
	12,134 tonnes full load
Length:	156m pp, 167m oa
Beam:	21.7m wl, 27m flight deck
Draught:	6.7m
Machinery:	Four Yarrow-Loire small watertube superheated boilers (two oil-fired, two oil/coal-fired)
	20kg/cm² (290 degrees); two-shaft Schneider-Zoelly geared steam turbines for 23,230shp;
	speed 21kts (designed)
Oil fuel:	1163 tonnes oil, 700t coal; radius 2000nm at 18kts + 2500nm at 10kts on coal
Armament:	Twelve 100mm/45 Model 1927 guns in single mountings (2760 rounds + 480 starshell + 120 tracer);
	eight 37mm/50 Model 1925 guns on single mountings (4000 rounds);
	twelve 13.2mm/76 Model 1929 Hotchkiss MGs in twin mountings Model 1931
Aircraft:	Ten Levasseur PL.14 torpedo-bombers, fourteen Gourdou-Leseurre 811 reconnaissance seaplanes
Protection:	magazines: 20-50mm; machinery bulkhead: 40mm; side belt: 36-50mm;
	deck: 24-36mm; steering gear: 26mm; conning tower: 30-80mm
Complement:	42 officers + 602 men

unit propulsion system of design F, the twin funnels being on the centre-line (these were later trunked together as a single funnel amidships).

The final design was approved by the General Staff in December 1925. The new ship, by now christened *Commandant Teste* in memory of the man who had done so much to make French naval aviation a reality, was part of the 1925 *tranche* of the Naval Programme, but construction was delayed for one year.

It was now envisaged that the air complement would comprise ten Farman Goliath torpedo-bombers, of which eight would be housed in the hangar and two would be carried dismantled in crates in the hold; and twelve fighter/recce floatplanes, of which four would be readied on the catapults, four would be in the hangar (they replaced two Farman Goliaths), and four in crates in the hold. Twenty torpedoes were to be stowed in the hangar, the warheads and bombs (up to 700kg) being stowed in a magazine deep in the hull, and 80 tonnes of aviation fuel was to be provided. When employed as a transport, the ship would carry twelve Goliaths, twelve recce floatplanes, and thirty-six aero engines.

The project was passed to the Conseil Général for approval in March 1926, by which time propulsive power had been increased to 20 knots by the adoption of a new superheated steam plant. It was felt that the *transport d'aviation* as a type had certain advantages over the *Béarn*. It could operate large, long-range torpedo bombers; by keeping displacement to 10,000tW it escaped the Washington Treaty constraints; and cost was relatively low. On the other hand there were clear limitations in the ways in which the ship could be employed. Operations in adverse weather conditions were impossible (they were in any case marginal with fleet carriers, given the aircraft and the technology of the day!); and she could not operate at sea with the main battle fleet due to her lack of stability.

Hull and Superstructures

The general configuration of the *Commandant Teste* was essentially that of a cruiser hull topped by a massive box hangar, the forecastle being raised to the same height as the hangar. The lower hull housed the machinery spaces with a single deck above (see inboard profile), which in the area of the hangar housed workshops, washrooms and messdecks. In a break with tradition, officers' accommodation was located forward. The broad forecastle section, which was five decks high, allowed a generous allocation of space to the crew; facilities included a recreation room and an eight-berth hospital.

At the after end of the forecastle was a raised structure incorporating an enclosed bridge, with a prominent pole foremast angled at 2.5 degrees, the forward AA guns being disposed forward and to the sides. The single funnel, which was broadly in the centre of the ship, was set into a two-deck structure with wing platforms extending almost to the ship's sides on which much of the light AA weaponry was mounted. There was a small built-up after structure atop the after end of the hangar to accommodate the after AA guns, surmounted by a second pole mast at an identical angle to the foremast, the main R/T aerials being slung between the two pole masts, and between the mainmast and the funnel.

The double hangar measured approximately 80m by 26.5m and was three decks (7m) high; it was divided into two by a longitudinal partition which incorporated the exhaust uptakes for the funnel and the ventilation trunking for the machinery rooms. The hangar was designed to accommodate ten large torpedo-bombers with folding wings; two folding-wing recce floatplanes could be stowed in place of each of the bombers (see cutaway drawing). Two additional large torpedo-bombers and four reconnaissance seaplanes were carried dismantled in cases stowed in a hold beneath the hangar. There was magazine space for twenty 450mm torpedoes, together with bombs ranging from 75kg to 700kg, and 75 tonnes of aviation fuel was provided in two tanks abaft the machinery spaces.

A system of Décauville rails extended through each half-hangar onto the low quarterdeck, the floatplanes being moved on wheeled trolleys. Once the massive torpedo-bombers had been prepared and wings deployed on

the quarterdeck, they were lowered into the water by a 7-tonne crane with a reach of 5-12m located on the centre-line directly above the stern.

A prototype landing 'mat' for seaplanes was trialled in the cruiser *Foch* during late 1931, then transferred to the *Commandant Teste* on the arrival of the cruiser at Toulon and again trialled during May/June 1932. An order for a Kiwul-type mat was duly placed in October 1934, and it was installed during February/March of the following year. The floating section of the mat measured 12m by 7.8m, while the upper section was 8.5m long. The mat was only partially successful, imposing serious constraints on the operation of the mother ship during recovery operations; speed was limited to 6 knots during the aircraft's approach, and embarkation then took a further twenty to thirty minutes. The mats, which were also fit-

Commandant Teste: *profile and plan views*
The profile and plan views are based on official plans dated Bordeaux 11 April 1934. The 100mm AA mountings have yet to be fitted with shields, but the revised light AA armament is in place. Note the large sliding hatch covers atop the hangar roof in the plan view.
(Drawn by the author)

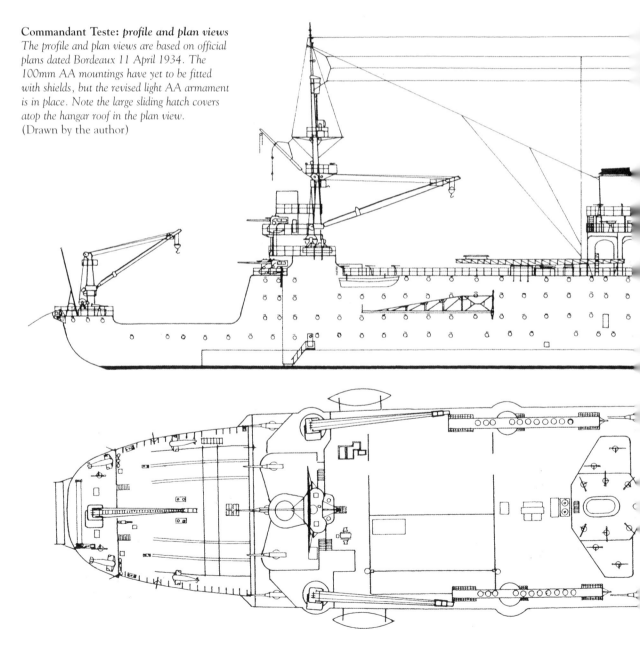

ted in the 7600-tonne cruisers of the *La Galissonnière* class, proved to be a maintenance nightmare, and were eventually removed from all ships.

Access to the hangar roof was via two large rectangular openings approximately 15m by 7m, covered by sliding hatches. Access for the port-side half-hangar was forward, that for the starboard-side half-hangar aft (see plan drawing). Four Penhoët compressed air catapults with a 20.5m boom and an initial launch capacity of 2.5 tonnes were fitted atop the hangar close to the deck edge. Used for launching the recce/fighter floatplanes, these proved particularly successful; in 1938 they were modified to permit the launch of the larger and heavier Loire 130, capacity being raised to 3.5 tonnes.

The hatches and catapults were served by four powerful cranes, mounted at the four corners of the hangar; each had a reach of 6-18m and could lift 12 tonnes (the forward cranes were also employed to handle the ship's boats). The cranes were judged robust but complex to operate and maintain. During trials in 1937 it took an estimated three hours to embark or disembark a flotilla of sixteen aircraft, seventeen minutes to embark a single GL 812 reconnaissance floatplane, and seven minutes to launch a section of four Gourdou floatplanes by catapult.

Machinery and Protection

The propulsion plant selected for the *Commandant Teste* was a mix of the traditional and the ultra-modern. Two of the four small-tube Loire-Yarrow boilers, rated at 20km/cm², had alternative coal-firing, while all four had

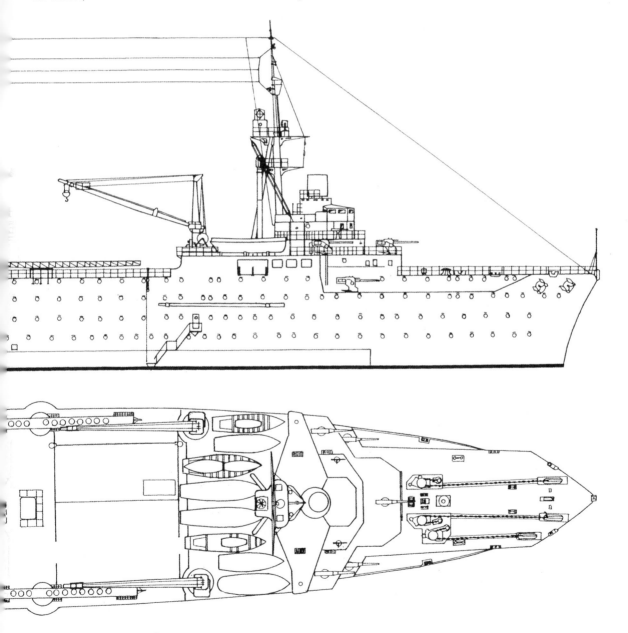

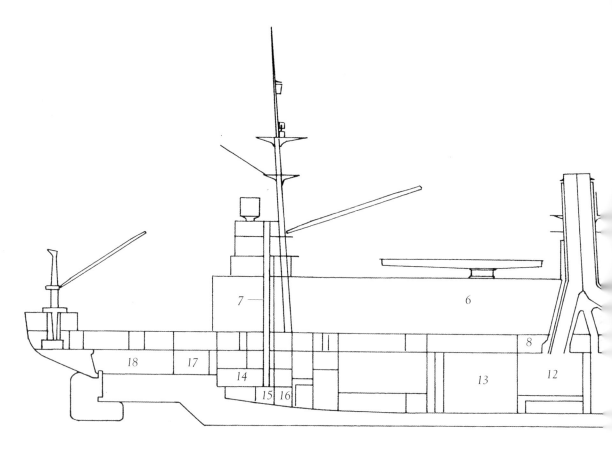

superheaters, rated at 290 degrees. The boilers were disposed in pairs in two boiler rooms separated by the forward engine room, the uptakes for the forward pair being angled aft to the single funnel amidships. The dual oil/coal-fired boilers were located in the after boiler room.

This was the first application of superheating in the Marine Nationale, the British and the Italians having recently adopted it for their latest destroyers. Unsurprisingly it was not a complete success, and modifications had to be made to the superheaters following trials, but it made possible a high power-to-weight ratio, and superheating would subsequently be extended to the later classes of *contre-torpilleur* and to the 7600-tonne cruisers of the *La Galissonnière* class.

There were two sets of Schneider-Zoelly direct-action geared steam turbines, each powering one of the two shafts and completely independent in operation, so that action damage or breakdown in one engine room would have no effect on the other. Each set comprised an HP and an LP turbine; a cruise turbine was linked to the shaft powered by the HP turbine via reduction gearing, while the reversing turbine was incorporated into the LP turbine. The cruise turbine was declutched above 12 knots and steam admitted into the HP turbine.

Apart from the problems experienced with the superheaters, the propulsion machinery was judged to be generally satisfactory and the designed power loading and maximum speed were both exceeded on trials. On 23 July 1933 just over 22 knots were attained on one run, and

the sustained speed of 20.5 knots over ten hours at normal power loading demanded in the contract was comfortably achieved.

Electrical supply was at 235V 'cruiser' standard. There were two turbo-generators each rated at 300kW (400kW max.), and three diesel generators rated at 150kW (180kW max.), primarily for use when alongside.

Protection for the machinery rooms and magazines was provided on a scale comparable to that of the cruiser *Suffren*, which was a close contemporary of the *Commandant Teste*, and employed the same 'armoured-box' principle. The machinery spaces were protected by a longitudinal bulkhead reinforced to 40mm from the keel to the main deck, enclosed at the ends by partial transverse bulkheads of 20mm. The magazines had 50mm walls with 20mm ends and ceilings. Outboard there was a reinforced belt 3.76m deep comprising two widths of 18mm plate (increasing to 20mm + 30 mm abeam the machinery spaces). The main armoured deck was constructed of double plates of 12mm steel (reinforced to 12mm + 12mm + 12mm above the boiler rooms). The steering gear was protected by 26mm of steel plate, while the conning tower had 80mm walls with a 30mm roof. All armour was of 60kg steel except for the decks, steering gear and walls of the CT, which were of 50kg steel.

There was concern from the outset that such a high-sided vessel would prove to be unsteady in rougher sea conditions, the bulky hangar acting like a sail in high winds. The weight of armour and machinery in the lower

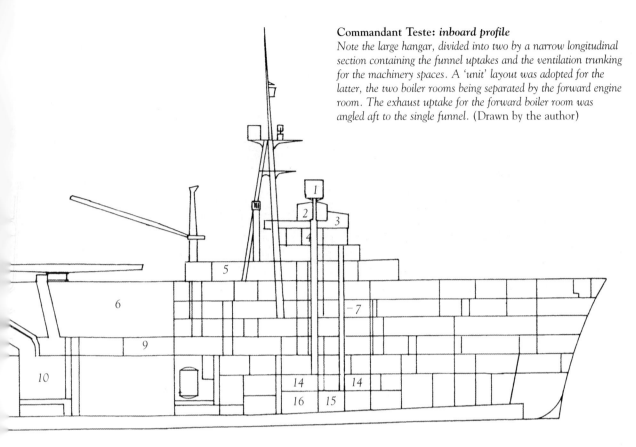

Commandant Teste: *inboard profile*
Note the large hangar, divided into two by a narrow longitudinal section containing the funnel uptakes and the ventilation trunking for the machinery spaces. A 'unit' layout was adopted for the latter, the two boiler rooms being separated by the forward engine room. The exhaust uptake for the forward boiler room was angled aft to the single funnel. (Drawn by the author)

Key to Inboard Profile:

1. HA/LA DCT for 100mm guns
2. conning tower
3. navigation bridge
4. main W/T office
5. dynamo room
6. aircraft hangar
7. 100mm hoists
8. after W/T office
9. workshops
10. fwd boiler room
11. fwd engine room
12. aft boiler room
13. aft engine room
14. 100mm magazines
15. 37mm magazines
16. bomb magazines
17. aviation fuel tank
18. steering gear

part of the hull contributed to stability, but there was also a concentration of weight high in the ship in the form of catapults, heavy cranes and AA artillery. It was therefore decided to fit a stabilisation system comprising two lateral tanks with a pressurized butterfly valve between. Trials in the long Atlantic swell off Morocco in 1933 were rated a complete success; the stabilisation system effectively deadened the roll of the ship by between 37 and 65 per cent. However, in the longer term the system was found to be difficult to maintain because of the difficulty of access to the tanks, and it was to remain experimental.

Artillery

In the early stages of the ship's design the Conseil Supérieur was particularly anxious to provide *Commandant Teste* with an anti-surface armament capable of protecting the ship against destroyers, submarines and even small cruisers. Following a demand for the complement of 138.6mm guns to be raised from four to six, it requested that range for this weapon be increased to 24,000 metres. Both the heavyweight Model 1910 and

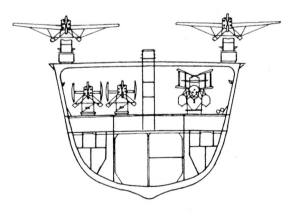

Commandant Teste: *cross-section at frame 54*
Each of the two half-hangars was designed to accommodate five (maximum six) large torpedo-bombers with wings folded; two reconnaissance seaplanes could be accommodated side by side in place of a single bomber. The planes were moved using wheeled trolleys on the twin rails which ran through the hangars and out onto the low quarterdeck, where the torpedo-bombers were prepared for launch. (Drawn by the author)

Commandant Teste at anchor in July 1931. The four large cranes atop the hangar, each of which had a 12-tonne capacity and a maximum reach of 18m, served the catapults and the access hatches to the hangar, and also (as in this view) handled the ship's boats, (Marius Bar)

four of the latest 155mm Model 1920 were considered, each involving a weight penalty of 60 tonnes. During this time the AA armament remained at four 75mm plus four 37mm guns, although it was proposed in August 1926 that this be increased by two 75mm and four 37mm guns (rangefinders for AA fire were considered unnecessary for wartime operations, so none were to be provided!).

By 1927, however, increasing recognition was being accorded to the aerial threat, and in August it was finally decided to suppress the anti-surface armament in its entirety, and to replace both the 138.6mm and the 75mm with a homogeneous battery of twelve single 100mm/45 Model 1927. The *Commandant Teste* was the only ship to receive this model (the Model 1932 was similar but had restricted elevation). The 100mm Model 1927 was a modern weapon with a sliding breech and alternative electro-mechanical or mechanical firing, and had a maximum elevation of 85 degrees. The mounting was designed for remote power control (RPC) in elevation and bearing, with manual operation and optical sights for back-up. A dual-purpose gun, it could fire the OPf Model 1927 armour-piercing shell or the OEA Model 1925S HE shell, of which 1840 proximity-fuzed and 920 percussion-fuzed rounds were to be provided. There was also magazine space for 480 rounds of star shell and 120 rounds of tracer.

The 100mm guns were disposed in three groups, each served by their own magazines and hoists; there were five mountings grouped around the forward superstructure, with a similar layout aft, and two mountings amid-

ships atop the hangar, located at the deck edge between the catapults. Production delays resulted in the late delivery of the mountings, which were installed only in October 1932. Protective shields with a thickness of 5mm were fitted during a refit in late 1935. The gun was generally successful in operation, but subsequently underwent a number of modifications to improve its performance against surface targets. The RPC also proved to be unreliable, as with other French gun mountings of the period.

The single 37mm/50 Model 1925, of which there were eight in the final design, were disposed as follows: two forward, two aft, and four on the wing platforms extending to port and starboard of the single funnel. They were installed during 1931. At the same time it was decided that the relatively ineffectual 8mm MG originally envisaged would be replaced by six of the new Hotchkiss twin 13.2mm mountings Model 1929. These would eventually be fitted in the bridge wings forward, on the upper funnel platform amidships, and on either side of the centre-line crane above the stern (see plan view).

Two fire-control directors, disposed fore and aft respectively and each equipped with a stereoscopic 3m range-finder, were provided for the 100mm guns. They provided control against both surface and aerial targets. It was later proposed that the range-finders be upgraded to a 5-metre base to improve performance against surface targets, but this modification was never carried out. There was also a single 1m range-finder forward of the single funnel for the midships 37mm mountings.

Air Group

The *Commandant Teste* was laid down only in September 1927, and construction at the Chantiers de la Gironde shipyard took just over three years. Extensive trials culminated in her entry into service with the First (Mediterranean) Squadron in April 1934.

Her air group, the *Flotille de Commandant Teste*, was formed on 1 September 1931. The lengthy gestation period of the ship meant that significant developments in naval aircraft had taken place in the interim. The scout floatplane to be carried was a folding-wing version of the Gourdou Leseurre GL 810. The Farman Goliath was by this time obsolete, and would be replaced by the Levasseur PL 14. No suitable float fighter had been developed by this time, so the first aviation complement would be built around the latter two types.

The scouting squadron, designated 7S2, was officially in service in October 1931. It was equipped as a temporary measure with the fixed-wing GL 810, which would be replaced by the folding-wing GL 811 variant in October 1933. An improved GL 813 model was embarked from early 1936. The Gourdou-Leseurre was a twin-float monoplane which proved very successful in service; maximum take-off weight was just below the 2500kg limit of the Penhoët catapult of the day, and the aircraft was to remain the standard French shipborne reconnaissance aircraft until the late 1930s, when it was replaced by the Loire 130. The latter was a much heavier aircraft, weighing in at 3500kg, and the existing catapults had to be modified in order to handle it. The Loire 130 replaced the GL 813 aboard the *Commandant Teste* from April 1938.

The torpedo-bomber squadron, designated 7B2, was officially in service from January 1932, but did not receive its first aircraft until April. The Levasseur PL 14 was adapted from a land-based bomber and had a take-off weight of 4250kg. Twelve were built, but the type remained in service for only a short period as it proved too fragile for landing at sea, the engine cowling sustaining frequent damage. It was succeeded by the PL 15, which entered service in July/August 1934 and remained in service until shortly before the Second World War. The PL 15 was replaced by the first genuinely modern torpedo-bomber to serve with the Marine Nationale, the Latécoère 298, which entered service March/May 1939. With a top speed of 295km/h and a payload of a single 400mm torpedo or two 150kg bombs, this aircraft was highly regarded by all those who flew in it; 130 were built, and it was used extensively during the Battle for France in May/June 1940, albeit not in the role for which it was intended.

In peacetime a reduced aviation complement was embarked. In practice this meant two/three sections each of three aircraft for the GL 810 series, plus an additional aircraft for the officer commanding the flotilla (it was given a distinctive pennant marking on the sides of the fuselage), and two sections each of three torpedo bombers. On 1 October 1938 the scouting squadron was redesignated HS1 (*Hydravions de Surveillance*), and the bomber squadron HB1 (*Hydravions de Bombardement*); at the same time the *Flotille de Commandant Teste* became F1H.

The catapult fighter long planned to provide a self-defence capability for this and other ships finally became a reality with the entry into service of the Loire 210 in mid-1939. Under development for the Marine Nationale since 1933, this modern monoplane, which featured a single large float virtually the length of the fuselage with smaller floats beneath each wing, was so far outclassed by contemporary land-based fighters by the time it entered service as to be virtually ineffectual, and only twenty were built. A new squadron, designated HC1 (*Hydravions de Chasse*) was formed at St Mandrier on 1 July 1939, but although formally attached to F1H the aircraft were never embarked.

COMMANDANT TESTE: Embarked Aircraft

	Levasseur PL.15	Latécoère 298	Gourdou-Leseurre 813	Loire 130	Loire 210
In service	1934	1939	1935	1938	1939
Length	12.85m	12.56m	10.5m	11.3m	9.5m
Span	18m	15.5m	16m	16m	11.8m
Height	5.1m	5.24m	3.86m	3.85m	3.8m
Weight (fl)	4350kg	4800kg	2460kg	3500kg	2150kg
Weight (empty)	2835kg	3000kg	1690kg	2050kg	1440kg
Power Unit	Hispano-Suiza 650hp	Hispano-Suiza 650hp	Gnome-Rhône 420hp	Hispano-Suiza 720hp	Hispano-Suiza 720hp
Max. Speed	210km/h	295km/h	200km/h	225km/h	345km/h
Ceiling	4500m	5500m	6000m	6000m	8000m
Armament	680/700kg torpedo or 700kg bombs; 1xII 7.5mm MG	400mm torpedo or 2 x 150kg bombs; 2xII, 1xI 7.5mm MG	1xI, 1xII 7.7mm MG	2xI MG; 2 x 75kg bomb or dc	4xII 7.5mm MG

Service

Following her entry into service, the *Commandant Teste* took part in a series of exercises with the Mediterranean Squadron, being attached for a time to the battleship *Jean Bart* in the *2ᵉ Division de Ligne*. She underwent a major refit from November 1935 to August 1936, and from September 1937 was based at Oran with the task of protecting neutral merchant shipping from commerce raiders during the Spanish Civil War. She returned to Toulon for refit in February 1938, when her catapults were modified to accommodate the Loire 130. She then saw extensive employment as an aviation transport between France and the French colonies in North Africa.

In August 1939 she embarked HS1 (six Loire 130) and HB1 (eight Latécoère 298) and left for Oran, where she was attached to the *6ᵉ Escadre*, which comprised a division of torpedo-boats and three divisions of submarines, with the submarine depot ship *Jules Verne* as flagship. When this was dissolved in December 1939, *Commandant Teste* was reattached to the 4th Maritime Region (Bizerta). She returned to Toulon that same month and disembarked her air squadrons. She was subsequently employed only as an aviation transport, ferrying aircraft between France and North Africa on behalf of the Armée de l'Air. In late June 1940 she was moved to Mers-el-Kébir to free a berth in the overcrowded port of Oran, and was present during the British attack on the French battle squadron there. She received some splinter damage but no casualties and returned to Toulon on 18 October, where she was disarmed. In June 1941 she was reactivated as a gunnery training ship, and provided anti-aircraft fire in defence of the submarines which tried to escape on 27 November 1942 before being scuttled with the rest of the French Fleet.

Conclusion

The hull was refloated in February 1945 and consideration was given to the completion of *Commandant Teste* as an escort carrier, but with the end of the war in Europe she was condemned and broken up, a sad end to a unique experiment in marine aviation. Although the attack squadron of large sea-launched torpedo-bombers represented something of a dead-end in naval warfare, the concept of a 'mobile aviation base' responded to French military requirements at a time when military facilities in the North African colonies were relatively underdeveloped, and the *Commandant Teste* was to have an undeniable influence on the Japanese seaplane carriers of the *Chitose* and *Mizuho* classes built during the mid-1930s.

Sources
Jean Moulin, Lucien Morareau and Claude Picard, *Le Béarn et le Commandant Teste*, Marines Edition (Bourg-en-Bresse, 1997?)
Francis Dousset, *Les porte-avions français*, Editions de la Cité (Brest, 1978)
Official plans of *Commandant Teste*, Centre d'Archives de l'Armement

A Loire 130 scout seaplane is catapulted from the fast battleship Strasbourg *in June 1942. The Loire 130 replaced the Gourdou Leseurre GL 813 aboard the* Commandant Teste *from April 1938. The catapults had to be modified in order to handle this heavier aircraft.* (Marius Bar)

THE 'BATTLE' CLASS DESTROYERS

The harsh circumstances that the Royal Navy faced in the Second World War, particularly in Norway and the Mediterranean, were to result in the need for a new fleet destroyer with a main armament capable of engaging enemy aircraft effectively. **George Moore** considers the evolution and circumstances surrounding the construction of these controversial warships.

Destroyer Characteristics: 1939-41

The early years of the war saw the Royal Navy concentrating resources on the ordering and production of intermediate destroyers, all of which were designed to carry a main armament of four 4.7in guns, but which had a limited elevation. In the first four 'emergency' flotillas of the 'O' to 'R' classes, the mounting had an elevation of 40 degrees; the succeeding 'S' to 'CA' classes mounted an improved gun, which had an elevation of 55 degrees (4.5in in Savage, 'Z' and 'CA' classes). The result was that the 1939-41 War Programmes included eighty-eight destroyers with a main armament which, as designed, had poor anti-aircraft capability, a problem perpetuated in the twenty-six destroyers of the 'CH', 'CO', 'CR' and 'CE' groups which were ordered under the 1942 New Construction Programme.

There were, however, some hopeful pointers emerging for the sloops of the Black Swan class, and the escort destroyers of the 'Hunt' class all mounted 4in high-angle guns. There were also four destroyers of the 'L' class, where construction was authorised before the war, which were completed between December 1940 and July 1941 with four twin 4in high-angle guns (albeit because of production delays with the planned twin 4.7in armament). All were better at combating enemy aircraft than the conventional destroyers with a low-angle main armament (and correspondingly limited capabilities).

Genesis

The situation had not gone unnoticed by the Director of Staff Duties and Training Division (DSTD) who had recognised the need for change in October 1940 when he stated that, 'In principle the long range weapons for destroyers and small vessels should be dual purpose HA/LA (High Altitude/Low Altitude) guns'. However, this is as far as the subject evolved for some six months.[1]

By April 1941 the debate was joined in earnest but at this stage there was clearly no consensus at all on how requirements should progress. The Director of Naval Construction (DNC) and the Director of Naval Ordnance (DNO) were against a completely HA/LA fleet destroyer and recommended an arrangement as in the rearmed 'Tribal'-class destroyer. This called for six 4.7in twin 40-degree mountings firing a 50lb shell as main armament plus a 4in twin 85-degree HA mounting. The Director of Plans (D of P) suggested two alternatives: three 4.7in single 40-degree mountings and one 4.7in single 85-degree mounting all firing 62lb shells or four 4.7in single 40-degree mountings and one 4.7in single 85-degree mounting all firing 50lb shells. DTSD suggested eight 4in in twin 85-degree mountings, the shells here weighing 35lb. The papers were now circulated by DTSD. His Department incidentally suggested that the close-range armament should be two multiple 40mm weapons and four Oerlikons. Two sets of torpedo tubes were required whilst operational endurance was to be 4000 miles at 12-14 knots.

The first response came from the Assistant Chief of Naval Staff (H) (ACNS (H)). He considered that the ideal armament, having summed up operational experience to date, was a destroyer having a secondary (defensive) gun armament, the ideal being a HA/LA 4.7in gun capable of 85-degree elevation. It did not exist. He wanted this worked for and the difficulties surrounding its use and design solved. Until such a mounting was in sight the best substitute had to be accepted. His immediate preference was for the main armament suggested by DNC and DNO, but he did not want the twin 4in mounting which he considered unlikely to worry high-flying aircraft. The close-range anti-aircraft armament was to be four-cornered and consist of four twin 40mm Bofors. One set of torpedo tubes was also required whilst the endurance suggested was again 4000 miles at 12-14 knots.

The Vice Chief of the Naval Staff (VCNS) went incisively to the core of the problem when he wrote: 'Experience in this war has shown quite clearly that for one day on which a destroyer fires her guns at another ship she probably fires them at aircraft twenty times. I consequently consider that we should not be satisfied with anything except the complete dual purpose HA/LA armament just like we have in the Dido class on a bigger scale.' He considered the 4in gun attractive because it was already in production. However, he did not regard it powerful enough for the job. Needless to say he did not like the suggestions put forward by DNO, DNC and D of P as 'they seem to me to fail to take account of war experience'. The answer was to press on as hard as possible with the development of a proper HA/LA gun capable of 85-degree elevation, which he regarded as long overdue. If the gun could not be ready for the 1942-Programme destroyers then in the first instance they should be fitted with twin 4in HA/LA guns before consideration was given to substituting the 4.7in HA/LA mounting when it became available. For the close-range armament he suggested four twin 40mm Bofors together with six or preferably eight 20mm Oerlikons in a four-cornered arrangement. The Controller concurred with the analysis produced by VCNS and on 9 May 1941 asked DNC for an approximate layout of a destroyer with four 4.7in (alternatively four twin 4in) guns and a four-cornered armament for close range.

And yet there were considerable misgivings among those involved in the decision-making, for on 14 May 1941, Sir Stanley Goodall, the DNC, recorded in his diary that in the morning at a Controller's meeting, 'a grand fight started on the fully high-angle guns for the destroyer'. Some six weeks later DNC produced three sketch designs.[2]

Design A. The main armament comprised four 4.7in (50pdr) 80-degree mountings. The close-range armament included four twin Bofors and eight Oerlikons. Machinery was repeat 'L' class, which was expected to give a speed of 32.5-36.5 knots according to loading. The complement was estimated to be 270 men whilst the costs were estimated at £840,000. The estimated standard displacement of 2250 tons was clearly a matter of concern to DNC for he drew attention to the reasons, which largely related to the characteristics of the secondary armament. The top weight of a twin Bofors was practically the same as a 4.7in 40-degree mounting whilst with these mountings in a four-cornered arrangement much space was taken up. In addition, the Oerlikons, with ready-use ammunition, added yet more top weight and space. The increase in size also resulted in difficulty at the shipyards for it would no longer be possible to lay down two destroyers side by side in certain of the yards. It was also anticipated that the ships would take two years and three months to build. DNC did not sound enthusiastic about the design for he considered it an elaborate, costly and unprotected ship with a comparatively poor main armament.

The DNC must have expressed his concerns, for the second design was produced on the verbal instructions of the Controller:

Design B. In this design the number of twin Bofors was reduced from four to two and the Oerlikons from eight to five in order to reduce the size of the ship. The result was

that the standard displacement reduced to 2000 tons. Machinery was now going to be a repeat of the 'Tribal' class with two boilers and one funnel. Speed was slightly reduced, the expectation being 32-36.25 knots according to loading. The complement reduced to 240 men whilst the cost was estimated to be £750,000. There were still, however, going to be the same constraints in building the ships although the time taken to construct the destroyers might be a few weeks less.

The DNC did not like the design of the new 4.7in 80-degree mounting which was only set out in a rough layout supplied by DNO. He felt that if a fully high-angle mounting was to be fitted into destroyers then it should be on the 'Between Decks' (BD) or semi-BD principle. The gun crews and ammunition supply parties would then work under cover, the desirability of a very high trunnion would be markedly less and it was thought that better shooting would result.

Design C. The main armament was now three twin-4.7in 50pdr semi-BD mountings. The gun design did not exist so the drawing was based on the 4.5in BD twin. This arrangement was adopted to meet criticism that to produce a destroyer as big or larger than a Tribal with only half the ahead fire seemed a retrograde step. The secondary armament was the same as that proposed for Design A. The forecastle deck was carried well aft as in the Black Swan class, which made for a dry ship but at the expense of size and silhouette. The torpedo tubes, however, had to be raised and there was a slight reduction in the arc of fire of the after 4.7in guns. The machinery was again a repeat of the 'L' class but the expected speed was 1.5-2 knots slower than Design A. The estimated complement was 260 whilst the cost escalated to £890,000. DNC felt that the ship would appear to be more of an unprotected cruiser than a destroyer but that the design nevertheless would be worth considering on that basis. The displacement is, unfortunately, not known.[3]

The size of Design C was daunting and the Controller now asked DNC to produce a design with no Bofors, the light anti-aircraft armament being limited to Oerlikons. Design C1 was produced. The revised requirement had the effect of reducing displacement by 175 tons but put up speed by a knot. Meanwhile, various opinions were obtained from officers serving in destroyers (among them Captain Lord Louis Mountbatten). All were said to 'swear by the "J" class design' and, according to the Deputy DTSD, wanted four main guns firing forward, some HA guns of about 4in calibre and plenty of Oerlikons. Mountbatten considered the 'J' class to be the most successful design yet but in need of a Tribal bow, a little more beam and plenty of Oerlikons. It was concluded that 'if we want 4.7in guns we must have a big expensive destroyer with twins forward and that if we want cheap destroyers they should be "Super 'Hunts'" with three twin-4in HA/LA.' The logic behind the suggestion was that with the main guns all mounted forward ability was improved: 'To fight her way against enemy destroyers to a position where torpedo hits could be gained on enemy ships'; also 'To drive off enemy destroyers attempting to torpedo our own ships.' DNC now produced Designs M and M1 with two twin 4.7in mountings all firing forward, two sets of torpedo tubes and a twin 4in HA/LA. Design M had two twin Bofors and six Oerlikons, M1 had eight Oerlikons but no Bofors.[4]

The basis of the design had now been developed but there did seem a divergence of purpose between the suggestions of the destroyer captains, who were fighting the battles, and clearly were seeing action with enemy naval forces, and the naval staff whose prime objective, in this instance, was to defeat air attacks. The precise timing of all the inputs into the debate are not known but the disasters off Crete in may 1941, when the cruisers *Gloucester* and *Fiji* together with the destroyers *Kelly* and *Kashmir* were lost, must have had a bearing on thinking.

The Design Progresses

The merits of all six designs were considered at a conference held by the Controller on 11 July 1941. It was now decided to prepare a design and produce draft staff requirements for 'The 1942 Programme fully high-angle destroyer'. The ship was described as an ocean-going destroyer for fleet work and general purposes at home and abroad. The vessel was to be armed with 4.7in 80-degree BD mountings forward, four twin Bofors, six Oerlikons, two sets of quadruple torpedo tubes, and have good endurance. The hull was to have a 'Tribal' bow and a 'J'-class bridge, thus meeting the suggestions of the destroyer captains. Endurance required was 7000 miles at 12 knots but there was some doubt about a requirement for 4000 miles at 20 knots. The main armament specification was still clouded with uncertainty, as it was not clear if the 4.7in twin could achieve 80-degree elevation. Possible alternatives were a 4.7in with 60-degree elevation or a new 4.5in with 80-degree elevation. Details of the preferred 4.7in mounting were still wanted from DNO. A further Controller's meeting was held on 18 August 1941 when sketch design 'N' was produced displacing 2250 tons with two twin 4.5in 80-degree mountings. This design was accepted but the debate must have been lively for Sir Stanley Goodall commented in his diary that 'there were almost as many opinions as Admirals'. The design was now rapidly developed and by 4 October 1941 such was the urgency of the matter that it was brought forward before the Board of Admiralty for approval.

There was reported to be little change from the design considered on 18 August 1941 other than an increase in displacement from 2250 tons to 2280 tons (standard). The reasons were the provision of extra dynamo power to enable the armament to be used when fires were drawn, extra oil-fuel tanks, provision of star-shell mortars, Type 272 RDF and higher powered machinery. It was confirmed that the main armament would comprise two 4.7in (50pdr) BD twin mountings with a maximum elevation of 80 degrees. A mock-up had been produced which indicated that it should be a satisfactory design. The close-range armament comprised four predictor-controlled Bofors 40 mm twin-mountings and six Oerlikons. Provision for firing star shells had not been definitely fixed, with the fitting of two mortars for this purpose under consideration. If the mortars were not fitted then the platform amidships was to be arranged to carry one 4in gun instead of two Oerlikons and two star-shell mortars. Two handworked 21in torpedo mountings were to be provided.

The machinery arrangements were similar to those of the 'L' class but slightly modified to develop 50,000 SHP, an increase of 2000 SHP, which was expected to give 31 knots in deep condition and 36 knots in standard condition. The improved performance was gained by raising the boiler pressure from 300lb to 400lb and the temperature from 660 degrees to 700 degrees. It had originally been hoped to achieve 32 knots in deep condition when the design was considered at the August meeting but the extra displacement resulted in the modest loss in performance. The endurance with a clean bottom was 4400 miles at 20 knots and 7700 miles at 12 knots, a figure which was 20 per cent better than the 'J' class, 10 per cent better than the 'L' class and only 5 per cent less than the 'Q' class destroyers. The radar arrangements were comprehensive for the time, with the main armament being controlled by a Type 285 whilst two twin sets of Bofors were controlled by a Type 282. Also to be fitted were a Type 290 (an aircraft and surface warning radar) and a Type 272 (a surface warning radar). The cost inclusive of guns, torpedoes and ammunition was estimated to be £827,000. Sir Stanley Goodall put his signature to the note for the Board of Admiralty on 22 September 1941, barely a month after the design parameters had been agreed at the Controller's August meeting. The Board of Admiralty duly approved the design.[5]

We do not know the manner in which the Board of Admiralty discussion evolved when the design was

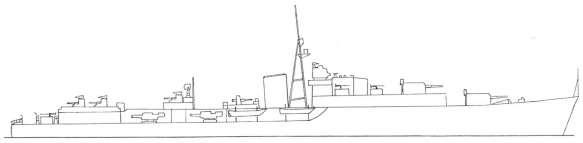

Battle class destroyer, March 1942. Based on an original plan held by the National Maritime Museum. (Drawing by Len Crockford.)

approved but it is clear that the First Lord of the Admiralty A V Alexander was one voice of dissent. On 14 October he submitted a memorandum to Winston Churchill in which he indicated that he was very unhappy about the weight of opinion against him. This was the start of what proved to be an onerous and protracted need for the navy to justify the construction of these destroyers. They were considered to be large, expensive and needing longer to construct than the intermediate destroyers which up to now had dominated the new destroyer construction programmes.[6]

There seems to have been some further uncertainty about the merits of the design, for two further studies designated 'O' and 'P1' both employing six 4.7in mountings as the main armament were considered at a Controller's meeting on the 11 November 1941. The likely instigators were the Naval Staff who had now changed their minds: they now wanted to split the main armament. The DNC was somewhat exasperated by the constant requests for alterations. He commented that the design had been prepared to meet staff requirements, if now different the board must rule that all work so far done was to be thrown overboard in order to start again from the beginning. These ideas were not taken any further, which was hardly surprising as the class was urgently needed in the fleet and delays caused by design changes would not have been acceptable. The studies were, however, the first hint of developments which were to lead to the *Daring* class.[7]

The 1942 Programme

The requirement for the new fleet destroyers became even more urgent with the entry of Japan into the war and the consequent loss of the *Prince of Wales* and the *Repulse* on account of virtually unchallenged Japanese air

power. Early drafts of the proposed 1942 Programme produced on 2 January 1942 outlined Programme A, which called for forty fleet destroyers. and Programme B, where fifty-five fleet destroyers were proposed. Plan B was based on the assumption that in the future it might be possible to transfer a large part of the shipbuilding effort from mercantile tonnage to warship tonnage in view of the very large amount of mercantile tonnage being constructed in the United States. The option of a massive expansion in the warship building programme was not followed, however.[8]

Following further consultations with the Controller, the D of P duly produced a draft new construction programme in February 1942. He wrote: 'Our losses of Fleet destroyers during 1941 have been heavy and have counterbalanced the number completing during the year. Experience has shown the weakness in AA fire power of our existing designs. A new design has been produced which mounts not only a good torpedo and L/A armament, but also develops very considerable AA fire power. Some ships of the 1941 Programme Emergency Destroyers will not be laid down for some time. It is proposed that, as soon as the 1942 design is ready, these destroyers should be laid down on all slips that can take them. The smaller slips should take the emergency destroyers which still remain to be laid down. It is therefore proposed to include forty destroyers of the 1942 design in this programme.' By the end of the month the situation had been reassessed. DNC indicated that there was capacity to build thirty of the new fleet destroyers and ten of alternative designs. There was still dislike of the new design being expressed by ACNS and the C-in-C Home Fleet, but it was suggested that sixteen of the new design should be built together with as many of other designs as possible. The Controller agreed and concluded that only sixteen of the new fleet destroyers could

Vigo pictured in 1946. (Author's collection.)

be built, the balance of the programme now being twenty-four intermediate destroyers.[9]

By the end of March details of the 1942 New Construction Programme were placed before Churchill. The first question he asked, no doubt primed by Alexander, was: 'What type will destroyers be and how long to construct? Numbers and speed of delivery are still overriding requirements.' Initially it would seem that only the briefest of responses was made by the Admiralty for on 2 April the Prime Minister, in a memorandum to the First Lord, wanted details of 2250-ton destroyers (actually 2280 tons). He went on to say that he was 'naturally prejudicial against destroyers taking twenty-one months to build—ship is neither a cruiser or a destroyer.'[10]

The response to the memorandum was detailed and it is worthwhile setting it out in an abbreviated form for it succinctly illustrates the case for the new design:

Careful consideration was said to have been given to the remarks regarding the proposed 2250-ton destroyer.
Functions of the fleet design –
To attack enemy heavy ships with torpedoes.
To attack enemy light craft with gunfire.
To screen heavy ships against submarines, aircraft (especially torpedo-bombing aircraft) and E-Boat attack.
To act as supporting forces in combined operations.
To be comparable with the enemy, the ship must have a gun of at least 4.5in throwing a 55lb shell.
Experience shows that the main armament must be able to fire against aircraft and therefore require a high elevation.
Need to be able to deal with torpedo-bombing aircraft before they have dropped torpedoes to attack capital ships.
Mutual support provides a large measure of security against low-level and dive bombing
Value of firing ahead arises from Narvik and Mediterranean experience.
Only ship to embody all features is the 1942 design.
Ability to operate in adverse weather is an advantage of size, on the other hand a smaller ship is desirable for anti-submarine work and speed of construction. This argument has led the Admiralty to continue with the smaller type for twenty-six out of the forty-two destroyers proposed in the Programme.
It was agreed that fighter aircraft were the best screen against heavy air attack. Nevertheless a gun screen is necessary.
Ships were designed before the loss of *Prince of Wales* and *Repulse*. The loss of these ships confirmed the arguments in favour of this design.
The screening destroyers would be two or three miles from the battlefleet to defend against air and submarine attack.
Ships are not intended to usurp the functions of cruisers.
In every type of ship the provision of AA weapons, splinter protection and wireless equipment has dictated an increase in size if the main features of armament, speed and endurance are not duly sacrificed.
If the intermediate type of destroyer were substituted we

could not lay down any more. We would only get the same number three months earlier.[11]

The Admiralty response seems to have temporarily satisfied Churchill, as there was no change in the programme when the First Lord of the Admiralty produced a memorandum 'New Construction Programme 1942' for the War Cabinet on 21 April 1942. The section on destroyers read: 'There is little likelihood of our ever having a sufficient force of these ships and our programmes for them are determined principally by the limit of the capacity which can be found for them. During 1941 our losses in fleet destroyers have been heavy, and have counterbalanced the number completing during the year. I propose to order as many destroyers as are likely to be found berths—forty-two. There is a requirement for a new type of destroyer having a greater power of AA fire than the existing type, and this has been designed. I propose to order sixteen of this type. The remaining berths will be employed on the construction of the intermediate type, which is the most suitable craft for general fleet work. I make provision for twenty-six of this type, two of which will be fitted for minelaying.' The cost of the sixteen fleet destroyers was quoted as £13,600,000, i.e. £850,000 for each vessel.[12]

The Treasury reaction to the cost and nature of the Destroyer Programme was very supportive. An official wrote: 'The sky is the limit for the number of destroyers required, and there can be little question that the Admiralty are right in building as many as can be provided within capacity. The normal period of completion for a destroyer is some fifteen to eighteen months, but some of the ships now proposed will not complete until rather later.' The War Cabinet duly approved the Programme on 27 April 1942, no member making any comments about the destroyer plans.[13]

The Main Armament

The quest for a fully high-angle mounting in destroyers commenced early in 1941 when the DNO was asked to investigate, as a matter of urgency, the 'cost' of installation. The initial investigations led to a 4.7in Mark XII gun as fitted in the 'Tribal' class being modified, which was soon followed by a 4.5in Mark II mounting coupled with a 4.7in Mark XIX cradle. It soon became clear that this combination would involve a complete redesign of the mounting in which little advantage could be taken of existing design work. The DNO therefore came to the conclusion that the only answer would be to accept the 4.5in gun as the new standard destroyer gun in lieu of the 4.7in weapon. This was not a straightforward decision for there were enormous stocks of 4.7in ammunition distributed all over the world and it could be difficult in wartime to build up stocks of 4.5in ammunition to necessary levels.

The 4.5in gun was first developed as a new anti-aircraft weapon in the mid-1930s, acting as secondary armament for battleships and aircraft carriers, one limitation being that it was then considered the largest calibre for which 'handleable' fixed ammunition could be produced. The overall weight of a round was 85lb and the length 50in. It was essential that a prototype of the new destroyer mounting was produced, an aim which was achieved by converting a spare Mark II mounting then under construction at Barrow. Considerable modifications were needed but the state of completion meant that little existing work was wasted. One early decision was to incorporate RPC (remote power control). It was also decided to adopt 'separate' ammunition the reason being that experience at sea in *Scylla* and *Charybdis*, two Dido-class cruisers which carried 4.5in Mark III mountings with 'fixed' ammunition, indicated that ammunition handling was difficult in bad weather even in these 5000-ton warships.

A wooden mock-up of the new weapon was constructed at Barrow in October 1941 to eliminate potential shortcomings; by March 1942 it was decided to go ahead with the detailed design work. Meanwhile, it was also decided that the prototype mounting should go to sea for evaluation in the new destroyer *Savage* then expected to complete in April 1943. It was also decided to convert her remaining two 4.7in Mark XIIs to take a 4.5in gun; these became the 'pilot' 4.5in Mark V mountings which were to see service in the 'Z' class destroyers and subsequent intermediate destroyer designs. In no sense was the 4.5in Mark IV, which fired a 55lb shell, a new design for it was regarded as a compromise solution produced quickly to provide an adequate answer to a very urgent problem. The development period for a mounting of this type was normally three to four years.

Even before the 4.5in Mark IV mounting had gone to sea an entirely new design of main armament for destroyers was under consideration. This design was to incorporate all the lessons of the war. The design of what became the Mark VI mounting was first considered in September 1942 and initially the required rate of fire was twelve rounds per gun per minute, which was the same as the rate of fire expected to be achieved by the Mark IV mounting. This was later raised to eighteen rounds per gun per minute. The new gun also had a higher performance in elevating and training, with the result that the peak electrical power needed to power a mounting rose from 80hp in the Mark IV to 117hp in the Mark VI. The first two mountings were expected to be ready in March and April 1945 when they were scheduled to go to sea on a trial basis in a 'Battle' class destroyer. The armament was also specified for some later units of the 'Battle' class, as we shall see.[14]

Uncertainties!

No sooner had the programme started to get underway in earnest when further distractions appeared. The catalyst this time was the decision to cancel four Fiji-class cruisers which were to be built under the 1942 New Construction Programme and in their stead to lay down nine new light fleet carriers in addition to four already planned. When the matter came before the War Cabinet on 1 August 1942, Churchill commented that 'the Admiralty should perhaps go further and cancel the laying down of the very large type of destroyers, which would take two years to complete, the capacity thus released being used to build a larger number of smaller destroyers, which would be completed within about a year's time'. The Cabinet agreed that the matter should be investigated, another aim being to see if it would be possible to reinstate the cancelled cruisers.

The result of the deliberations that this minute set in train was perhaps unexpected. The Cabinet minutes on 22 September 1942 recorded that three more light fleet carriers had been added to the programme and just one of the cancelled cruisers reinstated. Churchill also changed his views on the new fleet destroyers. He commented 'that since the Admiralty had agreed to substantial measures of cancellation and postponement in regard to the cruiser programme, he would withdraw the objections he had raised on the ground of the longer time which they took to complete, to the construction of these 16 special fleet destroyers.' Churchill's earlier comment about the need to build destroyers, which took a year to complete, was said to refer to the 'Hunt' class. It was explained that 'owing to their short endurance these vessels were only suitable for work in coastal waters or in the Mediterranean'. Opposition in the Cabinet to the construction of the class was at an end for now![15]

Meanwhile within the Admiralty, 'The Future Building Committee' had been formed and it duly commenced its deliberations in August 1942. As a result of Churchill's suggestions, one of the first tasks of the committee was to consider and settle a number of questions including functions of fleet destroyers, types of destroyer and alterations needed to the design of the 1942 fleet destroyers. The deliberations resulted in a multitude of ideas appearing yet again. As a result of views expressed by the Naval Staff, DNC produced two fleet destroyer designs BA and BC. Standard displacement was 2750 tons and 3250 tons respectively, BA being armed with three twin 55-degree UD (Upper Deck) mountings while BC was armed with three twin 80-degree BD mountings. The machinery in both designs produced 60,000shp. The D of P, however, was in favour of continuing the existing fleet destroyer design. He was supported by DNC who remarked that the Controller required the production problem considered. The best answer was to continue with the 1942 design but it would be possible to instigate a change if the overriding requirement was met by an alternative design. These new ideas were a further glimpse of thinking within the Naval Staff that was to lead to the *Daring* class.[16]

The 1943 Programme

The Future Building Committee considered the 1943 Programme on 22 November 1942. The first draft of the destroyer programme prepared by DNC included twenty-five fleet destroyers and seventeen intermediate destroyers. Fleet destroyers were to be placed on every slip which could take them. No cruisers were included in the plans, the first time this had occurred in a major warship build-

A fine view of Jutland *at anchor at Portland in 1948. Amonst the many other vessels visibile beyond her are* Barrosa, Aisne, *and* Alamein. *(Author's collection.)*

ing programme since 1923. The fleet destroyers were going to have to be the 1942 class as the DNC would not be able to get down to designing a new fleet destroyer until mid 1943. The only modification then considered possible was that what were described as two modern 4.5in guns could be fitted in ships later in the programme, a reference to the new Mark VI mounting then under development. Also underway were investigations by the Engineer-in-Chief into fitting machinery in destroyers, which operated with higher temperatures and at a higher pressure.[17]

The 1943 Programme was considered by the Controller on 25 November. One cruiser from the 1942 Programme was cancelled to enable production to be concentrated on aircraft carriers and destroyers. The result was that the planned number of fleet destroyers rose from twenty-five to twenty-six units. The maximum use of available production capacity was thus being utilised. The Future Building Committee was meanwhile considering the design of the destroyers; their deliberations were to lead ultimately to the 'Weapon' class being adopted for the intermediate type. At this stage, it was agreed that what were now described as the large fleet destroyers should not be restricted to the present tonnage but might go up to 3000 tons, although as we have seen there was no hope of designing let alone building them.[18]

The Memorandum by the First Lord of the Admiralty incorporating the 1943 New Construction Programme was drafted in March 1943. There was no change in the numbers of destroyers required. The reasoning behind the presentation is worth quoting in full: 'We are still short of our requirement for fleet destroyers, and I propose to continue the policy of ordering as many destroy-

ers as we can find berths for. I therefore include in the Programme forty-three destroyers—all destined for fleet work—twenty-six of the "1942" design, and seventeen of the "intermediate type", which has been designed for building in those berths which cannot accommodate the larger type. Further study has confirmed that the "1942" design provides the smallest hull which can accommodate the requirements of a modern fleet destroyer. War experience has emphatically shown that in addition to adequate gun power, torpedo armament, speed and endurance, a modern destroyer must have a heavy AA armament to give it a fighting chance of avoiding destruction by air attack.'[19]

When the matter came before the War Cabinet on the 1 April 1943 the main point of attention was the Destroyer Programme. Churchill 'deprecated the tendency to make more and more improvements in the design of destroyers which added to their size'. He raised further matters such as vulnerability, a lack of armour and considered them to be almost as big as light cruisers of the last war. He wanted to see more of our resources devoted to building vessels which could be completed more quickly.

The First Lord of the Admiralty and the First Sea Lord explained 'that these destroyers were required not for fleet protection but to form part of the Battle Fleet. The endurance, speed and armament required of such a destroyer could not be incorporated in a vessel of less than about 2300 tons. The Admiralty would have liked all destroyers included in the 1943 Programme to be of the 'Battle' type but there were not enough slips available to lay down vessels of this size, and they had therefore had to include seventeen destroyers of the intermediate

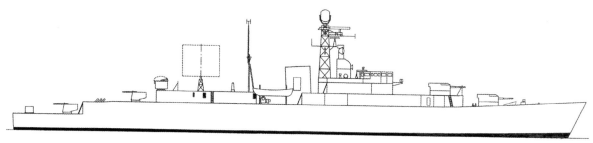

Original design for a conversion to a fleet radar picket which was approved in September 1956. It was ruled out because of the cost and the cheaper design substituted. (Drawing by John Roberts based on original plan held at the Natioinal Maritime Museum in Ships Cover ADM 138 860.)

type. We had suffered heavy losses in destroyers and had far fewer destroyers in service than we required. Furthermore we had lost many destroyers through air attack and it was essential to include anti aircraft guns with powered mountings.' The First Lord of the Admiralty went on to say, 'it was hoped to reduce to some extent the building time of both types so that from the time of laying down to completion they would take from sixteen to eighteen months.' The question was then raised, 'whether some reduction could be made in the number of destroyers in the Programme, additional frigates and corvettes being substituted for them.' The First Lord considered this would not be economic as destroyers were built by specialist firms, but he undertook to investigate the matter further. The War Cabinet called for a report but they did approve the construction of twenty fleet destroyers in order to avoid delays in their construction. The remainder of the 1943 Programme was approved. A report on the feasibility of substituting frigates and corvettes for destroyers was duly produced on the 12 April and illustrated emphatically the disadvantages of such a move. The whole of the 1943 New Construction Programme was then duly approved by the War Cabinet.[20]

Design Developments

There remained a lurking dissatisfaction with the 'Battle'-class design, which culminated in a minute being produced by the Deputy Controller in April 1943. The design was said to have been criticised in various quarters as being deficient in gun power, with the bunching of the main armament forward described as a weak feature. He indicated that a preliminary survey showed that the 1943 ships could be built without any disruption of production programmes with a main armament of six 4.5in mountings, the price being the elimination of one set of quadruple torpedo tubes. It was suggested that the two forward mountings should be the Mark IV design whilst the additional mounting aft would be the new Mark VI. When the matter came before the Future Building Committee, the reduction in the number of torpedo tubes was criticised and that there were said to be disadvantages in installing a combination of new and old mountings. The new mounting was not expected to go into production until the Spring of 1945 at the earliest which meant that

only the last five could be completed to a new design incorporating the Mark VI mounting. The possibility of a three-turret ship was, however, to be thoroughly explored.[21]

On 14 May, the Deputy Controller joined the Future Building Committee meeting when the armament of the 1943 'Battle'-class destroyers was again discussed. The minutes of the meeting noted: 'the present armament had never appeared to him to be satisfactory. The vessel was designed after Norway and Crete when we were, perhaps, excessively dive-bomber minded. He had always felt it desirable to improve long-range armament and had formed the opinion that this could be done without redesigning.' Among views expressed by members of the committee, that of the DNC was perhaps the most practical for he drew attention to the very considerable increase in weight and resultant stresses that the suggested new mounting would place on the ship. He could not say whether a redesign would be necessary or not. It was decided that the question of a redesign should be examined as soon as possible and that the views of the Commanders-in Chief should be canvassed on the proposed armament change.[22]

By 10 June 1943, replies from the Commanders-in-Chief (bar the C-in-C, Home Fleet) had been received. All of them regarded the existing armament unfavourably. The main criticism was that the proposed armament would produce an exclusively AA ship unsuitable for offensive operations. Against this, the 'Battle' class would only form a very small portion of the whole destroyer force and that formidable AA defences might be invaluable in certain types of operation. The result of all the deliberations was to alter the 1942 Design by fitting one 4.5in 55-degree mounting aft at the expense of the star shell gun (4in), one twin Bofors and one twin Oerlikon. Meanwhile, it was reported that DNC's Destroyer Section was now ready to commence work on the design of the Large Fleet Destroyer of the 1944 Programme.[23]

When the matter came before the Sea Lords on 27 June 1943 the Controller explained why, for reasons of weight and strength, it was not possible to add an additional 4.5in mounting. The consensus of opinion among the Sea Lords was that an additional 4.5in single gun should be mounted, if possible, amidships rather than aft as earlier suggested. The Controller was not sure, however, if this was feasible on account of ammunition supply difficulties. By the 28 July a full examination of the problem showed that a 4.5in single mounting could be sited amidships. At this time the new 4.5in Mark VI mounting was to be fitted into the new fleet destroyers as soon as it was practical even though this would mean surrendering the single 4.5in mounting as fire control arrangements were not compatible. However, it was not known when it would be possible to commence a regular supply of mountings hence the indecision. It had also desired that the last five ships of the 1943 Programme should be built to the new design, which was to carry three twin 4.5in Mark VI mountings. Draft staff requirements for the ship were by now known and first estimates showed that the standard displacement would be of the order of 3500 tons. Sir Stanley Goodall commented in a memorandum that 'such ships could hardly be termed destroyers, they are really small unprotected cruisers'. In his diary he was rather more forthright: '3500 tons, ridiculous for a destroyer'.

On 18 August the implementation of the 'Battle'-class Programme was discussed at a Controller's meeting. The Controller did not want to alter the design of the 1943 ships other than the fitting of the additional single 4.5in mounting but he did want to see what could be done to improve the last five ships and the later ships of the 1944 Programme. A sketch was produced showing a repeat Battle hull and machinery but the armament was substantially modified with the two twin UD Mark VI mountings placed fore and aft while the secondary armament now consisted of four twin Buster Bofors, a new system under development, and three twin Oerlikons. DNO was however against splitting the main armament forward and aft mainly because four guns bearing forward were considered a definite requirement but also because of blast difficulties which would affect the Bofors when 'X' mounting was firing on fine forward arcs. The Controller summed up the position. There was now a commitment to three types; the 1942 'Battle' as designed, the five-gun 1943 'Battle' and a 1943 'Battle' pilot with two twin Mark VI mountings. The possibility also remained that the last five ships would be built to a new larger design.[24]

Production

Authorising construction and ordering the 'Battle'-class destroyers was one matter, building them was a different task altogether. The War Cabinet was led to believe that ships of the class could be built in two years, with the First Lord of the Admiralty even espousing the possibility of getting the construction time down to eighteen months. The reality was that only the prototype *Barfleur* was built within this schedule and she was delivered without her director tower.[25]

The Controller outlined the constraints when the

The forlorn sight of J4922, ex-Jutland (1), launched but left incomplete, photographed possibly in January 1952, moored in stream off NCRE Rosyth. (Held in Ship's Cove ADM 138 662B, National Maritime Museum.)

1943 Programme was considered in March of that year. The control and allocation of materials was so strict that orders had to be placed at least six months before the hulls were laid down. The supply of castings and forgings was limited and here there was competition from both the Army and Merchant Navy for resources. Engine capacity was also limited. When it came to the process of fitting out, fire control, wireless gear, radar sets, guns, gun mountings and electrical equipment were also under tight control with the Army and Royal Air Force also making immense demands on the manufacturers. The Controller however envisaged laying down the first of the 1943-Programme ships in August with the final pair being laid down in September 1944. The programme started on time but it was to be June 1945 before the construction of the last pair commenced.[26]

The first imposed delay on the programme was the need for new landing craft for the cross-channel invasion of Europe. Orders were placed in October 1943 for seventy-one craft with shipbuilding firms, and of these thirty-six were placed with the major warship building yards. Warships under construction, including 'Battle'-class destroyers, were inevitably delayed by the landing-craft programme with its consequent diversion of labour and materials. This delay lasted for some six months. Worse was soon to come, however, when the LST (3) Programme was imposed on the shipyards in late 1943, with twenty-five units of the class being ordered from the major naval shipbuilding yards. The result was that nine

Battle-class destroyers were delayed, the initial estimate of the effect being between one and seven months on nine ships in the class. Delays in the LST (3) programme meant that the impact was actually worse than expected. Another cause of considerable delay was the delivery of the Mark VI Director, which was manufactured at Vickers' Crayford Works. The unit for fitting in *Barfleur* was produced seven months later than expected, those for *St Kitts*, *Camperdown*, *Trafalgar*, *Armada*, *Finisterre*, *Hogue* and *Lagos* were between eight and ten months late, those for *Solebay* and *Saintes* were between a year and fourteen months behind schedule. The 1943 ships were not affected by this problem, as from their inception it was intended that they carry the American Mark 37 Director Tower.[27] One major warship not delayed by the landing craft and landing ship programmes was the battleship *Vanguard*, under construction at John Brown, which had Priority One production status as a 'named' ship in the new construction programme; the result, however, was that the destroyers *Barrosa* and *Matapan* were delayed by a lack of labour.[28]

Naming the Ships

In May 1942 the Ships' Names Committee submitted their suggestions. The four leaders were allocated the names of Admirals. *Harman*, *Holmes*, *Hoste* and *Lawson*, while the remaining members of the class were given

Aisne converted to Fleet Radar Picket, pictured in March 1962. (Richard Osborne)

names in the 'A' and 'B' series: *Acasta, Acheron, Acorn, Ardent, Arrogant, Attentive, Basilisk, Bear, Blanche, Blaze, Brazen* and *Brisk*. By July, however, Plans Division wanted to see a distinctive series of names for the new fleet destroyers, which were comparable with the 'Tribal' class. The Committee agreed to substitute for the 'A' and 'B' names a series consisting of naval and land engagements which would be known as the 'Battle' class. The initial list included *Texel*, and *Portland*, which were not accepted being replaced by *St James* and *Vigo*. The 1943-Programme names were considered in May, the first draft of suggestions including *Lissa, Algiers* and *Plassy*. These three names were rejected, being substituted by *Albuera, Barrosa* and *Oudenarde*.[29]

Performance

In August 1945 a questionnaire was issued to the commanding officers of *Armada, Barfleur, Camperdown, Hogue* and *Trafalgar*. Comments were asked for on general arrangements, armament, habitability, seaworthiness, endurance, communications and radar. All the replies had been assessed by the autumn of 1946 when the D of P indicated that he was generally satisfied that the ships were capable of carrying out their function from strategic and tactical standpoints. There were, however, two important exceptions. First, the stated actual endurance of 3060-3440 miles at 20 knots fell considerably short of the Staff Requirement of 4400 miles at 20 knots. The Staff Requirement called for a ship with a clean bottom and no doubt the ships would have been out of dock for several months. Nevertheless, the performance achieved against the set target was poor. The second exception was inadequate storage for three months' provisions. There were also many comments on generally minor matters, most of which could be easily corrected, although a perceived lack of good ventilation in the tropics was an important issue as it would have affected the efficiency of the crew.

Performance on trials was up to expectations. A full-power trial involving *Cadiz*, carrying out six measured runs on the Arran Mile on 5 April 1946, produced a mean speed of 33.175 knots on a mean displacement of 2756 tons. Oil consumption averaged 18.58 tons an hour, the ship having last undocked on 6 March 1946.[30]

Evolution

As we have seen, there was uncertainty about how the last five ships of the 1943 Programme should proceed. The ships concerned were the last two at John Brown (*Talavera* and *Trincomalee*), the last ship at Cammell Laird (*Vimiero*) and the last two ships at Fairfield (*Waterloo* and *Ypres*). In April 1943 it was considered possible that they could be built to a new design.[31] Considerable vacillation occurred but what seems to have finally happened is that *Talavera* and *Trincomalee* were to complete with two Mark VI 4.5in mountings whilst *Vimiero* and *Ypres* were to be built to the new

Daring-class design, a decision made in November 1944. There was always the intention of sending the Mark VI mounting to sea for trials and initially this pilot mounting was to be fitted in *Jutland*, which was being constructed by Hawthorn Leslie. Delays in production meant that it was 1947 before the new gun went to sea in *Saintes*, mounted temporarily in B position—a Mark IV twin 4.5in being carried in A position.[32]

The end of the war in August 1945 inevitably resulted in a considerable slowdown in the programme as priority now shifted, as planned, to the construction of liners and merchant ships. Cancellations were not long in coming and on the 15 October 1945 it was agreed that sixteen members of the class should not be completed. The First Lord of the Admiralty however gained an understanding that 'certain replacements should be made in the future on a long term basis which will supply the shipyards with a steady flow of work'. Nevertheless in December eight of the *Daring* class were cancelled, including *Vimiero* which had been renamed *Danae*. Eight ships of the *Daring* class survived, including *Ypres*, which was ultimately completed as *Delight*, thus honouring the undertaking given to the First Lord.[33]

Work was well forward on many of the cancelled ships. *Oudenarde, Namur* and *Albuera* had all been launched in the normal course of construction and had machinery shipped. *Jutland* was launched in a sub-normal condition but had machinery shipped whilst *Poitiers, Belle Isle* and *Navarino* were launched in a sub-normal condition with no machinery. These three hulls were quickly scrapped. *Talavera* was launched in the normal course of construction whilst *Trincomalee* was launched in a watertight condition. Some work continued on these two ships after they were cancelled to keep men employed, and at one stage it was thought possible that they might complete for a Dominion Navy. Both these ships were, however, sold for scrap early in 1946. In April 1946 the Dutch expressed an interest in the acquisition of *Albuera, Jutland, Namur* and *Oudenarde*. The discussions ran on until June 1946 but ultimately nothing came of the proposal. There was also talk of them being sold to Norway but this requirement was ultimately met by the sale of four smaller 'CR' class destroyers. The four incomplete survivors lingered on for several years. *Namur* was considered for use as a trials ship for machinery in 1949-50 but she had not been docked since launching and as a result corrosion was rife; she was scrapped in 1951. The hull of *Albuera* was subjected to stress tests and broken in half in 1950, after which she was scrapped. *Jutland* and *Oudenarde* were used to test the effects of explosions on ship hulls; both were then scrapped in 1957.[34]

The completed ships provided a powerful destroyer force for the Royal Navy. There were numerous modifications made while they were in service, including the fitting of the new twin 40mm 'Staag' mounting, twin Bofors 40mm Mark V and single Bofors 40mm Mark VII. Four of the 1943 ships, *Agincourt, Aisne, Barrosa* and *Corunna*, were considerably modified when they were fitted out as aircraft-direction ships carrying the Type 965 radar. All were recommissioned in 1962 but their operational lives in the new role were short, the last ships pay-

Matapan, *as sonar trials ship, pictured in 1975.* (Richard Osborne)

Anzac. *She and her sister Tobruk had the distinction of being the first destroyers to mount the new radar controlled 4.5-inch Mk.6 twin mounting in operational service. She served with distinction during the Korean War.* (Richard Osborne.)

ing off in 1968. The final member of the class to be reconstructed was *Matapan*; she was converted into a sonar-trials ship between 1971 and 1973 after lying in reserve for some twenty-four years. *Matapan* was laid up in 1978, the last of the class to be in service with the Royal Navy. Two of the class, *Cadiz* and *Gabbard*, were transferred to Pakistan in 1956, while *Sluys* was sold to Iran in 1967. The remainder were scrapped between 1961 and 1972.[35]

Perspective

The 'Battle'-class destroyers, from the moment they were conceived, seemed to excite controversy and doubt. Admiral of the Fleet Viscount Cunningham of Hyndhope, in his autobiography *A Sailor's Odyssey*, epitomized the prevailing Jekyll-and-Hyde philosophy when he became First Sea Lord in October 1943. 'Destroyers were much too large', he wrote. 'They had become carriers of radar and radar ratings; and although they could detect the approach of enemy on the sea, under the sea and in the air, they could do little about it when in range because of their lack of gun power.' He then, however, continued in a different vein: 'In justice it must be said that the destroyers were good ships for the abnormal sort of war being fought in the Pacific—carrying an air war to enemy territory in aircraft carriers, with battleships and cruisers providing anti-aircraft protection for the carriers, and destroyers as the outer ring against aircraft and submarines.' In March 1946 he crossed the Irish Sea in the new destroyer *Solebay*: 'A fine enough ship which seemed to carry every mortal weapon and gadget except guns... These 'Battles' fulfil my worst expectations. An erection like Castle Rock, Edinburgh on the bridge. They call it a director, and all to control four guns firing a total broadside of about 200lb. We must get back to destroyers of reasonable size and well gunned.'[36]

But was the former First Sea Lord right? The judgement of history, as shown by the way warship designs have evolved, clearly indicates that the 'Battle' class was at the forefront of a trend where the ability of a warship to fight an enemy on the sea, under the sea or in the air has been enhanced by ever-improving methods of detection, fire control and weapons. The result has been the ever-increasing size of destroyers which Churchill, Cunningham and Alexander all deprecated, but this was an inescapable consequence of their growing technological sophistication. The concept behind the development of the 'Battle' class can therefore be said to have been the right one for the Admiralty to pursue given the nature of the threats that were being faced. One weakness was perhaps the retention of two banks of torpedo tubes but the possibility of action with an enemy fleet meant that it was too early in the war for a reduction in the numbers of this weapon.

The design was, however, rather rushed and it had to make use of weapons, machinery and proven construction techniques which would theoretically enable the class to be produced with all speed. The few ships completed before the end of the war were, however, too late

to be effective so we cannot make a judgement on their fighting qualities. They were very much an interim solution and they have to be judged on the basis of what could be done at a time when the British Empire and Commonwealth was fighting alone against Germany and Italy as well as being threatened by an aggressive Japanese Empire. The successor design, the Daring class, had a better armament, better machinery and was built with more advanced techniques but they could not have been ordered when the 'Battle' class was conceived. As an answer to a proven threat the 'Battle' class can be seen as the right design at the right time.

Acknowledgements
My thanks are due to David K Brown RCNC for reading the manuscript and providing helpful comments which have been included in the text, Richard Osborne of the World Ship Society for the provision of photographs and to Len Crockford and John Roberts who have produced the drawings. I would also like to thank the staff of The Naval Historical Branch, Cambridge University Library, The Public Record Office, Glasgow University Business Archives and Bob Todd and his team at the National Maritime Museum for all their help and kindness.

References and Footnotes
1   ADM 138 662. BATTLE Class Ships Cover. (NMM) The four 'L' Class Destroyers to mount eight 4in guns were *Lance*, *Gurkha* (ex-*Larne*), *Legion* and *Lively*. There were only two destroyers in the 'CE' Group, *Celt* and *Centaur*. Both were later to be units of the 'Weapon' class. *Centaur* was completed as *Scorpion*; *Celt* became *Sword* and was cancelled at the end of the war. By the end of the war the 'Z' and subsequent members of the group had better directors and were capable of firing eighteen rounds in the first minute, a rate of fire that could not be sustained. In *Chivalrous* they regarded themselves to be better than a 'Battle'. (D K Brown RCNC)

2   The background to the discussions is fully documented in the Ships Cover. The Diaries of Sir Stanley Goodall are held at the British Library. Extracts have been produced courtesy of D K Brown RCNC.

3   Drawings and Legends were produced but unfortunately they are not held in the Ships Cover.

4   ADM 138 662 BATTLE Class Ships Cover contains only brief details of the design options.

5   The Memorandum for the Board of Admiralty—'Fleet Destroyers of the 1942 Programme'—is held in ADM 167 113 (PRO). The fleet destroyer was first on the list of new design priorities given by the Controller on the 27 October 1941. Other new designs underway at the time in order of priority were aircraft carrier (fleet aircraft carrier which was to lead to *Eagle* and *Ark Royal*), 8in cruiser ('Admiral' class) and 6in cruiser (*Fiji* with longer endurance). ADM 138 624 Armoured Cruiser Designs to carry 8in or 9.2in guns. (NMM) The boiler temperature and pressures are detailed in *The Design and Construction of British Warships 1939–1945* (London 1995)

6   The memorandum written by A V Alexander is held in PREM 3 322-11. (PRO)

7   ADM 138 655 'U' and 'V' Classes. (NMM) See also *British Destroyers* by Edgar J March. DNC had been working on

'Draft Staff Requirements'. The full Staff Requirements were not available until the 2 January 1942. The six 4.7in mountings in Studies 'O' and 'P1' were probably twins.

8 ADM 229 25 Director of Naval Construction: Reports March 1941–March 1942. (NMM)

9 ADM 116 4601 1940–1942 Naval Construction Programmes. (PRO) See also *British Destroyers* by Edgar J March.

10 CAB 120 281 contains personal minutes drafted by the Prime Minister. (PRO)

11 ADM 205 13 First Sea Lord's Records. (PRO) Note that the number of destroyers in the Programme has now risen from 40 to 42.

12 CAB 66 24 War Cabinet Memoranda. The early drafts of the 1942 Programme included two fast minelayers. These were replaced by the two 'CE' class destroyers which were to be fitted out for minelaying.

13 T161 1105 S36130/42/1. (PRO) The Cabinet discussion is recorded in CAB 65 26. (PRO)

14 The Development of Destroyer Main Armament 1941 to 1945 by Captain (E) G C De Jersey, RN (*Journal of Naval Engineering* 1953/54). Fixed ammunition included the brass cartridge case; separate ammunition kept the charge and the shell apart.

15 CAB 65 27 War Cabinet Conclusions WM (42) 101 and WM (42) 128. (PRO) Opposition to the fleet destroyers emerged again when the 1943 Programme was presented to the War Cabinet and yet again when the Daring class destroyers were included in the 1944 New Construction Programme.

16 ADM 116 5150 Destroyers FB (42) 2. (PRO)

17 ADM 116 5150 1943 Programme FB (42) 11 (PRO) The new machinery developments planned would move the standards in use in the Royal Navy closer to those achieved by the USN. They were not incorporated in the 'Battle' class.

18 ADM 205 21 First Sea Lord's Papers. (PRO) and ADM 116 5150 Destroyers FB (42) 7. (PRO) The cruiser was to have been built by Cammell Laird and started late in 1943. No order was placed.

19 CAB 66 33 War Cabinet Memoranda. WP (43) 122. (PRO)

20 CAB 66 34 War Cabinet Memoranda. WM (43) 47 contains the War Cabinet discussion. The Memorandum on the 'Effect of Replacing Fleet Destroyers by Additional Frigates' (WP (43) 145 is held in CAB 66 33, Cabinet confirmation of the whole of the New Construction Programme (WM (54) 43 is held in CAB 65 34. (PRO) The row in Cabinet about the fleet destroyers seems to have obscured the increase in size and cost of the light fleet carriers: *Colossus* (14,000 tons) = £1.8m, *Hermes* (18,300 tons) = £2.5m. This matter surfaced in the summer of 1943 and took many months to resolve.

21 The minute by the Deputy Controller (FB (43) 32) and subsequent discussion (FB (43) 15) are held in ADM 116 5150. (PRO)

22 ADM 116 5150 Armament of the 1943 BATTLE Class Destroyers (FB (43) 16) (PRO)

23 ADM 116 5150 1943 BATTLE Class Destroyers FB (43) 19,
BATTLE Class Destroyers: Armament (FB (43) 20 and FB (43) 18 Design for the Large Fleet Destroyer of the 1944 Programme. (PRO) The large fleet destroyer became the Daring class.

24 ADM 229 30 Director of Naval Construction. Reports June 1943–August 1943. The Buster Bofors was a computer-controlled mounting. 102 sets were ordered from Vickers Armstrong but considerable difficulty was experienced in building the system and only one was delivered after the war. The remainder were cancelled. (Vickers Archives, Cambridge University Library.)

25 CAB 65 34 War Cabinet Conclusions. WM (43) 47. (PRO)

26 ADM 205 29 First Sea Lord's Papers (PRO)

27 CAB 102 524 Execution of Naval New Construction Programmes 1939-1945 D.C.M. Bolster, and CAB 119 93 1944/45 Landing Ships and Craft: Future Requirements and Provisions. (PRO) The first production Mark VI Director was fitted in *Barfleur*. The next four were fitted in the battleship *Anson* to the detriment of the destroyer programme. ADM 138 677 1943 BATTLE Class Destroyers. (NMM)

28 John Brown Archives. (University of Glasgow Business Archives.)

29 Minutes of the Ships Names Committee. (Naval Historical Branch, Whitehall.)

30 ADM 1 19739 1946–1949 BATTLE Class Destroyers–Performance Reports and Departmental Comments. Details of the *Cadiz* four-hour full-power trial and other trials are recorded in ADM 138 662A BATTLE Class Destroyers. (NMM) Design endurance was calculated on a standard formula, which it was found resulted in overstated performance expectations. (D K Brown. RCNC)

31 ADM 229 29 Director of Naval Construction: Reports March–May 1943 (PRO)

32 ADM 229 36 Director of Naval Construction: Reports August 1944-March 1945. Notes taken at Deputy Controllers meeting on 14 November 1944 record the decision to complete the last two 'Battle' class destroyers to the 1944 Design. (PRO) According to Conway's *All the Worlds Fighting Ships 1922–1946* eight members of the class were to complete with four 4.5in Mark VI mountings and a 41-foot beam. The destroyers involved were *Jutland, Poitiers, River Plate, St Lucia, Somme, Talavera, Trincomalee* and *Waterloo*. Delays in constructing the ships could have made it possible to modify the original armament production plans to accommodate this suggestion.

33 ADM 167 124 1945 Board Memoranda and ADM 1 19096 1945 Cancellation of Warship Contracts. (PRO)

34 ADM 138 662A BATTLE Class, ADM 138 677 1943 BATTLE Class (NMM) John Brown Archives (University of Glasgow Business Archives.), *A Century of Naval Construction*, D K Brown RCNC.

35 The post-war history of the class is documented in various editions of *Janes' Fighting Ships, Battle Class Destroyers* by Peter Hodges and *Warships since 1945-Part 3—Destroyers* by Mike Critchley.

36 *A Sailors Odyssey–The Autobiography of Admiral of the Fleet Viscount Cunningham of Hyndhope.* Pages 577-78 and 66.

Appendix 1: THE BATTLE CLASS DESTROYERS.

1942 Programme.

Job Number	Yard Number	Name	Builder	Ordered	Laid Down	Launched	Completed
J 4583	1691	BARFLEUR	Swan Hunter	27. 4.42	28.10.42	1.11.43	14. 9.44
J 4585	1693	TRAFALGAR	Swan Hunter	27. 4.42	15. 2.43	12. 1.44	23. 7.45
J 4587	1695	ST KITTS	Swan Hunter	27. 4.42	8. 9.43	4.10.44	21. 1.46
J 4584	658	ARMADA	Hawthorn Leslie	27. 4.42	29. 12.42	9.12.43	2. 7.45
J 4586	659	SOLEBAY	Hawthorn Leslie	27. 4.42	3. 2.43	22. 2.44	11.10.45
J 4588	660	SAINTES	Hawthorn Leslie	27. 4.42	8. 6.43	19. 7.44	27. 9.46
J 11707	707	CAMPERDOWN	Fairfield	27. 4.42	30.10.42	8. 2.44	18. 6.45
J 11708	708	FINISTERRE	Fairfield	27. 4.42	8.12.42	22. 6.44	11. 9.45
J 4681	1705	GABBARD	Swan Hunter	12. 8.42	2. 2.44	16. 3.45	10.12.46
J 3630	1124	HOGUE	Cammell Laird	12. 8.42	6. 1.43	21. 4.44	24. 7.45
J 3653	1125	LAGOS	Cammell Laird	12. 8.42	8. 4.43	4. 8.44	2.11.45
J 3608	1127	GRAVELINES	Cammell Laird	12. 8.42	10. 8.43	30.11.44	14. 6.46
J 3615	1128	SLUYS	Cammell Laird	12. 8.42	24.11.43	28. 2.45	30. 9.46
J 11711	711	CADIZ	Fairfield	12. 8.42	10. 5.43	16. 9.44	12. 4.46
J 11712	712	ST JAMES	Fairfield	12. 8.42	20. 5.43	7. 6.45	12. 7.46
J 11713	713	VIGO	Fairfield	12. 8.42	11. 9.43	27. 9.45	9. 12.46

Note: HOGUE and LAGOS were originally ordered from White on 27. 4. 42. Job Number J 6094 and J 6148, Yard Numbers 1926 and 1927 respectively. Initial cause of transfer was bomb damage at White's yard. Firm was then able to concentrate on the production of welded Intermediate Destroyers. Contracts and material were originally to be transferred to Fairfield.

1943 Programme.

Job Number	Yard Number	Name	Builder	Ordered	Laid Down	Launched	Completed
J 4870	664	AGINCOURT	Hawthorn Leslie	10. 3.43	12.12.43	29. 1.45	25. 6.47
J 4876	665	ALAMEIN	Hawthorn Leslie	10. 3.43	1. 3.44	28. 5.45	21. 5.48
J 4869	74	AISNE	Vickers (Tyne)	10. 3.43	26. 8.43	12. 5.45	20. 3.47
J 4873	75	ALBUERA	Vickers (Tyne)	10. 3.43	16. 9.43	28. 8.45	Canc. 15.10.45
J 1615	615	BARROSA	John Brown	10. 3.43	28.12.43	17. 1.45	14. 2.47
J 1616	616	MATAPAN	John Brown	10. 3.43	11. 3.44	30. 4.45	5. 9.47
J 4923	1713	CORUNNA	Swan Hunter	24. 4.43	12. 4.44	29. 5.45	6. 6.47
J 4926	1715	OUDENARDE	Swan Hunter	24. 4.43	12. 10.44	11. 9.45	Canc. 15.10.45
J 4929	1717	RIVER PLATE	Swan Hunter	24. 4.43	11. 4.45	-	Canc. 15.10.45
J 11603	603	DUNKIRK	Stephen	24. 4.43	19. 7.44	27. 8.45	27. 11.46
J 11604	604	MALPLAQUET	Stephen	24. 4.43	27. 11.44	20. 2.46	30. 4.47
J 11605	605	ST LUCIA	Stephen	24. 4.43	19. 1.45	-	Canc. 15.10.45
J 11714	714	BELLE ISLE	Fairfield	24. 4.43	10. 11.43	7. 2.46	Canc. 15.10.45
J 4922	667	JUTLAND	Hawthorn Leslie	24. 4.43	14. 8.44	2. 11.45	Canc. 15.10.45
J 4925	668	MONS	Hawthorn Leslie	24. 4.43	29. 6.45	-	Canc. 15.10.45
J 4928	669	POITIERS	Hawthorn Leslie	24. 4.43	9. 2.45	4. 1.46	Canc. 15.10.45
J 3694	1152	NAMUR	Cammell Laird	24. 4.43	29. 4.44	12. 6.45	Canc. 15.10.45
J 3672	1153	NAVARINO	Cammell Laird	24. 4.43	22. 5.44	21. 9.45	Canc. 15.10.45
J 3651	1154	SAN DOMINGO	Cammell Laird	24. 4.43	9. 12.44	-	Canc. 15.10.45
J 3633	1155	SOMME	Cammell Laird	24. 4.43	24. 2.45	-	Canc. 15.10.45
J 1617	617	TALAVERA	John Brown	5. 6.43	4. 9.44	27. 8.45	Canc. 15.10.45
J 1618	618	TRINCOMALEE	John Brown	5. 6.43	5. 2.45	18. 1.46	Canc. 15.10.45
J 11716	716	WATERLOO	Fairfield	5. 6.43	14. 6.45	-	Canc. 15.10.45
J 11717	717	YPRES	Fairfield	5. 6.43			
J 3675	1157	VIMIERO	Cammell Laird	5. 6.43			

Notes: YPRES and VIMIERO to DARING Class. MALPLAQUET renamed JUTLAND when sister ship cancelled.

Australian 'BATTLE' Class.

		Name	Builder	Ordered	Laid Down	Launched	Completed
		ANZAC	Williamstown Dockyard	23. 9. 46	20. 8. 48	22. 3. 51	
		TOBRUK	Cockatoo, Sydney	5. 8. 46	20.12.47	17. 5. 50	

Appendix 2: *FLEET DESTROYER WITH FULLY HA ARMAMENT.*

Sketch Design 'N'.	4. 10. 1941. (ADM 167 113)	21. 5. 42 (ADM 167 115)
Length between perpendiculars.	355'	355'
Length on waterline	364'	364'
Length overall	377'	379'
Breadth extreme	40' 3"	40' 3"

STANDARD CONDITION

Displacement	2280 tons	2315 tons
Draught, mean	10' 3"	10' 3"
Freeboard to top of deck at side, forward	24' 0"	23' 11"
" " " amidships	11' 9"	11' 8"
" " " aft	12' 6"	12' 5"

DEEP CONDITION

Draught, mean	12' 10"	12' 11"
Shaft Horse Power of Engines	50,000	50,000
Number of propelling shafts	2	2
Speed in Standard Condition (knots)	36	35³/4
Speed in Deep Condition (knots)	31¹/2	31¹/4
Oil Fuel Capacity (tons)	700	700
Endurance at 20 knots (miles) clean bottom	4,400	4400
Complement of Officers and Men (as War)	235	236

GUNS and TORPEDOES

Two 4.7in (50lb shell) twin 80-degree BD mountings with predictor control. (350 rounds per gun with space for 400 rounds per gun). Later: Two 4.5in (55lb shell) (325 rounds per gun with space for 375 rounds per gun)

Four 40mm twin Bofors (1800 rounds per barrel). Later (1440 rounds per barrel)

Six 20 mm Oerlikons (2400 rounds per barrel)

Two Star-shell mortars (30 rounds per gun). Later 1 – 4in Mk XXIII (60 rounds).

Two 21in Quadruple handworked torpedo tubes. Eight Mark IX torpedoes.

Depth Charges	60	60
Throwers	4	4
Depth Charge Rails	2	2

Minesweeping Equipment – Capable of being fitted with TSDS (Twin-Speed Destroyer Sweep) when required; when fitted, after set of torpedo tubes to be landed.

ARMOUR AND PROTECTION

15lbs protection to gun working spaces and EC hoists. (Later 10lbs protection to EC hoists.)

20lbs protection to shields of BD mountings.

15lbs (later 10lbs) zareba protection to close-range armament.

15lbs protection on front and sides of wheelhouse, upper bridge and plotting office.

15lbs (later 10lbs) protection on Bofors offices, transmitting station and cables to director.

DISPLACEMENT.	(Tons)	(Tons)
General Equipment	100	105
Machinery	645	655
Electric Generators	30	30
Armament including Stabiliser	357	360
Armour and Protection	30	30
Hull	1118	1135
Board Margin	-	
Standard Displacement	2280	2315

Notes: It was originally planned to fit stabilisers in the class but only *CAMPERDOWN* and *FINISTERRE* were so fitted. The remainder gained space for an additional 60 tons of oil fuel.

Leaders displaced 2325 tons.

Appendix 3: STAFF REQUIREMENTS FOR *1942* PROGRAMME FLEET DESTROYER. (TSD 1066/41)

General

The requirement is for an ocean going destroyer for Fleet work and general purposes at home and abroad.

It is considered that the design should be based on the following main requirements which war experience has shown to be desirable.

Main armament to be fully HA/LA.

Main armament guns not to be less than 4.7in calibre.

Four main armament guns to be fired forward.

Adequate close range AA armament.

Very good sea keeping qualities and high endurance.

Two sets of torpedo tubes.

Four charge pattern Depth Charge equipment

It is considered that the ship should be very seaworthy at speed in adverse weather conditions in the open ocean. A stabiliser should be provided. Good provision is required for lookouts.

The ship should be capable of being fitted with TSDS when required, and arrangements made for adequate weight compensation.

A gangway from the forebridge to the after superstructure passing over the torpedo tubes is considered desirable.

Two ships of each flotilla should be fitted as leaders.

Speed

It is considered that the speed should be not less than 31 knots in deep condition.

Endurance

It is considered that the endurance starting in the deep condition with clean bottom should be 4400 miles at 20 knots and 7700 miles at 12 knots. (This is 20 per cent greater than 'J' and 'K' classes and only 5 per cent less than 'Q' class)

Armament

Main Armament.

Four 4.7in HA/LA guns in twin BD mountings with a maximum elevation of 80 degrees, both mountings to be mounted forward. It is considered that two mountings should be accepted in order to give the ship an adequate close range armament without excessive displacement. There is consequently no main armament fire aft. Experience is that we rarely need to fire aft, but two mountings should be given the maximum possible arcs. It is considered that special attention should be given to making the mountings watertight and to ease of maintenance.

Close Range Armament.

i. Four Predictor Controlled Bofors Twin Mountings.

ii Six Oerlikons. (See note after paragraph 12.)

The close range armament to have the widest possible arcs of fire and to be arranged on the 'four cornered system'.

Star Shell Equipment.

One 4in HA gun or two Star Shell Mortars. (Note. The provision for firing Star Shell is not decided. If Star Shell mortars now under construction give satisfactory results then these will be installed. If not, the platform amidships will be arranged to take one 4in HA/LA gun instead of two Oerlikons and two Star Shell Mortars. Provision for using Bofors to fire star shell is also being examined.)

Ammunition Stowage

i. Main armament – 400 rounds per gun (325 rounds per gun outfit and six months practice allowance).

Bofors – 1440 rounds per barrel.

Oerlikons – 2400 rounds per barrel

4in Star Shell – 60 (see note after preceding paragraph). Or, Star Shell Mortars – 30 rounds per gun.

Torpedo Armament

Eight 21in in two quadruple mountings

Asdics

To be fitted with Asdic equipment

Depth Charges

To be fitted with –

Four Depth Charge Throwers.

Two DC Rails.

60 Depth Charges.

Searchlights

The provision to be as in 'J' class Destroyer.

Communications

As in 'J' class. (Note: If HF/DF is required it can be provided in place of the RDF set Type 290.)

Added in manuscript – (TSD1604/42 – A battery operated WT transmitter and receiver is to be supplied and stored in a position remote from the main W/T Office for use when the latter is put out of action.)

RDF

The following are required

Air and surface warning sets.

Main armament – one set.

Bofors – four sets in two offices.

Electrical Equipment

It is considered that sufficient electrical power should be available to fight the armament in harbour with fires drawn.

Habitability

As in 'J' class destroyers with improvements that DNC can provide without prejudice to fighting qualifications. (It is proposed that space should be provided on the bridge structure where lookouts and bridge personnel stand off and relax.)

Silhouette

It is considered that silhouette should be small.

GERMAN MOTOR MINESWEEPERS AT WAR, 1939-1945

To many students of naval warfare during the Second World War, the German Navy's schnellboote bore the brunt of fighting in coastal waters. However, as **Pierre Hervieux** shows in his latest instalment on the war experiences of minor German warships, the raumboote (or R-boats) played a major part. They were more numerous and proved doughty opponents for their Allied counterparts.

[Because of lack of space, the article does not cover the operations against the Soviet forces in the Arctic, Baltic and Black Seas, nor the Anglo-American forces in the Mediterranean.]

The German motor minesweepers were known as *räumboote* or *R-boote* in the Kriegsmarine. The prototype, *R1*, displaced 45 tons and was launched in 1931. She was followed by an enlarged group *R2/R7, R9/R16* (60 tons) and *R8* (63 tons) which were launched between 1932/1934. They were followed by the groups:

R17/R24 (120 tons) launched between 1935/1937,
R25/R40 (126 tons) launched in 1938/1939,
R41/R129 (135 tons) launched between 1941/1943,
R130/R150 (155 tons) launched in 1943/1944,
R151/R217 (128 tons) launched between 1940/1943,
R218/R290 (*R271, R291/R300* were unfinished, *R277/R287* were cancelled) (154 tons) launched between 1943/1945,
R301/R312 (*R313/R400* were cancelled) (190 tons) launched in 1943/1944,
R401/R419 (*R420/R427* were unfinished, *R428/R545* were cancelled) (150 tons) launched in 1944/1945.

From the prototype to the biggest model the overall length rose from 24 to 41 metres and the maximum speed from 17 to 25 knots. Apart from *R1*, commissioned in 1931, all the others were commissioned between 1932 and 1945. Those 299 *räumboote* were used for coastal convoy protection, minesweeping, minelaying and the rescue of air crews. According to the type of operation, depth charges or 10 mines were carried in addition to the original armament. Prior to, and early in the war that armament comprised one or two 20mm AA guns (1x1 or 2x1), later increased to four 20mm AA guns (2x2), or one 37mm AA gun, and three or six 20mm AA guns (3x1/2). *R301/R312* were later re-classed GR301/GR312

(*geleit-räumboote*) and two 21-inch (2x1) torpedo tubes were added. This article will only cover the operations of the German-built R-boats

The R-boats first went into action in the Baltic during the campaign against Poland. The 3rd Flotilla (Kapitänleutnant Küster) with *R33, R34, R35, R36, R38, R39, R40* and the tender *Von der Gröben* was employed in the operations against Westerplatte, Gdingen and Hela. The flotilla did not suffer any damage despite being fired on several times by Polish coastal batteries. Sometimes this was without any possibility of returning the fire, such as on 25 September, off Hela, when the Poles opened fire on the boats at a distance of 15,000 metres with their 150mm guns. On 1 October, north-east of Heisternest, the old minesweeper M85 was sunk by a mine laid by a Polish submarine (probably the *Zbik*). Two-thirds of her crew were rescued by R-boats and the old minesweeper *M122*.

At the beginning of January 1940 it was so cold—minus 20°C—that on the Elbe seven R-boats were trapped in the ice in Brunsbüttel, and it was this weather that caused the first R-boat loss in the Second World War Two. R5 sank in the Baltic, off Stolpmünde, on 3 January 1940, after suffering ice damage and becoming stranded.

The next big operation in which R-boats were involved was the occupation of Norway, which started on 7 April 1940. During that operation (*Weserübung*), three flotillas were employed.

The 1st Flotilla (Kapitänleutnant Forstmann) was directed to Oslo, with *R17, R18, R19, R20, R21, R22, R23, R24* and two whalers. The 2nd Flotilla (Korvettenkapitän Von Kamptz), with *R25, R26, R27, R28, R29, R30, R31* and *R32* was assigned to the Esbjerg and Nordby in Fanö area. Finally, the 3rd Flotilla, with the same boats as in Poland, plus *R37*, went to Tyborön in Lim fjord. In addition, *R6* and *R7* were part of group 9

The R11 was launched on 27 June 1934 and is here seen before the war. She was transferred in November 1941, with sister-boats, to the Mediterranean, via Rotterdam, the Rhine, the French Rhine/Rhone canal, through 167 locks(!), and then via other French rivers. She was sunk by a British bomber, on 2 August 1942, in the Bay of Bardia (Drüppel)

R-boats of the R9/R16 type were modified in 1939. Here is one in Nouregian waters. They had been launched between April and September 1934 (ECPA)

directed to Middelfart and Belt Bridge. It was only at the naval arsenal of Horten, in the Oslo fjord, that strong resistance from Norwegian warships was met. The R-boats were no match for the Norwegian minelayer *Olav Tryggvason* (1763 tons, 1932) which, with her four 120mm guns, sank *R17* and heavily damaged *R21* on 9 April. During the same battle, the Norwegian minesweeper *Rauma* (370 tons, 1939) was damaged by gunfire from an R-boat (*R27?*) and lost two men killed and six wounded. Later in the day she was captured by Germans, together with the *Olav Tryggvason*. On 9 April, also in the Oslo fjord, the Norwegian submarine A2 (268 tons 1913) was captured by R22 and R23. On 18 April, *R25* and *R27*, with three torpedo boats, escorted the minelayers *Hansestadt Danzig*, *Kaiser*, *Roland*, *Cobra*, *Preussen* and *Königin Luise* which laid anti-submarine barrages in the Kattegat.

Thanks to the charts of English minefields captured with the British submarine *Seal* on 5 May, R-boats swept 111 moored mines off the Ems.

During the second half of May, the 2nd Flotilla was back back in Germany, ready for action in the Netherlands, together with the newly-formed 4th Flotilla. The 2nd Flotilla swept Vlissingen and then sailed for Boulogne, where English moored mines were destroyed. In the Belgian and Channel French harbours 263 German magnetic mines laid by aircraft were recovered. The German land forces were progressing down

south at an unexpected speed, Cherbourg being reached on 18 June and Brest within the next four days, followed by all the harbours in the Bay of Biscay, stopping in Hendaye near the Spanish border. The 2nd Flotilla had the task of clearing the harbours and the approaches of Brest, Lorient and St. Nazaire. By August those harbours and all the others were free of mines. During the second half of July, sweeping was effected off the Dutch, Belgian and French coast down to Boulogne. While working near Cap Gris Nez, the 4th Flotilla was attacked by British destroyers. The R-boats zigzagged and made artificial smoke and, nearing the coast, they were lucky enough to be supported by an 88mm coastal flak battery. Then a few German aircraft came to help, and the destroyers turned back.

By the middle of August there were 20 R-boats in the West:

2nd Flotilla with 8, in Lorient and Brest,
4th Flotilla with 10, in Boulogne and Calais,
11th Flotilla with 2 and 8 old cutters in Holland and Belgium.

The 3rd Flotilla was expected soon. During the Battle of Britain, R-boats and other small craft recovered German fliers shot down at sea. Fifty of them had been rescued in this way by the middle of September. They were, of course, attacked at sea by British aircraft, and 20mm guns

An R-boat of the R21/R40 type, close to the French north coast near Malo les Bains, with the wreck of the French destroyer Jaguar *after she was torpedoed by the German motor torpedo boats S21 and S23 and grounded on 23 May 1940 (ECPA)*

A close-up of an R-boat's bridge during the summer of 1940 (ECPA)

were always ready, even in rescuing missions. During these operations *R44* and *R45* shot down four of the attackers.

On 1 November 1940, there were 5 flotillas in the West with 36 R-boats and 5 depot ships: the 1st, 2nd, 3rd, 4th and 7th Flotillas. It was just enough, for the Kriegsmarine had to protect 900 sea miles (about 1700 kilometres) of coast, and a lot of shipping from Holland to the Bay of Biscay sailing from 22 harbours. On 4 November 1940, the Kriegsmarine reported that seven R-boat flotillas were necessary: one in Holland, two in the Dover Strait area, one in the Seine Bay, two in the Bay of Biscay and one in reserve.

The number of mines swept in between September and December 1939 and through 1940 is not available but, to give an idea, north of Ijmuiden, in October 1940, 204 moored mines were swept by the 4th Flotilla and the pinnaces from the *MRS.11* (a depot ship for minesweepers).

The situation, by 1 April 1941, was even worse than in November 1940 for, because of the planned attack against the Soviet Union, only 4 R-boat flotillas were left in the West, with a total of 40 boats.

In April, off Brest, in two weeks, 22 mines were swept and destroyed. British planes frequently strafed the R-boats. Though they could not sink them, the crews were suffering heavy casualties. During the second half of April, off the French coast, 19 men were killed and 31 wounded on R-boats, while 11 planes were confirmed as

shot down. British aircraft attacked individually or in small groups, but things were going to change in the coming autumn.

At the end of June 1941, the 4 flotillas in the West were made of:

1st Flotilla:	12 R-boats (+ 1 non-operational)
2nd Flotilla:	8 R-boats
3rd Flotilla:	13 R-boats
4th Flotilla:	9 R-boats (+ 2 non-operational)
TOTAL:	42 R-boats (+ 3 non-operational).

When the Soviet Union was invaded on 22 June 1941 half the operational R-boats were sent to the Baltic.

During the summer of 1941, the 7th Flotilla had been sent to northern Norway for operations on the Polar Coast, between Hammerfest and Kirkenes. On 7 September, by night, off Porsanger fjord, a small German convoy comprising 2 freighters, carrying about 1500 troops, escorted by the gunnery training ship *Bremse* (1596 tons, 1931), *R162* and 2 patrol boats, was attacked by the British light cruisers *Aurora* and *Nigeria*. (See *Warship* 1987) After a courageous defence, the *Bremse* was sunk, allowing the freighters to escape safely. *R162* and 4 patrol boats rescued 37 survivors.

When autumn arrived in the Channel, British fighters and fighter bombers attacked in much greater numbers, in groups of 30 to 50 planes. For instance, on 1 October

Two fine views of the same R-boat, armed with 2/20mm AA guns without shields, off Holland. Note the heart emblem amidships on the hull and 3 depth-charges on each side, between the forward gun and the bridge: R21/R40 type or even RXX onwards...
(ECPA)

1941, R-boats of the 3rd Flotilla were sweeping off Dieppe, when they were suddenly attacked by a swarm of British planes. In few minutes the boats had lost 40 per cent of their crews, killed or wounded. The Commander of the 2nd Security Division, Kapitän zur See Weniger, the Flotilla Leader Kapitänleutnant Rossow, 2 officers and 8 seamen were killed, 20 were seriously and 16 slightly wounded. It became necessary to equip the guns with armoured shields and to armour the bridges as well, and to do this as soon as possible.

During 1941, in the West, mineweepers of all kinds swept 399 ground mines and 678 moored mines for the loss of one minesweeper and one auxiliary minesweeper. In addition, they also escorted 687 U-boats sailing in and out of harbours in the Bay of Biscay.

At the beginning of 1942, in the Channel and in the southern North Sea, the 2nd, 3rd and 4th R-boat Flotillas were involved in minesweeping work before the start of Operation Cerberus, the famous Channel dash of the *Gneisenau*, *Scharnhorst* and *Prinz Eugen*. A total of 21 grounds mines and 98 moored mines were swept by R-boats, M-boats and auxiliary minesweepers. One of the latter was sunk by a mine, and *R42* sank after colliding with a wreck, on 11 February 1942, in the Channel near Ambleteuse, at 50°49N/01°37E; there were no casualties.

On the night of 13/14 March, the German auxiliary cruiser *Michel* passed through the Channel, escorted by 9 R-boats from 2nd Flotilla, 8 M-boats and 5 torpedo boats. In fierce engagements with British MTBs, MGBs and escort destroyers, two of the latter, *Fernie* and *Walpole*, were damaged without German loss. The *Michel* reached Le Havre on 14 March, St. Malo on 15 March and La Pallice on 17 March from where she set out for the Atlantic on 20 March.

During the night of 22/23 April, the 2nd R-boat Flotilla escorted the *Sperrbrecher 4* and the seaplane tender *Immelmann* from Boulogne to Le Havre. The sea was so rough that *R86*'s forward 20mm gun was considerably bent.

On 9 May, near Dunkirk, west of Ambleteuse, at 50°49N/01°36E, *R45* collided with the old minesweeper *M533* (508 tons, 1919, ex-*Raule*, ex-*M133*) which sank, while the wrecked *R45* was brought in. On 12 May, the auxiliary cruiser *Stier* left Rotterdam escorted by six R-boats, ten M-boats and four torpedo boats. Two of the latter (*Iltis* and *Seeadler*) and the British *MTB220* were sunk during transit of the Straits of Dover but, by small stages, the *Stier* safely entered the Gironde Estuary on 19 May.

During the night of 14/15 June, a unit of MGBs (6, 13, 41, 46) plus the Polish *S3*, and a unit of MTBs (201, 203,

The R33 was launched on 1 February 1939 and is seen here in the West in May 1941. Among other boats, 23 R-boats were sent by the Kriegsmarine to the Black Sea. They were carried overland from the Elbe Tiver, below Dresden, to the Dambe, below Regensburg. Among them was the R33 and the first units arrived in May 1942. R33 was sunk by a Soviet bomber, off Yalta at 44°30N/34°10E, on 19 July 1943 (Koehlers)

A crew manning a 20mm AA gun aboard an R-boat (ECPA)

229) attacked a German convoy proceeding from Boulogne to Dunkirk, which comprised the following ships and boats: tanker *Memelland* (6200 tons) in tow of five tugs (*Cherbourgeois V*, *Vulcan*, *D126S*, *D127S*, *C72S*) escorted by *R77*, *R78*, *R79*, *R80*, *R81*, *R82*, *R83*, *R84*, *R85*, *R86*, *R87*, *R88*, *Vp1501*, *Vp1505*, *Vp1507*, *Vp1509*, *Vp1512*, *Vp1514*, *Vp1802*, *Vp1805*, *Vp1806*, and *Vp1813*.

MTB201 (40 tons, 1941) was badly damaged, having come under heavy fire and being set ablaze as a result. Though she was abandoned, her crew were able to re-embark half an hour later and got clear of the enemy high speed launch soon after daylight some 10-miles east of Dover, but sank, however, whilst efforts were being made to tow her in. It would appear that the combined fire of the escorts at the rear of the convoy (*Vp1514*, *R79*, *R77*, *R82*, *Vp1505*) was responsible for the damage to *MTB201*, which at one stage passed so close to *R77* that the signalman aboard *R77* was able to hit the MTB's bridge with a grenade thrown by hand.

On 16 August, three days before the ill-fated landing of Dieppe, the 10th R-boat Flotilla laid a flanking mine barrage off Calais. But at 20:30 the Dover radar detected them. The British *MGB6* and *MGB10* sailed from Ramsgate, and *MGB330*, *MGB331* and *MGB609* from Dover to attack them. The battle began around 21:30. The Germans fought vigorously. Right from the start the British leader, *MGB330*, was crippled; her wireless transmitter was destroyed, and her 2pdr pom-pom gun put out

of action after having fired only about thirty shots. However *MGB330* succeeded in ramming *R184*. *MGB331* and *MGB609* were also seriously hit, while *MGB6* and *MGB10*, having a smaller silhouette, were not so badly damaged. On the German side, three R-boats were more or less damaged, whilst the wrecked *R184* was given the coup-de-grace by German coastal guns. Both sides suffered dead and wounded; eight Germans were rescued by the British brought back to Dover. The action ended at 22:45.

On 6 October, following reports from Dover of a large merchant vessel proceeding north-east from Boulogne, MGBs *75* and *76* and MTBs *29*, *30*, *70* and *72* were sent to intercept. Just after midnight the unit encountered a force of twelve R-boats (*R77* to *R88*, that had sailed from Dunkirk) and four M-class minesweepers, (*M21*, *M25*, *M38* and *M153*). Two actions ensued, and it was during the second that *MGB 76* (37 tons, 1942) came under heavy fire from *R77*, *R83*, *R85* and *R87*, receiving hits in the petrol tank compartment, which caught fire. The fire appeared to have been brought under control when suddenly the boat blew up without warning and subsequently burnt fiercely. MGBs *61* and *64*, returning from patrol, fought the fire and rescued all the crew except the motor mechanic, who had been killed.

When the German auxiliary cruiser *Komet* tried to break out on a second raiding cruise, she was escorted by the 2nd R-boat Flotilla, but on 8 October they ran onto a newly-laid moored acoustic minefield off Dunkirk, at

Two more good views of R-boats with two totally different patterns of camouflage early in the war (1940 or 1941) (ECPA)

Another 'hearted' R-boat with an increased AA armament, later in the war, off the coast of Brittany (ECPA)

51° 02'N 102°22'E, and *R77, R78, R82* and *R86* were sunk. Those moored acoustic mines were a very dangerous device, primarily aimed at R and S-boats. The R-boats, not being equipped against them, suffered badly.

On 26 November, West of Fécamp, at 49°46'N/00°21'E, *R109* was sunk by a German mine.

In the Western theatre, during 1942, R-boats, M-boats, auxiliary minesweepers, sperrbrecher, etc. escorted 5275 ships, representing a total tonnage of 4,226,000 tons. Eight of these ships were sunk: 4 by torpedoes from MTBs, 2 by mines and 2 by air attacks, representing a total tonnage of 11,500tons. Ten ships, representing 3,600 tons, were sunk by hazards of the sea and by navigational errors. Total losses represented less than 1 per cent of the escorted tonnage. In escorting, minesweeping and patrolling, minesweepers of all kinds lost 42 boats (7 during 1941), including motor luggers, motor fishing cutters, sardine boats and lobster boats. They shot down 78 aircraft (confirmed), and sank or damaged several MTBs and MGBs; 542 moored mines were swept for the loss of two minesweepers and no loss of escorted ships. 624 ground mines were swept for the loss of 17 boats of all kinds, one escorted steamer and one transport ferry. The sperrbrecher suffered heavier losses, 6 being sunk and 11 severely damaged.

On 1 January 1943 there were 51 R-boats with four R-boat tenders in the West. On 23 January the U.S. 8th Air Force flew daylight raids against Lorient and Brest; in the latter *R44* was sunk at about 14:30 (all times given are

German). On 12 March, south-west of Boulogne, at 50°44N/01°36E, *R74* was sunk by an air-laid mine at 18:27, and *R187* badly damaged by another. On 17 March it was the turn of *R40* to hit such a mine at 19:12, the wreck being towed in and on 19 April stricken for cannibalisation.

After their transfer on 19 April from Germany through the North Sea, the Dover Straits and the Channel, *R194* and *R195*, after having left Le Havre, were on their way to Auxerre for the Mediterranean via French canals. On the same day, *R34* and *R210* left Le Havre for the Mediterranean too. At that same date *R38, R178, R188* and *R211* were being prepared before a similar transfer, and *R39* was also in Le Havre, in a shipyard, being repaired before also sailing for the Mediterranean. In Fécamp *R177* was also being repaired and was later sent back to Germany. Many other R-boats were also later sent, in the same way, to the Mediterranean: *R161, R162, R185/R187, R189/R192, R198/R201, R212* and *R215*.

On 26 April *R114* struck a mine between Dunkirk and Calais. She sank the next day while under tow.

In the southern North Sea, during the night of 13/14 May, the minelaying operation 'Stemmbogen' took place, west of the Hook of Holland. The 9th R-boat Flotilla and 2 flotillas of minesweepers laid the barrage SW12 and were attacked on the return by 4 British MTBs, the minesweeper M8 being torpedoed and sunk. On 19 June *R41* was also the victim of a British MTB, in the Seine Bight near Barfleur.

A 37mm AA gun with a shield aboard an R-boat (ECPA)

Two views of different styles of bridges: the first with chinks and armour, with 2/20mm AA guns protected by shields, late war appearance; the second with usual apertures, but the guns (1/37 and 1/20mm) with protective shields too, probably in 1943. (ECPA)

On 20 August, R84 was sunk near Boulogne, at 50°44'N/1°36'E, by an aircraft bomb and gunfire, while R94 was sunk by a mine in the Channel on 6 September. On 16 September, during a U.S. 8th Air Force raid, R19 was sunk in the harbour of Nantes, at 16:10. R93 was sunk by a mine off Dunkirk, on 23 September at 51°02'N/2°22'E.

In the Channel, during the night of 26/27 September, the 2nd R-boat Flotilla and patrol boats escorted a convoy from Le Havre to Dunkirk, and came under attack by British MGB108, MGB117 and MGB118. At the same time the Dutch MTB202, MTB204 and MTB231 attacked from the shore side, off Fécamp and Berck-sur-Mer, and sank the patrol boat Vp1501, the cargo ship Madali (3019 tons) and the R-escort boat Jungingen (ex-M534, 721 tons, 1919), the latter at 50°28'N/01°27'E, 3 miles west of Berck-sur-Mer. (Contrary to what I wrote in Warship 1995, page 118, Jungingen was not a German freighter of 800 tons.)

On 13 December, during a daylight attack on Kiel by bombers of the 8th U.S. Air Force, R306 was among the ships sunk. She was raised on 5 February 1944 and cannibalised. On 16 December, R54 hit a mine and sank, at 10:31, north-west of the island of Anholt in the Kattegat. There were no casualties.

Through 1943, in the Western Theatre, R-boats, M-boats, auxiliary mimesweepers, sperrbrecher, motor fishing cutters, motor luggers, etc. swept 792 ground mines and 246 moored mines for the loss of 12 vessels; from all causes 43 were lost, with 458 men killed and missing, 965 being wounded. They shot down a confirmed total of 69 enemy planes. They also were very active in escorting U-boats in and out of the Bay of Biscay, no less than 1452 of them. They escorted a total of 3,400,000 tons, and sank or damaged several MTBs and MGBs.

On 21 February 1944, a German convoy was attacked by 37 British Beaufighters of Coastal Command, south-west of Den Helder, and R131 was sunk at about 09:31, at 52°55'N/04°26'E, the wreck being part-raised later. On the same day, R222 was sunk by British air-laid mine, east of Schleimünde, near the Kiel Bay. On 25 February R52 was damaged, in Dieppe harbour, by an aircraft bomb at about 20:00, and was then stricken. She nevertheless was used after the war, by the German Minesweeping Administration under Allied control and, in 1947, became a U.S. prize. On 16 April, in the North Sea off Terschelling, R108 was sunk in collision with R229, at 53°22'N/05°21'E.

On 29 May, off Le Havre, R123 was sunk by aircraft bombs at 49°29'N/00°06'E, at 02:50.

In the run-up to Operation Neptune (the amphibious phase of Operation Overlord), the major Allied landing in Normandy, from 30 April to 5 June there was an intensive mine offensive by RAF Bomber Command. In 31 nights, 1008 sorties were flown against the French Biscay, Brittany and Channel ports, the Belgian and Dutch coasts, the Heligoland Bight, the Kattegat and the Western Baltic up to the Pomeranian Bay. Mosquitos laid, for the first time, mines in the Kiel Canal. Eleven aircraft were lost. Among other ships, the following R-boats were victims of those air-laid mines:

On 15 May, in the approach to Le Havre, R179 at 49°29'N/00°15'E.
On 29 May, off Calais, R116 at 51°04'N/01°17'W, at 04:05.

Two R-boats preparing to tie up in a western French harbour (Drüppel)

The R156, launched on 23 October 1940 she survived the war and served in the German minesweeping administration, under allied control. On 1 December 1945 she became the Danish MR156 and was renamed Dyrnaes in 1951. Stricken in 1957, she was broken up in 1958 (Drüppel)

On 10 June, off the Hook of Holland, *R110* at 52°05'N/04°07'E.
On 12 June, off Gravelines, *R95* at 50°59'N/02°03'E.

On the night of 17/18 May, S-boats, coming back from mining operation against a British convoy between Folkestone and Dungeness, had had a brief engagement with a German convoy comprising the 4th R-boat Flotilla, their tender and KFKs (naval drifters), without any damage being done.

On 13 June, off Trouville, *R50* was sunk by a German shallow water mine, at 49°22N/00°05'E, but there were no casualties. In the meantime, during the night of 6/7 June, off Le Havre, the 4th R-boat Flotilla (Kapitänleutnant Anhalt) had become involved in an engagement with the British 55th MTB Flotilla and the Canadian 29th MTB Flotilla, while laying the barrage Blitz 25. *R49* was badly damaged, as were *MTB624* and *MTB682*. On 6 June *R221* had been sunk by air attack at Blainville, on the Orne Canal.

On 13 June, off Boulogne, the 2nd Flotilla of S-boats was heavily attacked by Beaufighters of Nos. 143 and 236 Squadrons of the RAF. Three of the four boats were sunk. *R97*, who came to their assistance, was also sunk by a rocket, at 50°44N/01°36E, and *R99* was damaged. On 15 June *R51* was sunk near the coast by mine, but she was raised. With the D-day landings, June had already been costly for R-boats, and it was not over.

At the time of D-day, there were 65 R-boats in the West (France, Belgium and Holland). On the night of 14/15 June, a big air raid of 362 Lancasters against the harbour of Le Havre sank many ships, including *R182*; but she was raised. On the following night the harbour of Boulogne was attacked by 155 Lancasters and 130 Halifaxes. Both raids also included 28 Mosquitos, which only dropped flares. Again many warships were sunk, and this time it was even worse for the R-boats, five being sunk at about 23:00: *R92*, *R125*, *R129*, *R232* and *R237*. Three others were badly damaged: *R96*, *R100* and *R117*. On 16 June *R81*, at about 01:00, was sunk by a British aircraft bomb, off Boulogne at 50°44'N/01°36'E. On 23 June, off Boulogne, *R79* was sunk by two aircraft rockets, at 50°44'N/01°36'E. On the next day, *R141* was sunk in an air attack on Wesermünde while under repair.

On the night of 25/26 June, eight control and nine explosive boats ('Linsen'), towed by R-boats tried a first attack against the Allied Operation Neptune but because of bad weather one of the explosive boats smashed against *R46*, exploding and sinking her, off Le Havre, at 49°29'N/00°06'E. The operation was a failure.

R-boats of the 10th Flotilla (Kapitänleutnant Nau) were attacked off Fécamp by British *MTB632* and *MTB650* on 2 July; at 02:65 *R180* was torpedoed and sunk at 49°46'N/00°20'E while *MTB632* was put out of action by other minesweepers coming on the scene.

In the North Sea, on 5 July, *R111* was sunk by a British aircraft bomb and gunfire, at 05:20, near the Dutch Island of Vlieland, at 53°18'N/05°00'E. On the next day, *R224* was sunk in an explosion caused by sabotage, which destroyed the torpedo repair depot in the harbour of Le

Havre. On 18 July, in the North Sea, off the German island of Norderney, at 23:16, *R139* was sunk by aircraft rockets causing her ammunition to explode, at 54°N/07°37E. The S-boats *S90* and *S135*, which had arrived at Dieppe, were transferred to Boulogne on 25 July along with the 4th R-boat Flotilla.

In the night of 5/6 August, the 14th R-boat Flotilla had an engagement off Cap d'Antifer with the British frigates *Thornborough* and *Retalick*. On the night of 7/8 August, the 14th R-boat Flotilla again had an engagement with the *Retalick*, this time together with four American MTBs, two of them, *PT520* and *PT521*, being damaged. In the night of 9/10 August there was a further engagement between the same R-boat Flotilla and an MTB group. On 10 August, in Norway, a British carrier force, including the *Indefatigable*, *Trumpeter* and *Nabob* (Canadian), escorted by two heavy cruisers and eight destroyers, attacked the German airfield at Gossen, near Kristiansund North. Six German planes were destroyed and three steamers damaged. *R89* was damaged by air attack, at Lepsoe, near Aalesund, and sank after an ammunition explosion at 19:50.

In the Channel, during the night of 12/13 August, the 4th R-boat Flotilla, in a mining operation off Etaples, had an engagement with an MTB group. In the North Sea, near Sylt, *R20* was sunk by a German mine and lost 9 men on 16 August. On the same day *R182*, *R213* and *R217*, being under repair and unable to sail away, were scuttled on the river Seine near Paris. In the Channel, on the night of 18/19 August, there were engagements near Le Tréport and Cap d'Antifer, between the 14th R-boat Flotilla, auxiliary minesweepers and the British *MTB208*, *MTB209*, *MTB210* and *MTB212*, supported by the escort destroyer *Melebreak*. During these actions *R218* was sunk by torpedo and gunfire from the MTBs. On the night of 20/21 August, two R-boats of the same flotilla and one submarine chaser suffered damage during engagements with the British *MTB471*, *MTB476* and *MTB477*, off Cap d'Antifer. On 22 August, as Allied troops approached, *R51*, under repair after being salvaged, was scuttled on the river Seine at Rouen.

The evacuation of German ships from Le Havre started in the night of 23/24 August when two R-boats with two more in tow, together with two armed trawlers, one submarine chaser and sixteen KFKs moved from Le Havre to Dieppe. Off Cap d'Antifer and Fécamp the boats were attacked, first by the British frigate *Thornborough*, the escort destroyer *Talybont* and *MTB692*, *MTB694* and *MTB695*; and then by the frigate *Retalick*, the escort destroyer *Melebreak*, and *MTB205*, *MTB208* and *MTB212*. *R229* and an armed trawler were damaged, while *R219* was sunk at Dieppe harbour entrance, at 49°56N/01°04E, by fighter-bombers following the engagements with British vessels. On the night of 24/25 August, *R117* moved from Dieppe to Boulogne with five armed trawlers, sixteen drifters, three KFKs and a naval ferry barge. They were successively attacked by American MTBs *PT250*, *PT511* and *PT514*; the British frigate *Seymour* with *MTB252*, *MTB254*, *MTB256* and *MTB257*; another group comprising *MTB447*, *MTB452* and *MTB453*; and finally the British escort destroyers

Talybont and *Bleasdale*, the frigate *Retalick* and *MTB205*, *MTB209* and *MTB210*. In engagements, *S91* from the 6th S-boat Flotilla, deployed as cover, was sunk by *Talybont* and *Retalick* north of Fécamp. The auxiliary minesweeper *M3857* was also sunk and one patrol boat damaged, while the naval ferry barge *AF103* was sunk by a mine. On the night of 26/27 August, the frigate *Retalick* with *MTB208* and *MTB210*, the British escort destroyer *Middleton* with the *MTB252*, *MTB256*, and the American MTBs *PT511*, *PT514* and *PT520* attacked the 14th R-boat Flotilla and gun ferries, three of the latter being sunk. On the night of 27/28 August, seven boats of the 14th R-boat Flotilla (*Kapitänleutnant* Nordt) sowed mines in the Seine estuary, near Le Havre, and proceeded to Fécamp with 2 submarine-chasers. Off Cap d'Antifer they were attacked first by the frigate *Thornborough*, the French escort destroyer *La Combattante*, *MTB447*, *MTB450* and *MTB482*; and then by the British *MTB692*, *MTB693*, *MTB695* and the American MTBs *PT512* and *PT519*. The submarine-chaser *UJ1433* was sunk and *R231* was towed in to port in a damaged state.

On the night of 29/30 August, 9 R-boats, 1 submarine-chaser, 1 patrol boat, 1 MFL minesweeper, 6 gun ferries and 1 tug moved from Le Havre to Fécamp; they were the last units to leave the great Norman harbour, and they were covered by S-boats. Attacks by frigate *Retalick* and the British escort destroyer *Cattistock* were beaten off, the latter being damaged with her Commanding Officer, Lieutenant Keddie, being killed. The fights in the Channel were over for the R-boats.

On the night of 29/30 August, 402 British and Canadian heavy bombers attacked the harbour of Stettin in the Baltic. *R193* and 1 merchant ship were sunk and 7 merchant vessels were damaged, 23 bombers being shot down by German defences.

Between 6 June and 16 August, in the Western area (France, Holland and Belgium) R-boats, M-boats auxiliary minesweepers, sperrbrecher, etc. were involved in 445 fights with enemy ships and aircraft, more than 100 of the latter being shot down and a number of MTBs and MGBs being sunk or damaged, while two destroyers were damaged and 747 mines were swept.

On 6 September, at about 01:30, *R304* was sunk by a mine, near Egerøy, southern Norway, at 58°25'N/05°57'E. While being transferred from Belgium to the Netherlands, *R235* was so badly damaged in a collision, on 7 September, that she had to be scuttled 15 kilometres from the Merwede canal (Holland). In Holland again, on 11 September, *R80* was sunk by an aircraft bomb, off Houfdplaat, at 51°22'N/02°40'E. In the North Sea, on 17 September, *R171* sank after hitting a wreck at 53°53'N/08°01'E. On the night 30 September/1 October, a German towing convoy with new constructions and the sloop *F6* was on its way from Rotterdam to Borkum. A barrage group of 3 R-boats of the 13th Flotilla (Korvettenkapitän Eizinger), 6 patrol boats and 5 auxiliary minesweepers were protecting the convoy when, off Ijmuiden, they were attacked by British *MTB347*, *MTB349*, *MTB350*, *MTB351* and *MTB360*. All the attacks were beaten off, and *MTB347* (40 tons, 1943)

An R-boat of the R307/R312 type in Norway, in 1944 or 1945, with twin 20mm AA guns fore and aft of the bridge and one single on top of it. (Drüppel)

and *MTB360* (40 tons, 1943) were sunk by the escort's gunfire.

After a stop in Den Helder on the night on 2/3 October, the convoy continued on its way, suffering air attacks off the Dutch north coast. The new 'Hansa' construction No. 922 (1923 tons) was sunk. After a British naval force of 2 cruisers and 4 destroyers (one being Canadian) had sunk 2 freighters, 2 M-boats and 3 submarine-chasers, *R32* helped to rescue survivors, but was then sunk on the morning of 13 November by aircraft gunfire, south-east of Egersund, at 58°26'N/06°00'E. *R32* was raised, recommissioned, and served after the war in the German Minesweeping Administration. She was taken as a Danish prize in December 1945, returned in 1947 to the Allies, and then broken up in Britain.

On the night of 27/28 November, off Sogne Fjord, the Norwegian *MTB627* and *MTB717* attacked a German convoy and torpedoed the steamer *Welheim* (5455 tons) which had to be beached. *R312* and 2 patrol boats obtained hits on the MTBs. On 8 December, off Bomlo Fjord, *R56* was sunk by gunfire from a British fighter-bomber. On 22 December, at 09:34, *R402* was sunk by a mine which had been laid, on 19 December, by the French submarine *Rubis* (Capitaine de Corvette Rousselot) north-north-west of Feiestein, 13 men being killed. The submarine chasers *UJ1113* and *UJ 1116*, and the steamer *Weichselland* (3654 tons) were also sunk on the same minefield. *R57* was damaged beyond repair in a collision with the submarine *U1163*, on 28 January 1945, in Trondheim Fjord, and was broken up.

On 5 February, at Arendal in Norway, *R202* sank after an explosion in the engine room, at 58°28'N/08°47'E. In the Baltic, on 28 February, *R177* was sunk by a British air laid mine off Stolpmünde, 10 men being killed.

In the Baltic, B-17s and B-24s of the 8th USAAF dropped 1435 tons of bombs on Swinemünde on 12 March. In the harbour, among other ships, *R243* was sunk and *R272/276* were destroyed or heavily damaged on the stocks. The latter was repaired and completed by the Polish Navy as *OP-301* and stricken in 1956. On 16 March, in Swinemünde again, *R239* hit a wreck and sank. On 3 April, about 700 bombers of 8th USAAF dropped 2200 tons of bombs on the harbour installations in Kiel. *R59*, *R72*, *R119* and *R261* were sunk, together with 6 submarines and other ships. On 14 April *R126* was sunk by a mine in the Great Belt. On 4 May *R104* and *R247* were scuttled in the Kaiser Wilhelm canal where, four days later, *R88* had the same done to her.

THE ADMIRALTY FIRE CONTROL TABLES

Between the two world wars, the Royal Navy developed a new generation of elaborate fire control tables. **John Brooks** describes the debt owed to earlier tables, how they were designed and built, their principal features and their performance in battle.

At the end of 1916, when Admiral Sir John Jellicoe left the Grand Fleet to become First Sea Lord, he was accompanied to the Admiralty by Frederic Dreyer, his Flag-Captain in HMS *Iron Duke*. Dreyer already had an established reputation as a captain of ships and as the inventor of the fire control tables named after him. In March 1917, he was appointed Director of Naval Ordnance (DNO). His principal task was to drive through the development of new and effective armour-piercing shell, though, as we shall see, his staff in the Ordnance Department also introduced a number of detailed improvements to 'his' tables.[1] By April 1918, the first batch of the new shell had been delivered to the Grand Fleet: and, in the following month, the First Sea Lord (by then Admiral Sir Rosslyn Wemyss) was corresponding with the Commander-in-Chief, Admiral Sir David Beatty, about appointing Dreyer to the Naval Staff in order to make use of his 'exceptional abilities'. Beatty, however, expressed his opposition in outspoken terms:

> In fact I am the Director of Gunnery of the Grand Fleet and will surely clash with any gentleman appointed as Director of Gunnery at the Admiralty, where there is no practical gunnery and where they cannot be up to date in gunnery problems which can only be worked out in the Fleet at sea.

In his reply of 3 June, Wemyss assured Beatty 'that there will be no interference with the gunnery policy or gunnery training of the Grand Fleet' and, on 20 June, Captain H R Crooke took over as DNO, while Dreyer was appointed Director of Naval Artillery and Torpedoes (DNA&T).[2] Beatty's hostility to this attempt, as he saw it, to interfere with his prerogatives suggests that, while the Grand Fleet remained in being, Wemyss's efforts to establish an effective naval staff were likely to be frustrated. These tensions between the Admiralty and the Fleet would soon have an impact on the early gestation of the new generation of fire control tables that are the subject of this article. However, before these developments can be explained, it is necessary to begin with an outline of the main features of the fire control tables that had served in ships of the Grand Fleet throughout the First World War.

The Dreyer Fire Control Tables

In the summer of 1914, the first Dreyer Fire Control Table Mark IV was installed in HMS *Iron Duke*. Thereafter, this model and the almost identical Mark IV* (which differed only in its maximum range of 28,000 rather than 25,000 yards) became the standard equipment in the transmitting stations of the Royal Navy's modern capital ships. These tables, although more elaborate and automatic, were based on the same principles as the Original Dreyer Table of 1911 and, like it, had been designed and manufactured by the firm of Elliott Brothers under the direction of Keith Elphinstone.[3]

Target ranges (from multiple rangefinders) and compass-bearings were plotted separately against time on paper moving at a steady speed, the range plot being much the wider of the two. Between the two plots of the Marks IV and IV* were the Electrical Dumaresq and, beneath it, the two 'clocks' (actually variable-speed drives) that generated predicted values of range and bearing. The Dumaresq was set initially with own speed and course, mean target bearing, and estimates of the target speed and course; its mechanical linkages were then able to calculate automatically the rate of change of range (more concisely, the range-rate) and the Dumaresq-deflection. The latter quantity was expressed in knots and was also called the speed-across. It represented the component of the apparent speed of the target that was perpendicular to the target line-of-bearing; when adjusted for range, it determined the deflection from the line-of-bearing needed to allow for the change in target bearing in the time-of-flight of the shell to the target. The Electrical Dumaresq had been introduced in the Mark IV so that, by means of electric motors, the rate of rotation of the range-clock could follow automatically the range-rate of the Dumaresq–though a handwheel for setting the clock rate manually was also provided. Likewise, the rate of the bearing-clock could also be maintained automatically, though an additional linkage was needed to convert speed-across (in knots) into bearing-rate (in degrees/minute).

The range-clock was coupled to a long threaded rod that extended across the range-plot and determined the position of a pencil plotting clock-range. This enabled

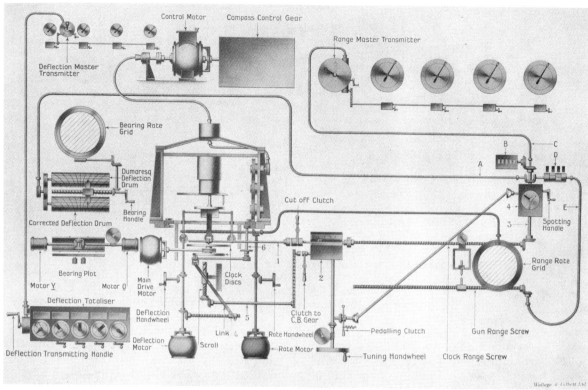

Schematic for the Dreyer Tables Mark IV and IV*. The paper for the range plot ran under the Clock and Gun Range Screws. The discs and rollers of the range and bearing clocks are beneath the Electrical Dumaresq. The positions of the rollers were set automatically by the Rate and Deflection Motors, the latter working through the Link and Scroll, which together converted speed-across into bearing-rate. Changes of own course were set automatically on the Dumaresq by a flexible shaft from the Control Motor; the Compass Control Gear contained a gyro-compass receiver. The bearing plot illustrated here was probably fitted to only a few tables before being superseded by the GCT gear. (Handbook of Dreyer's Tables, 1918, Plate 9)

the predicted ranges to be compared with the actual rangefinder ranges. Any errors in the predicted range could be corrected by 'tuning' the clock-range pencil to the mean of the rangefinder ranges. If the current estimates of target course and speed were incorrect, the range-rate would be wrong, so the clock-range would tend to diverge from the mean trend-line of the rangefinder ranges. A revolving grid with parallel wires was mounted above the range-plot to measure the slope, and hence the equivalent rate, of this trend-line. A similar grid over the bearing-plot measured the mean rate of the observed target-bearings, and, by means of curves engraved on the surface of a revolving drum next to the bearing-plot, the bearing-rate could be converted into an equivalent speed-across. The values of range-rate and speed-across obtained from the plots could then be compared with the values indicated by the Dumaresq. If they differed, the target speed and course set on the Dumaresq were adjusted together until the new indicated values corresponded with those obtained by observation and plotting; this process was known as making a cross-cut. If time permitted and the target held its course, the accuracy of the cross-cut could be improved by further plotting.

It must be emphasised that making a cross-cut depended on the trends of the plots being sufficiently clear to allow the rates to be measured. If this was not the case,

the Dumaresq could only be set by visual estimation of target speed and course–the latter expressed most conveniently as the inclination, the angle between the line-of-bearing and the target-course. Any consequent errors in range, range-rate and deflection were then corrected after opening fire by spotting the fall of the salvos.

If the target did change course, it was necessary to make a new estimate or cross-cut once the course had steadied. While alterations by the target unavoidably threw out the predictions of the clocks, the Mark IV and its derivatives were designed to correct automatically for the changes in range-rate and speed-across that resulted from changes in target bearing and/or changes in own course. This was possible because the bearing dials of the Electrical Dumaresq were coupled appropriately both to the bearing-clock and to a relay motor controlled by a gyro-compass receiver. These features, together with the electric transfer of rates from the Dumaresq to the clocks, meant that these tables (the Marks IV, IV* and V) can be characterised as both automatic and helm-free. If the target speed and course were correct and steady, they could continue to predict target ranges and bearings without any operator intervention, even if the target became obscured or own ship altered course.

Many valuable details of the different marks of Dreyer Table have recently been published in a series of articles by William Schleihauf.[4] However, while the description of the Mark IV/IV* refers to the handwheel for setting range-rate manually, it does not mention that the clock rates could be maintained automatically.[5] It also echoes Professor Sumida's conclusion that 'The clock mechanism bore an unmistakable resemblance to the disc-ball-roller arrangement of the Argo clock'[6] and that 'this mechanism...probably introduced errors due to slipping because the friction wasn't enough to hold the rollers in position'. Yet Schleihauf himself confirms that the Dreyer clock mechanism was of the simpler pattern in which the edge of a single, narrow roller (sometimes called a wheel) ran in direct contact with the disc.[7] In contrast, in the Argo design, a ball was held in contact with the disc by not one but two long rollers in a sliding carriage; their two functions were to position the ball by rolling it along a diameter of the disc: and to transfer its rotation to an output shaft. With this arrangement, the ball remained in rolling contact with the disc, even if the rate (determined by the distance of the ball from the centre of the disc) was changing. In the Dreyer mechanism, a change of rate required that the roller be dragged sideways, so that the consequent disruption of rolling contact was liable to induce slipping between the disc and roller. This did become a problem, though apparently only later in the First World War when a number of ships in the Grand Fleet were adding experimental fittings of their own design:

> **Overloading the Dreyer Table.** Attention is drawn to the necessity of circumspection in adding fittings to the Dreyer Table; if driven by the rate disc it is essential that they should be fitted with great care and thoroughly tested to ensure against overloading and slipping, as occurred in one ship.

Even so, the standard tables do not appear to have suffered from excessive slippage, even when the rate changed rapidly while under helm:

> In certain firings [during the first quarter of 1918] the range and deflection were maintained very successfully during turns of twelve points and upwards.[8]

As well as experimental modifications, a number of standard design changes and enhancements were introduced, including a typewriter for differentiating between the ranges from different rangefinders, a wind Dumaresq (invented by Dreyer) and a deflection totaliser. These were probably the results of Admiralty initiatives, but the need for an additional pencil to plot gun ranges was determined by experiments in the Fleet. Likewise, the Admiralty initiated development of improved bearing transmitters working with steps of four minutes rather than the previous ¼ degree steps. However, this was soon overtaken by much more radical ideas originated after the inconclusive action of 17 November 1917; a Committee of the Grand Fleet,

> ...evolved a design, which was largely the work of Lieut. Dove, RN and Lieut. Clausen, RNVR, for an instrument,

which, by a combination of the gun-director, Gyro compass, and the bearing clock of the Dreyer table, enabled the Director to be kept on for direction when the enemy was hidden, provided that he had been effectively engaged before his disappearance.

After further development by HMS *Excellent*, a production design was developed by Elliott Brothers, before an order was placed in January 1919. This Gyro Director Training (GDT) gear introduced an important new principle, that of the 'straight-line' plot, in which a straight line up the middle of a narrow strip of moving paper always represented the target compass bearing predicted

N.1568.

The Gyro Director Training (GDT) Gear that replaced the bearing plot in the later Dreyer Tables. The slewing (coarse) and training (fine) dials had red hands indicating the bearing of the Director and black hands indicating the bearing being transmitted from the GDT gear back to the Director. When the target was visible, the slewing and training handles were used to keep the red and black pointers aligned; this also resulted in a plot of the difference between the director bearing and the bearing predicted by the bearing clock. The transparent plate with parallel lines measured the angle of the plot and hence the error in bearing-rate; an illuminated scale beneath the paper showed the corresponding error in speed-across. In indirect fire (target not visible), the bearings transmitted to the director were generated automatically from the bearing-clock (though spotting corrections from aircraft could be imposed manually using the three push-buttons) or were obtained from the target's 'datum compass bearing' received from another ship; the Gyro Dial Box made the necessary allowance for 'position-in-line'. (N. 1568 in 1.24/4, EA).

by the bearing clock. Each observed compass bearing was plotted as its *difference* from the current predicted value; thus, as well as showing the deviation of observed and predicted values, the slope of the mean line through the plot of observed bearings also indicated the error in the clock rate. The GDT gear also incorporated the new four-minute bearing transmitters but, during the War, these were only fitted in the final Mark IV* table, for *Ramillies*.[9] The retention of the earlier pattern of bearing plot, with its coarse ¼ degree transmission steps, explains the comment of an American officer with the Grand Fleet that: 'The bearing plot instrument is not generally taken seriously';[10] also, after the War, the Admiralty's *Technical History* admitted: 'Bearing plots have not been an unqualified success but recent improvements will do much to counter this'.[11]

While the design of the Dreyer Tables did not change greatly during the War itself, after the Battle of Jutland:

> The development of [new] spotting rules and afterwards the solution of the problem of concentration of fire, constituted the main work of the Fleet during the latter half of 1916, and in 1917 and 1918. The progress has been enormous…[12]

Action ranges of 15,000 to 18,000 yards were assumed.[13] Practices were conducted at ranges up to 24,000 yards, while the new technique of 'throw-off' firing allowed gunnery to be tested while employing realistic tactics at full speed, including frequent changes of course by both sides.[14] By mid-1918:

> It is considered to be definitely established that at normal fighting ranges the range and bearing plots alone cannot be expected to provide either an accurate rate or a prompt indication of changes of enemy's course, and that it is therefore necessary to devote increased attention to direct estimation of inclination.[15]

Although 13.5in as well as 15in ships had been provided with 15-foot range-finders,[16] at the ranges now practised in full-calibre firings it was accepted that 'small rangefinder spreads were the exception'.[17] Nonetheless, the *Grand Fleet Gunnery and Torpedo Orders* warned against:

> …the neglect of the range plot which on numerous occasions during throw-off firings provided information which could have been utilised to great advantage.
> …Of the range plots examined after the firings many were excellent and afforded throughout a good indication of the rate and true range; on the other hand some present large and varying differences between hitting gun range and mean plotted range.[18]

They also insisted that the range plot:'…is of immense value as a check on gun range, and especially so when fire has been opened at short notice'. It had also assumed a new importance as a means of recording the ranges in use by consorts during concentration firing.[19]

In the last year of the war, when the limitations of

rangefinding were all too apparent and the GDT gear was still being developed, the direct measurement of inclination appeared to be particularly promising in countering the loss of rate resulting from defensive zig-zagging. In addition to observations from aeroplanes, several simple inclinometers were being tested, while an automatic instrument with integral calculator was under construction. Special five-minute prisms were also issued as a stop-gap, so that rangefinders could be adapted to measure inclination. However, whatever the optical details, all inclinometers depended on measuring the angle subtended by two widely separated features on the target, for example, its masts or bow and stern; then, if the target range and the distance between these features were known (the latter depended on recognising the class of ship correctly), the inclination could be calculated as an angle less than 90 degrees. However:

> The chief defect which is common to all inclinometers is that by the instrument itself it is impossible to say on which side of 90 degrees the inclination lies. It is therefore essential that the inclinometer should be worked in close conjunction with the rangefinder and gun range plots.[20]

And, when the inclination was close to 90 degrees, even a substantial change of course resulted in only a small change in the subtended angle. In reality, the early promise took many years to realise. The first automatic inclinometer (the Langley SJ1) was too defective to put into production, while the Barr and Stroud SF3 was in service, but only in limited numbers and with mixed results, in 1923 and 1924. After further development, their SF7 was tried with complete success and supplied to capital ships in 1927. However, by that time it was accepted that inclination could only be measured to an accuracy of 2 degrees for inclinations less than 70 degrees or greater than 110 degrees.[21]

The Dreyer Table Committee

On 9 September 1918, a letter from the Admiralty to the C-in-C (almost certainly sent with Dreyer's knowledge and perhaps at his instigation) requested 'proposals…as to the type of consort's gun range pencil for fitting on the Mark V table of HMS *Hood*, observing that several types are understood to be fitting in the various ships of the Grand Fleet'. To respond, Beatty ordered the establishment of the Grand Fleet Dreyer Table Committee. Its First and Second Interim Reports, submitted as one short report on 19 November 1918, concerned the Mark V, the latest and most elaborate version of the Dreyer Table. However, the recommendations covered much more than just the consort pencil; in particular, they criticised the excessive number of fittings obscuring the plot, and also repeated the earlier concerns about:

> **The drive of the Frictional Clock Disc**—many complaints have been received that this disc is not sufficiently strong for the work now imposed on it. It is considered

that the power of the motor should be greater, and that the diameter of the shaft carrying the roller should be increased.[22]

These changes allowed an increase in the pressure between disc and roller, thereby reducing slippage when the rate was changing.

Beatty evidently soon realised that the Committee could also be used to put the Grand Fleet's stamp firmly on all future developments in fire control. On 18 October 1918, he ordered them to consider two much broader questions. The first, which was addressed in their Third Interim Report of 29 January 1919, concerned 'standardising the alterations which are being made by various ships to their Dreyer Tables'. This report repeated the request to strengthen the friction drive. Despite the inadequacies of the old bearing plot, it emphasised that:

The measurement of rate of change of bearing is considered of great importance owing to the accuracy with

which bearings can be observed, even when the visibility is poor…bearing observations can be obtained *continuously* and *accurately*.

It accepted that 'The Gyro Director Training Gear…will standardise the arrangements for dealing with rate of change of bearing'; though it also acknowledged that 'the present system of correction' of the gyro-compass, with which 'oscillations take place when course is altered', must be improved.[23]

Concerning the utility of the time-and-range plot, the Committee adopted the more pessimistic of the conflicting views found in the GFG&TOs:

*Experience has shown, and it must be accepted, that it will very seldom, if ever, be possible to obtain the rate of change of range from rangefinders….*The frequent alteration of course at high speed which are now the accepted conditions of action will preclude the rate…being obtained with sufficient rapidity from a time and range plot. The setting of the enemy bar must, therefore, be obtained

'*General Progress of Table as at 14/7/23*'. *The Dummy Range and Bearing Plots are nearest the camera, with the Gun Range Plot and the Clock behind them. Note the shafting running back from the Dummy Range Plot and the projectors on the overhead beam. The unit at the right rear is the incomplete Range Correction Unit based on links designed by H F Landstat; it was not used in the production tables.* (N. 1496 in 1.24/5, EA)

from the rate of change of bearing and the inclination found by inclinometer, observation or outside reports (*e.g.* aeroplane)....[24] It is considered that the primary object of plotting the rangefinder observations is to enable them to be 'meaned' by inspection for the purpose of checking gun range...and to allow the value of the rangefinder readings to be assessed...[25]

The second part of the Committee's extended brief was 'To draw up recommendations as to the Fleet's requirements for the future development of Fire Control Tables generally'. The recommendations in their Final Report of 1 February 1919 did not depart from the essentials first brought together in the Dreyer Table Mark III of 1911-12; namely separate plots of ranges and bearings and a combined clock generating predicted ranges and bearings. They proposed that the bearing plot should be on the same general lines as the GDT gear, but that the straight-line principle should now be extended to the range plots, of which there would be two. One should show the ranges from all rangefinders (or, to be more exact, the differences between their ranges and the clock range) and have a pencil capable of being tuned to the mean of the rangefinders. The other should plot this mean range as well as own gun range and the gun ranges (corrected for position-in-line) of up to three consorts.

The top face of the Clock, Unit A. The larger dial represents the enemy ship and has angular scales for inclination and enemy compass course. The intersection point of the two suggestion wires showed the best estimates of speed-across (in knots) and range-rate (in yards-per-minute). The corresponding enemy speed and course were set by altering the inclination and speed until the small pin lay at the intersection. The smaller own-ship dial showed own course relative to the target line-of-bearing represented by the thick arrow running across both dials. This is the prototype clock of 1923; the production model had a number of other dials on top, including one for own-speed. (N. 1480, 1.24/3, EA)

The Committee also recommended a simple plot of inclination against time: and held to their previously stated axiom that: 'it is not considered that at any time and under any action conditions will it be possible to obtain a useful rate of change of range by rangefinder'. However, while true-course plotting, as advocated by Arthur Pollen, was considered as an alternative, it was decisively rejected:

> When observations and information of the enemy's movements and fall of shot becomes so good and rapid as to enable a correct track to be plotted, these results can be set direct on the clock, and the necessity of plotting for gun control purposes vanishes.

Yet, while the Committee had no interest in reviving the Argo plotter, they accepted that, in the Dreyer Tables: 'The drive of the automatic Dumaresq...is not the best available type of variable speed gear'. They proposed that the new table should be a 'combination of all the good points of the Dreyer table, Ford clock, and Argo clock'.[26]

In forwarding the Committee's conclusions to the Admiralty on 7 February, Beatty acknowledged that:

> The difficulties of putting into effect the recommendations of the Committee, both from the technical and commercial point of view, are realised. It is held, however, that the matter is of such importance that every endeavour should be made to surmount these difficulties, and further that financial considerations should not be permitted to stand in the way.... As regards the question of design, it is clear that the highest engineering skill available, together with a clear understanding of the practical requirements, must be brought to bear on the problem.
> ...It is suggested that a committee of experts should be formed [and] the names of the following are proposed:
> Lieut. J S Dove, RN, HMS *Royal Sovereign*.
> Lieut. Hugh Clausen, RNVR, HMS *Benbow*.
> G K B Elphinstone, Esq. of Elliotts.
> H Isherwood, Esq. formerly of Argo Company.[27]

Changes at the Admiralty

In view of Beatty's earlier attitude, it is most unlikely that Dreyer was allowed any part in the Committee's deliberations. In November 1918, Jellicoe accepted the War Cabinet's invitation to lead the Empire Mission on naval defence and immediately asked Dreyer to accompany him as Chief of Staff; on 1 February 1919, Dreyer was superseded as DNA&T by Captain J W L McClintock.[28] Thus Dreyer also had little opportunity to comment on the Interim Reports, while the Final Report arrived after his departure. Even so, although the Grand Fleet Committee had successfully set the broad agenda for future fire control developments, the dissolution of the Grand Fleet on 7 April ensured that, in the future, only the DNA&T would be responsible for the further definition of requirements, not only for fire control but for naval weapons in general. This clear separation from the responsibilities of the Controller's departments for development and supply was an important reform. Under the Controller, the DNO retained the principal responsibility for gunnery material, but he also depended on the expertise in electrical equipment (including communications instruments) of the department of the Director of Torpedoes and Mines (DTM).[29] The skills available to the latter were considerably enhanced in February 1920 by the creation of the Low Power and Fire Control (LP&FC) Section, which was accommodated at 80 Pall Mall. There are signs that, in 1919, this group was not set up without some dispute within the Admiralty about whether it should be controlled by the DNO;[30] however, once it was established, it provided, throughout the inter-war period, an expertise in electrical and mechanical design that was available to all Admiralty departments.[31]

The DNO, Captain Crooke, accepted the recommendations of the Grand Fleet committee wholeheartedly, including those in favour of the inclinometer and against obtaining the range-rate from a time-and-range plot. He also suggested that his newly-appointed Assistant (later Deputy) DNO, Captain C V Usborne, should preside over the committee of experts recommended by Beatty; however, this did not happen, perhaps because Osborne was made president of the important Anti Aircraft Gunnery Committee. In 1913, Usborne, with Dreyer, wrote the technical report that justified the Admiralty's rejection of Arthur Pollen's Argo system in favour of the Dreyer Tables.[32] Thus another possibility is that the ADNO later proved less enthusiastic than his chief about the proposed departures from Dreyerite principles–we shall return to this idea later. Crooke himself probably had an open mind about earlier controversies; in the past, he had contributed to favourable reports on some of Pollen's equipment but, by 1919, he also recognised the inventor's commercial dealings as 'not at all satisfactory or encouraging'.[33] This view explains why the DNO was against the appointment of Pollen's chief designer, Harold Isherwood, to the committee of experts 'unless he is employed...by the Admiralty and also pledged to maintain secrecy both now and in the future'.

By May 1919, a new Fire Control Table Development Committee was being formed in the Admiralty. Its membership comprised representatives of the DNA&T, DNO and DTM and, in accordance with a further proposal by the DNO, Professor J B Henderson, the Professor of Applied Mathematics at the Royal Naval College, Greenwich and an expert on gyroscopes; the fifth member was Lieutenant John Dove.[34] His co-inventor of the GDT gear, Hugh Clausen, was not appointed to the committee but, as a civilian, he (along with the DTM's representative on the committee, Commander W B Mackenzie) joined the LP&FC section on its foundation in 1920.[35] Contrary to Beatty's recommendation, the committee itself did not include either Isherwood or Elphinstone. But it is probably not a coincidence that, soon after Beatty became First Sea Lord on 1 November 1919, Isherwood (with H F Landstad, previously a senior draughtsman at Argo) was engaged to assist the committee with mechanical design; in 1920 and 1921, both men worked at 80 Pall Mall.[36]

The table committee had not reached any firm conclusions on the design by March 1920[37] but continued working together until January 1921, after which some of the members were assigned to other duties. The committee itself was no longer sitting in April 1922, but other officers in the departments of the DNO and DTM joined the project, while Dove remained in the DNO's department until July 1922.[38] A month earlier, Commander Bruce Fraser had joined the DTM's department at 80 Pall Mall to represent the DNO and, until July 1924, advised the designers on matters ranging from performance to installation.[39] The design of the new table was later described as 'a co-operative effort by the FC Tables committee, designers on Messrs. Elliott Bros. staff and the LP and FC section of the DTM Department':[40] while 'The construction was carried out by Messrs. Elliott Bros., under the supervision of Admiralty Officers'.[41] Unfortunately, no clear indications have been found of when Elliotts began to contribute to the design process nor, therefore, of whether Isherwood and Elphinstone (by now Sir Keith) had worked for a time in collaboration.

In April 1920, Frederic Dreyer returned to take up his previous duties (with the title originally intended by Wemyss) as Director of the Gunnery Division (D of GD) of the Naval Staff. If Dreyer had then found himself in serious disagreement with the assumptions underpinning the committee's work, he had the opportunity to interfere well before they produced any detailed designs. Further, Usborne did not relinquish his post as DDNO until June 1922;[42] if he had been similarly opposed, he could have attempted to influence the Committee during Dreyer's absence, while the two men would have made a formidable alliance once the latter was back in the Admiralty. In fact, there are no indications that Usborne had any involvement with the Committee, while, a year after his return, Dreyer's only concerns were unrelated to plotting:

> ...D of GD was for a long time very anxious as regards the effect of the very complex proposals for the new Fire Control Table, but eventually arrived at the conviction that they were necessary in order to face the problems with which we are confronted....I am in complete agreement with the procedure now being carried out, by which, under the direct superintendence of the DNO [Captain R C C Backhouse from September 1920] designs of Fire Control Tables...are being prepared to meet requirements.[43]

A year after writing this, in April 1922, Dreyer returned to sea in command of *Repulse*. At about the same time, the Fleet was informed that:

> ...the design [of the new fire control tables] is now well advanced, some of the mechanisms are manufactured, and shop trials are being carried out. It is hoped to carry out sea-going trials of the whole system early in 1923.

The report also indicates some of the additional complexity that had concerned Dreyer. In order to engage invisible targets in indirect fire and indirect concentration, a master gyro unit was also under development, though it was not expected to be ready until after the table; it was intended to give 'gyroscopically stabilised datum lines for both elevation and direction, and also applying the cross levelling error'.[44]

Unfortunately, the hopes for trials in *Repulse* (also Dove's new ship) in April 1923 proved unduly optimistic and, by that date, it had been accepted that trials could not be held before the end of 1924. However, progress had been made and, at a meeting with the DNO (now Captain J C W Henley, another long-standing associate of Dreyer's)[45] on 17 July 1923, Elphinstone was able to report that:

The clock, gun range plot, two dummy plots, and automatic PIL instrument have been completed, together with portions of the straddle and deflection units.... The date previously given for completion can be adhered to provided no further difficulties arise.

Sir James Henderson, whose title was now 'Adviser on Gyroscope Equipment', was also present. The minutes show that he was involved with a more accurate transmission system from the gyro-compass (working with the LP&FC Section); with trials of five different gyro-compasses for gunnery purposes; with development of a vertical gyro reference; and with gyro-sights–the priority given to the last-mentioned had delayed the design of the master gyro unit.[46] In addition to what appears an excessive workload, Sir James was probably not the best person for the task in hand. In the opinion of Hugh Clausen, who during the Second World War became the Chief Technical Adviser to the DNO:

His analytical and mathematical work was often really brilliant, but he had no sense of mechanical design at all. He also had the bad luck of being unable to recruit first class people to help him with the design work...he seemed to me to work on the principle of 'heads I win, tails you lose'. Any failure of his material was always attributed to poor design.[47]

Even without these personal limitations, the work in hand was clearly too much for a single adviser; Henderson's work for the Royal Navy ceased in 1925, while the Greenwich team working on gyro-compasses for gunnery moved to the Admiralty Research Laboratory (ARL) at Teddington.[48]

However, despite the delays, the Master Gyro Unit and three constrained gyros, for measuring roll and yaw velocities, were included in an outline description of the new table circulated in 1923.[49] These units were intended 'to provide an under-water position from which the guns can be accurately laid, trained and fired, and which will be independent of any outside point of aim'. The outline also identified the majority of the units that would be incorporated in the completed design, usually by the same letters employed in the final handbook; thus the overall architecture was already well defined. While the core conception of the Grand Fleet committee, of an automatic clock, bearing plot, gun range plot and separate rangefinder plot, remained intact, there had been one important shift of emphasis. The table itself had no inclination plot, though it was suggested that a substitute might be found in the plot incorporated in the Langley automatic inclinometer; unfortunately, the same progress report also described the disappointing trials of this instrument,[50] while, as already explained, the first satisfactory inclinometer did not enter service until 1927. Nonetheless, the table was designed to use whatever source of inclination might be available: but, as we shall see, at the clock.

The 1923 description and photographs of the clock establish that it was already pretty much in its final form. It differed in some respects from the Argo clock but still used the Argo-pattern variable-speed drives; Isherwood's influence is clear and he probably made his greatest contribution to this unit.[51] On the top face, a fixed line represented the line of bearing. Two circular dials were let into this face, one for own ship, the other, larger one for the enemy. The angles between the centre-lines of their ship-shaped pointers and the fixed line corresponded, respectively, to enemy bearing and inclination. The enemy's speed was indicated by a small pin in a slot along the enemy centre-line. Two adjustable 'suggestion wires' were mounted at right angles above the enemy dial. Their point of intersection was determined firstly by the values of enemy speed and inclination in use i.e. the settings currently determining the range-rate and bearing-rate of the clock. However, the wires were further displaced by the errors in the range-rate and speed-across obtained from the range and bearing plots. (The reader will recall that, on these straight-line plots, the deviation of the mean line through the plotted points from the straight line up the middle was a direct indication of rate error).[52] Thus the point of intersection of the wires provided one indication of how to alter enemy speed and inclination in order to tune the clock rates into closer correspondence with observations. However, an alternative suggestion for enemy course was given by an inclination line projected from above onto the enemy dial, using values of inclination obtained from an inclinometer or aircraft observation.

Thus, by 1923, inclination had been recognised as just one more item of imperfect fire control information. The designers of the new tables had implicitly rejected the axiom of the Dreyer Table Committee that range-rate could not and should not be obtained from the range plots. Instead, they recognised that all the available data must be used. The suggestion wires were a physical realisation of the cross-cut of range-rate and speed-across so long advocated by Dreyer, while the inclination projector extended the principle by providing for the alternative cross-cut of inclination and speed-across proposed by the committee.

After it became clear that no installation could be made in *Repulse*, *Courageous* was for a time under consideration as the trial ship, but this intent also had to be abandoned in February 1924, when the table was still not ready and the decision had been taken to convert the cruiser to an aircraft carrier. It was then decided that 'further proposals for sea trials should wait until the whole

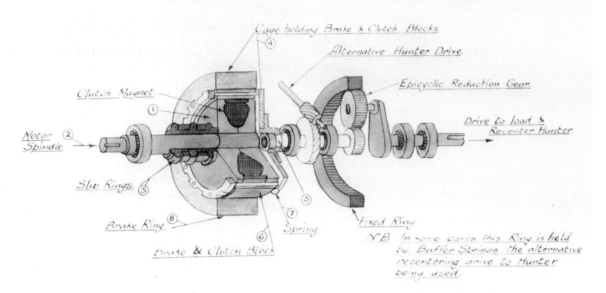

CLUTCH BRAKE MOTOR.
ARRANGEMENT OF CLUTCH & BRAKE MECHANISM.

Clutch Brake Mechanism. The Motor Spindle (2) was driven by a reversible electric motor. The Clutch Magnet (1), which was fixed to (2), was energised through the Slip Rings (3) by the motor armature current. (8) was a fixed Brake Ring. A Cage (4) was coupled to the transmission drive shaft (5) (the upper arrow pointing to the Brake Ring should be ignored); the Cage located a number of mild steel Blocks (6) in the gap between the Clutch Magnet and the Brake Ring. When the Magnet was energised, the Blocks were attracted inwards, thereby coupling the Motor Spindle through the magnet casing to the Cage and thence to the transmission shaft. When the current was turned off, the Blocks were forced outwards by the Springs (7) into contact with the Brake Ring; thus a brake was applied to the transmission shaft as the motor was disconnected from it. (Handbook AFCT Mark I, Figure

system...is on a much firmer material basis'.[53] One protracted technical problem was recalled by Clausen:

> ...in early days of fire control tables, all development work was held up for lack of suitable power follow up gears...and was unable to proceed until these had been produced.[54]

The difficulty arose because the delicate, precise calculating mechanisms in the table were unable to drive directly the many mechanical devices that were needed to obtain automatic operation and to implement straight-line plotting. It was therefore necessary to devise follow-up gear (today we would call it a servo follower) so that a sufficiently powerful motor could follow accurately the movements of a low-power mechanism. The first power follower to be developed, initially by ARL, was the 'clutch-brake motor', in which the output shaft was either held stationary by a brake, or coupled to an electric motor by a clutch; both clutch and brake were operated electro-magnetically.[55] A 'hunter' mechanism, incorporating electric contacts operated by a mechanical differential, detected whether the output shaft was aligned with the low-power input shaft. If it was, relays controlled by the contacts held the brake on and disengaged the clutch. If not, the brake was released, the clutch engaged and power applied to the motor with the polarity necessary to drive the output shaft into alignment. When this position was reached, the power was

removed; at the same time, the clutch disconnected the inertia of the motor itself from the output shaft, and the brake was applied.[56] Thus overshoot was minimised, but, even so, operation was inherently discontinuous, with the particular disadvantage that slow movements could only be followed in a series of jerks.

A smooth following action required some form of proportional control, in which the drive torque from the motor was proportional to the difference (error) between input and output. The solution was found before Bruce Fraser left 80 Pall Mall in December 1924, though the actual date remains unknown. As he recalled to Clausen after his retirement, as Admiral of the Fleet, in 1952:

> I think it was Clark of Elliotts [an under-manager with the firm] who changed from the brake-clutch [sic] motor to compressed air.[57]

In this follower, the power drive was provided by an air motor, with four cylinders arranged in a V, while the hunter controlled the balanced piston valves that regulated the supply of compressed air to the motor. Because, as the difference between output and input increased, the valves opened further, control was proportional (at least, for small errors) and gave a smooth following action. The air motors became the preferred option, though the clutch-brake motor was retained, particularly for use 'where the sensitive [input] side of the drives was insufficiently powerful to operate the air valve'.[58]

While the development of the air-motor follower removed one major technical hurdle, no such breakthrough was made with the gyro units. As we have seen, it had already been assumed that these would not be ready until after the table itself. This proved to be a fortunate precaution; according to Clausen, writing in 1949:

> HM ships *Nelson* and *Rodney* had two compartments allocated to 'Master Stabilising Units'; but they were never fitted and we hardly have an effective one [an artificial horizon or stable vertical] yet.[59]

By 1931, a device called a balancer had been developed that delivered smooth bearing transmission from the standard gyro-compass, despite the latter's intrinsic tendency to 'hunt', although it was not sufficiently accurate for indirect concentration. Development by ARL of a gyro-compass specifically for gunnery purposes was painfully slow, even though they received assistance from the Admiralty Compass Observatory. Despite some promising prototypes, by 1938 a sufficiently robust unit for sea service had still not been developed, and the DNO agreed that the ACO should undertake the design of what became the Admiralty Gyro Transmission Unit Mark I; even then, this did not enter service until 1943.[60]

In June 1924, the difficulties facing the development of satisfactory gyros had still not been fully recognised, the intention being that: 'Apparatus in hand to be completed for trial'.[61] Although direct evidence is lacking, it may well be that the dashing of these hopes gave the final push to the departure of Sir James Henderson. Nevertheless, despite this setback, the shop-trial of the completed prototype table was carried out successfully by the staff of *Excellent* at the end of 1925. Afterwards, the DNO (Captain C M Forbes) minuted:

> Though the new Table may be thought, at first sight, to be complicated and difficult to operate, it is clear from [*Excellent's* report] that further acquaintance with it removes this impression.

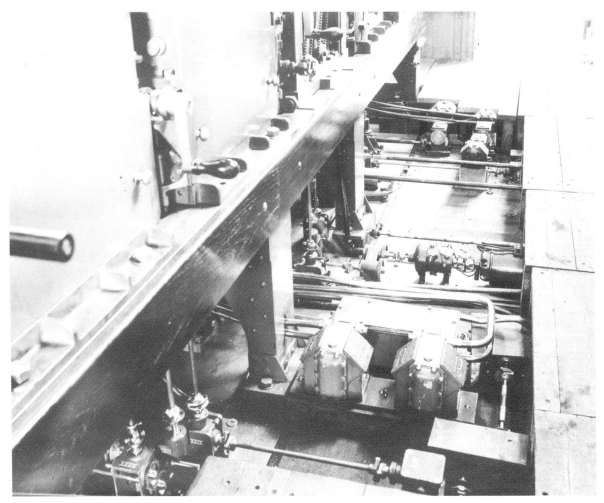

'*Arrangement of Clock Range Power Motors Nos. 1 & 2, also No. 12 Electric Clutch Brake Motor (Measure of Bearing Rate)…*'. *Because of the large number of mechanisms that were connected to the range clock, two air motors (the V-configuration of the cylinders can be seen) were coupled together to generate the required torque. The electric motor and clutch-brake mechanism are between the two groups of air motors. (N. 1722 in 1.24/2, EA)*

However, he admitted that the new table was very expensive (about £45,000) and that:

> …complete success in:-
> (a) concentrated indirect fire
> (b) automatic laying, training and firing from the TS
> (c) to a less extent any form of indirect fire
> depend now entirely on the production of improved vertical and azimuth gyroscopes… Progress has been made although further research is necessary.

The D of GD, Captain H T Walwyn, was more sceptical:

> The fact that the successful evolution of satisfactory vertical and azimuth gyros has not yet been attained, detracts from the full value of this new table which in [their] absence…does not…compete with the fire control problem to a much greater extent than the existing fire control tables…. It is also interesting to note that one of the chief requirements laid down by the Grand Fleet…Committee…has been dropped…. D of GD is of the opinion that an inclination plot…will eventually be necessary.

Frederic Dreyer, now Rear Admiral and ACNS, concurred with both minutes, adding:

> I agree that the Inclination Plot will probably be required… I am quite sure that the Policy pursued and the money expended in connection with these experimental Tables are fully justified.

The Controller, Rear-Admiral Chatfield, while confirming that the new design would be used in all new cruisers (as well as *Nelson* and *Rodney*), stated that:

> It is not intended to substitute the new tables for the existing ones in any ship now completed.[62]

This decision may have been motivated mainly by the need for economy, although, with no less than seven (soon to be nine) 8in cruisers already laid down and six more to follow in 1927-8,[63] the Admiralty probably considered that Elliotts had their hands full. In addition, after the Great War, the Dreyer Tables were considerably elaborated, while earlier concerns about slippage in the range-clock had been resolved by arranging for the clock to drive the range-plot through a clutch-brake motor; by 1930 these had been fitted to *Hood's* Mark V table and to the Mark IV* tables, the standard table in all other capital ships.[64] Thus there was no immediate necessity to replace the Dreyer Tables and, in fact, they were retained even into the next war, except in the four ships that were comprehensively reconstructed.

The AFCT Mark I

Compared with the Dreyer Tables, the new Admiralty Fire Control Tables (AFCTs) were a great technical advance in terms of both automatic operation, and

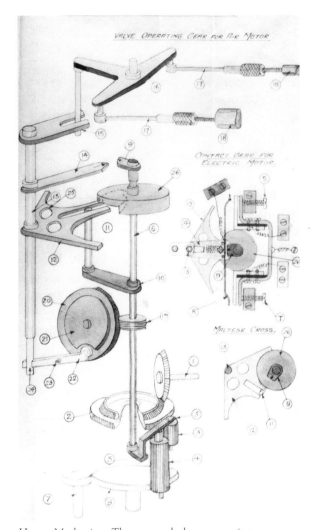

Hunter Mechanism. The gears at the bottom constitute a differential; the rotation of shaft (6) is proportional to the difference between the low-power input shaft (1) and the shaft driven by the motor (7). The diagram shows the controlling gear for either an air motor or a clutch-brake motor. When the positions of shafts (1) and (7) are equal, the mechanism is 'centred', pointers (9) and (14) are in line and the motor is unpowered. If the shaft positions become different, pin (11) displaces the 'Maltese Cross' (12). Power is applied to the motor in such a way as to 're-centre' the hunter; if an air motor is used, the valve openings are proportional to small differences, though larger differences result in the valves opening fully. The mechanism is designed to function correctly even if, for a time, the differences become very large. Once the air valves are fully open (or a contact is held fully closed), the cam (21) lifts the Maltese Cross so that it locks in position on the disc (26) and its slot no longer engages with the pin 11. Shaft (6) and pin (11) can then rotate many times in either direction until the difference again approaches zero, at which moment the pin (11) again engages with the slot. (Handbook AFCT Mark I, Figure 26)

mechanical design and construction. The Mark I for *Nelson* and *Rodney* consisted of no less than twenty-one modular units, mounted on two pedestals in separate compartments, all being interconnected by a maze of

Units of the Admiralty Fire Control Table Mark I (*Nelson* and *Rodney*)[65]

Unit		Principal Functions
A	Clock	To generate continuously clock range and bearing and to produce separately both own and target speeds along and across the line of sight.
B	Gun Range Plot	To enable a continuous comparison to be made between gun range, mean rangefinder range, consort's range, and fall of shot.
BD	Dummy Gun Range Plot	To plot consort's ranges, times of firing and fall of shot reports on to Unit B.
C	Rangefinder Plot	To obtain the mean rangefinder range and to transfer it to Unit B. [This unit plotted automatically the ranges received from seven rangefinders, one in each turret and a duplex instrument in each of the two DCTs.]
D	Bearing Plot	To enable a continuous comparison to be made between observed bearing, bearing generated by the clock and fall of shot for line.
DD	Dummy Bearing Plot	To plot times of firing and line fall of shot on to Unit D.
E	Range Correction	To compute and apply corrections for own ship, enemy and true wind 'along' and for the ballistic coefficient.
F	Deflection Correction	To compute and apply corrections for own ship, enemy and true wind 'across' and for drift.
FB	Gun Deflection Transmission	Group of transmitters that transmit gun deflection to all positions.
G	Auto PIL Instrument	To compute and apply corrections to range and bearing for position in line.
H	Recorder	To record information [from firings] required for analysis.
J	Inclination Calculator	To compute inclination from observations made at Inclinometer (SF5) [probably superseded by SF7].
JA	Inclination from Aircraft Dial	To enable aircraft reports of target course or inclination to be transmitted (as inclination) to clock.
K	Time of Flight	To convert gun range into time of flight and operate fall of shot hooters.
L	Timing	To control the electric clocks and the speed of the Table main drive motor.
M	Wind	To convert 'wind you feel' into 'true wind' and to apply the components of the latter 'along' and 'across' to units E and F.
N		For setting own speed on to the clock.
S	Aircraft Spotting Dial	To enable fall of shot reports received in 'clock code' to be converted into terms of distance along and across the line of fire.
T	Girder above table carrying repeat receivers and other instruments [including rate error and inclination projectors].	
UA	Gun Range Transmission	Group of transmitters which transmit gun range to all positions.
X	Mechanical Cut Off Gear	To prevent damage to mechanisms at extreme range limits.

shafting beneath the floor of the Transmitting Station (TS). These units are listed and briefly described in the Table. While too much technical detail would not be appropriate, some further information on the clock and the main plotting units should be given here.

As already noted, the clock relied on variable-speed drives of the Argo disc/ball/dual-roller pattern to integrate the rates in order to generate the changes in target range and bearing. The mechanism for dividing speed-across by range to give the bearing rate was entirely new and, unlike earlier designs, it could not jam even if the clock-range was very small.[66] This was possible because it incorporated a power follow-up; presumably, in order to limit the load on the linkages generating the speed-across, a clutch-brake motor was used for this purpose. The mechanisms that generated the range-rate and speed-across in some respects resembled those in the American Ford Clock. Rather than the single, Dumaresq-type link used in both the Dreyer and Argo

clocks, Hannibal Ford employed two links, one for own ship and one for the target. This had the advantage for the AFCTs (though not for the simpler Ford clocks) that the components of the speeds[67] due to the movements of own ship and the target were generated separately, as was necessary for the automatic calculation of some ballistic corrections. Both designs then required differentials to add these components together to obtain the clock range and bearing rates. While the Ford clock used conventional bevel gears,[68] the AFCT design was particularly simple and elegant, since the differential action was integral with the sliding speed resolvers; these 'linear differentials' minimised mechanical backlash.

The AFCT Mark I had no less than five plotting units, two for bearings and three for ranges, all on the straight-line principle. In addition to data and observations from the firing ship itself, the plots could record spotting corrections from aircraft and, for use in concentration firing, information from consorts. To avoid too much activity

'General Arrangement of Fire Control Table…'. Admiralty Fire Control Table Mark I photographed in the Elliott Brothers works at Lewisham, probably in December 1925 at the time of the first shop trial. From left to right, the units are G (PIL) with E (Range Correction) behind it, C (Rangefinder Plot), B (Gun Range Plot), A (Clock), D (Bearing Plot), the main group of hunters and M (Wind Unit). The Error in Rate (Range and Bearing) and Inclination projectors are carried on the beam above the main units. (N. 1797 in 1.24/2, EA – many of the related photographs in this album are dated 9.12.25)

around the table itself, separate range and bearing plots (the so-called 'dummy' plots) were installed in a separate compartment, where the operators plotted all fall-of-shot observations as well as consort ranges (corrected for position-in-line) and times of firing; the dummy plots were linked by shafting to the main range and bearing plots so that all the information could be repeated there.

In direct fire, i.e. when the target was visible, the actual target bearing was obtained by the Director; the main purpose of the bearings from the clock was then to determine the correctness of the estimated target course and speed. The clock and Director bearings were indicated by two pointers; if the bearing-rate on the clock was wrong, the clock bearing was corrected continuously by means of a tuning handle. These corrections were plotted on the bearing plot (D); by measuring the slope of this plot with a grid projected from above, the error in bearing-rate could be measured and, after conversion to error in speed-across, used to set the speed-across suggestion wire on the top of the clock. As soon as the target became invisible, the bearing clock became the source of bearings; now the Director trainer followed the clock pointer. However, if the bearing rate was still in error and aircraft spotting observations were available, the plotted falls-of-shot could still indicate the error in bearing rate.[69]

The table itself had two range plots, the Gun Range Plot being linked to the dummy plot. The Rangefinder Plot, which, after the Clock, was probably the most complex unit in the table, had been designed by the LP & FC Section and was manufactured by Barr and Stroud, the supplier of the Navy's rangefinders and range transmission equipment; the other atypical unit was the Position-in-Line Unit, which was not only manufactured but also designed by the Glasgow firm.[70] On the rangefinder plotter, the ranges, which were registered by a multiple range receiver connected to the ship's seven main rangefinders, were recorded automatically by a typewriter that scanned continuously across the full width of the plot. Since the scanning cycle took 10 seconds, this was the maximum delay between a rangetaker transmitting a new range and the indication that the range had been plotted and that he could 'throw off' before making a new 'cut'. By means of a tuning handle, the operator of the rangefinder plot adjusted a pen to draw a line representing his best assessment of the mean range. He was also provided with a range-rate projector to measure the slope and hence the error in range-rate as indicated by the rangefinders.

This mean rangefinder range was also drawn as a red line on the Gun Range Plot, where a pen loaded with blue ink plotted the gun range. In addition, two typewriters recorded the same fall-of-shot and consort ranges that had been plotted on the Dummy Gun Range Plot. The centre-line of the Gun Range Plot represented the corrected clock range, i.e. the clock range plus the corrections calculated automatically by the Range Correction unit. The gun range pen was coupled directly to the handle by which spotting corrections were added to the corrected range. Thus the deviation of the pen from the centre line showed the further corrections needed to compensate for errors in the clock range and range-rate. The slope of the fall-of-shot plot also gave an alternative indication of range-rate error. Thus a second rate-projector was mounted above the gun range plot to measure these slopes. The actual range-rate error used in setting the position of the range-rate suggestion-wire was the best compromise between the values indicated by the two projectors.

Straight-line plotting allowed the plots to be accurate without being too wide, since they only showed errors in range and bearing (of ±3,000 yards and ±3½ degrees respectively). However, when the pens deviated too far from the centre line, they had to be recentred without altering the predicted values. Recentring required additional tuning handles working in conjunction with differentials, clutches and (in the case of the range plots) moving range-scales. Nonetheless, these elaborations did not alter the essential principles: that ranges and bearings were plotted separately: that range and bearing rates were corrected by measuring the slopes of the plots both of observed values and of the falls of shots: and that the rate errors were used (in conjunction with directly measured inclination where available) to correct the enemy course and speed set on the clock.

Later AFCTs

The technology developed for the AFCT Mark I was used immediately for further developments. For *Nelson* and *Rodney*, Elliotts constructed Secondary Armament Clocks which kept the true range and bearing of the target and calculated automatically the gun-range and deflection. The firm also employed some of the Mark I units in the AFCT Mark II for the seven County-class cruisers. The main difference from the Mark I was that the Mark II had no dummy plots nor a separate rangefinder plot; the rangefinder ranges were plotted manually on the single Range Plot. The Mark III table was provided for subsequent 8in cruisers; this was generally similar to the Mark II except for a different range transmission system, supplied by Evershed. The Mark IV, fitted in *Leander*, was much like the Mark III, except that the ballistic units were redesigned for her 6in guns.

Despite its mark number, the Mark IV*, fitted in *Orion*, *Achilles* and *Neptune*, introduced two important innovations. The clock was altered so that it integrated speed-across (rather than bearing rate) to generate 'travel-across': and the bearing plot was replaced by the so-called speed-across plot. Working on the straight line principle, this compared the clock's travel-across (represented by the centre-line of the plot) with the observed

target travel-across; in direct fire, this was calculated automatically by multiplying the change in target compass-bearing (derived from the bearings observed with the director) by the range. In indirect fire, aircraft spotting corrections (expressed as yards left or right) were also plotted, their slope again indicating the error in speed-across. While the clock was simplified, the speed-across plot, which contained two Argo-type variable speed drives, was much more complicated than the previous bearing plot. The advantage of the new design was that it avoided all conversions between travel across and bearings (and their respective rates) so that the operators could address the whole fire control problem in terms of yards and yards-per-minute.

The Mark IV* table reverted to the earlier type of range transmission gear: and it was also the first model to incorporate lagless oil servo control gear.[71] However, with greater elaboration came increasing cost and, at their meeting on 10 November 1932, the Admiralty Board accepted that, after *Neptune*, cruisers should be fitted with less expensive, and less automatic, tables.[72] While the new AFCT Mark V retained a speed-across plot, at first only a simple range-plot was provided, though in this and the similar Mark VI, spotting and 'Error in rate' plots were added later, as can still be seen in the TS of HMS *Belfast*. The clock in these tables was based on the Admiralty Fire Control Clock (AFCC) Mark I. This had been designed originally, principally by Hugh Clausen of the LP & FC Section, for destroyers;[73] rather than the Argo-pattern of variable speed drive, he preferred the Ford type, in which two balls were held in a sliding cage, one above the other, between the disc and a single roller in fixed bearings.

Both Elliotts and Barr & Stroud manufactured the AFCC Mark I and Elliotts supplied some of the ships fitted with AFCTs Mark V and VI. Although direct evidence has not been found, it appears that, by utilising its own design expertise, the Admiralty had successfully introduced competition in the supply of clocks and tables that were required in quantity.

Elliotts were, however, able to retain their monopoly in tables for capital ships.[74] The AFCT Mark VII, for *Warspite* and the other three reconstructed ships, continued the line of development begun with the Mark I, though without the dummy plots. These tables were given a new type of rangefinder plot, the enemy-rate plot, on which the range-scale moved at own ship's range-rate i.e. the component of own speed along the line of fire. The typewriter plotted ranges relative to this scale; thus the slope of the plot indicated the enemy-rate and showed immediately whether the enemy inclination was towards or away from the firing ship. At the enemy-rate plot, an operator tuned a pen to follow the mean of all the plotted ranges. As with the Mark I, the mean rangefinder line was also plotted on the range plot (which now showed true rather than gun range); the error in range-rate could, as before, be measured as the slope of this mean line.[75] The tables for the battleships of the King George V class were designated Mark IX; at last, an inclination plot was provided but, in other respects, they consisted of the same units as the Mark VII.[76]

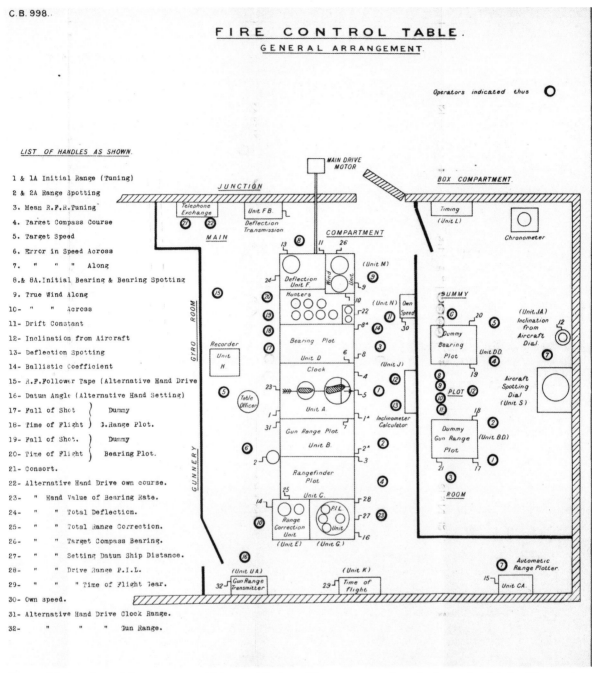

Layout of the Fire Control Compartments in Nelson *and* Rodney. *The operators are shown by the numbered circles. The team in the Main Compartment comprised 4 officers, 16 ratings, 3 telegraphists and 1 signalman: and in the Dummy Plotting Room, 1 officer, 7 ratings, 4 telegraphists and 1 signalman. (Pamphlet on the Drill Procedure and Upkeep of the Admiralty Fire Control Table Mark I.... 1927, ADM 186/277)*

The Royal Navy developed one more battleship fire control table, the Mark 10 for HMS *Vanguard*. Although made by Elliott Brothers,[77] this final table used Ford rather than Argo type integrators. By 1946 radar provided accurate ranges at the longest ranges and in all visibilities: while the latest gyro-compass could give a precise directional reference even under helm. With all obstacles to Pollen's vision of true course plotting at last removed, *Vanguard's* Mark 10 table, in addition to the usual rate

plots, also had a plot of enemy's course and speed.[78]

Conclusions

Before the Great War, the Admiralty had no research-and-development facilities dedicated to fire control, although HMS *Excellent* continued to perform its established function as the principal experimental establish-

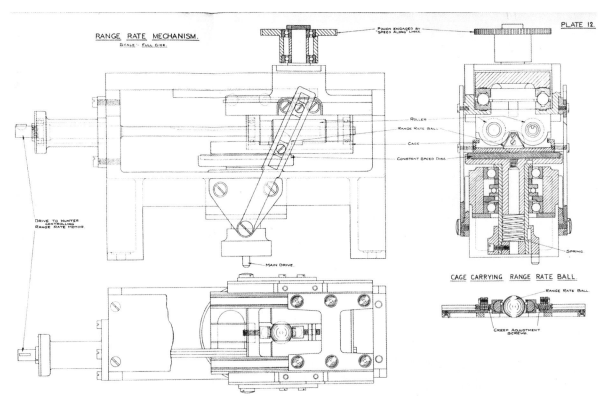

Variable Speed Drive. Apart from the pinion engaging directly with a pair of speed-along links, this was almost identical to the Argo design described in patent 17,441 of 1912. The two slotted links at the sides ensured that the cage carrying the rate ball was positioned correctly relative to the rollers. This variant was used in the Secondary Armament Clocks; the disc was 3.1 inches in diameter and rotated at about 1,800 rpm. The drives use in the main armament tables differed only in minor mechanical details. (Handbook on Secondary Armament Clock, HM Ships "Nelson" and "Rodney", 1930, ADM 186/299)

Clock: Bearing Mechanisms. The large heart-shaped cam in the centre was cut according to the inverse-tangent function. The hunter behind and to the right controlled the No. 12 clutch-brake motor that set the rate of the bearing-clock. The pair of sliding links at upper left had racks cut along their inner edges, which engaged with the large pinion gear between them; together, they acted as a differential, the pinion moving in proportion to the speed-across of the enemy relative to own ship. The bearing-clock variable-speed drive, with its slotted side lever, was underneath the sliding links. The handle was used to set the bearing-rate manually. (N. 1656, 1.24/5, EA)

ment for all aspects of gunnery. New equipment was developed either by industry (such as the rangefinders supplied by Barr & Stroud) or by industry in collaboration with inventive naval officers such as Dreyer (working with Elliott Brothers) or Percy Scott (with Vickers).[79] By 1920, R&D for the Royal Navy had been transformed. In the LP & FC Section, the Controller's Department had its own design and development group. The Admiralty Research Laboratory had been established at Teddington,[80] while the research group formed during the War at Greenwich continued its work on gyroscopes under the direction of Sir James Henderson. Even so, the Admiralty continued to work closely with its specialist industrial suppliers, including Elliott Brothers and Barr & Stroud.

In early 1919, the Dreyer Table Committee laid down very ambitious objectives for a new generation of fire control tables, while the Admiralty Fire Control Table Design Committee added further demanding goals that would require major innovations in gyroscopes. Unfortunately, successive DNOs assigned the gyro developments first to Henderson and then to ARL. These decisions were probably influenced by an unpleasant dispute that erupted after the War concerning the invention of the gyro-compass liquid ballistic.[81] Whatever the rights and wrongs, Henderson proved to be ill-suited to the task, while ARL's experimental designs, although

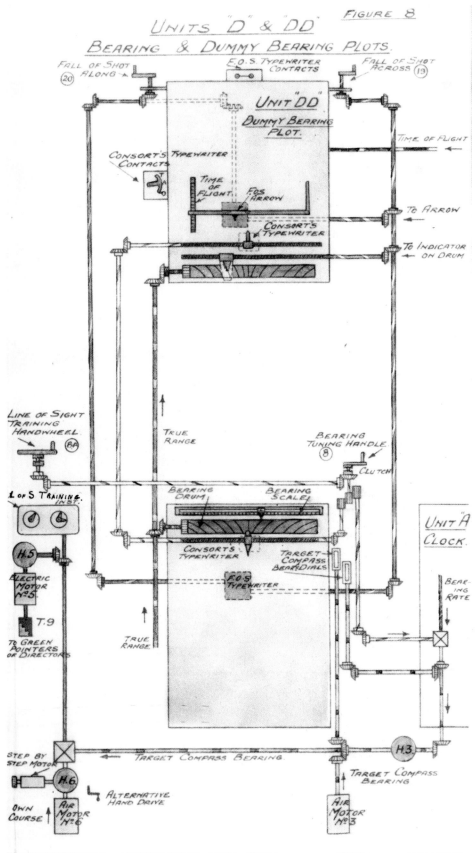

FIGURE 8

UNITS "D" & "DD"

BEARING & DUMMY BEARING PLOTS.

Bearing and Dummy Bearing Plot (D and DD). The bearing pens of both plots were coupled together; they were briefly displaced sideways to mark each time a salvo was fired. In direct fire (target visible), the pens plotted the movements of handle (8A) as the operator corrected any difference between the clock and director bearings. The slope of the plot, measured by the bearing-rate projector, was set on the pointer of the 'Bearing Scale'; the error in speed-across was then read off the 'Bearing Drum'. In indirect fire, the fall-of-shot was recorded with arrows printed by the FOS Typewriter on the Bearing Plot, but the typewriter was controlled by the operators at the Dummy Bearing Plot. With handle (19) the indicator on the drum was set to point to the line corresponding to the observed fall-of-shot to left or right expressed in yards; the lines were graduated to convert FOS from yards to degrees. By means of handle (20), an operator followed the salvo mark in the bearing plot with the FOS Arrow; thus the printed arrows were level with their related salvo mark. The salvoes of consorts firing in concentration were recorded by letters printed by the Consort's Typewriter; their falls-of-shot could also be plotted with the aid of the Time of Flight scale.
(Handbook AFCT Mark I, Figure 8)

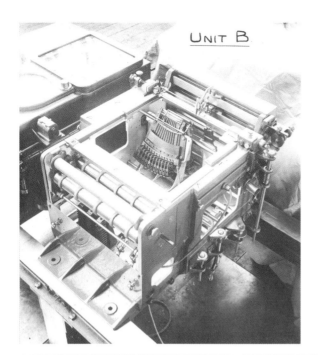

The Prototype Gun Range Plot (Unit B). The two pens, positioned by screwed shafts, plotted Mean Rangefinder Range (from the Rangefinder Plot) and Gun Range; the Gun Range pen was briefly displaced sideways to mark each time the guns fired. The width of the plot was 6,000 yards; the sliding range scale beneath the pens was graduated from 2,000 to 53,000 yards. The fixed pen to the left drew a 'saw-tooth' line to mark minute intervals. The paper moved away from the pens and across the top of the unit between glass plates (not in place). The large typewriter beneath the paper recorded fall-of-shot by printing one or more arrows on the underside of the paper, which was illuminated from below. It was controlled from the Dummy Range Plot; the arrow bars were spaced at intervals corresponding to 100 yards so that the distance of the fall-of-shot could be shown relative to the gun-range in use (multiple-arrow codes were used to signify e.g. 'far-over', 'straddle', etc.). As in the bearing plots, the fall-of-shot typewriter could move both across and along the plot: and there was a consort typewriter (visible to the right of the FOS typewriter). (N. 1486 dated 4.7.23 in 1.24/5, EA)

Admiralty Department Workshop, Elliott Brothers, Century Works, Lewisham. The item on the trolley to left of centre is a Secondary Armament Clock of the type supplied for Nelson and Rodney. The four units to its right are Type G Gyro Director Sights, as fitted in the two battleships and the 8-inch heavy cruisers. The commissioning dates of these ships suggest that this photograph was taken before mid-1927. (N. 1944, 1.24/6, EA)

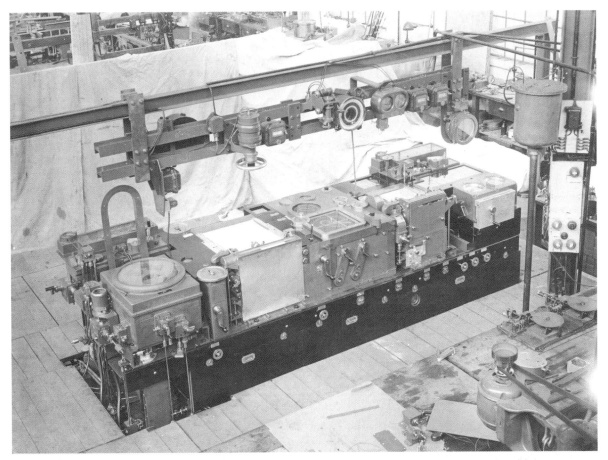

'*Kent Class Cruiser Table*'. *Admiralty Fire Control Table Mark II photographed at the Lewisham works of Elliott Brothers. From left to right, the units are G (PIL) with E (Range Correction) behind it, B (Range Plot), A (Clock), D (Bearing Plot) and M (Wind) with, behind it, the hunters and F (Deflection Correction). (N. 1936, 1.24/6, EA)*

eventually achieving the required accuracy, were insufficiently robust.[82] Thus the master stabilising units were never produced; the goal of blind firing was not realised: and assistance in the difficult task of compensating for ship's motion while aiming and firing was limited to the stabilisation of the line-of-sight, though in elevation only, by a gyroscope incorporated in each Director sight.

In contrast, in the development of the AFCTs themselves the Admiralty was successful in co-ordinating the technological resources at its disposal. Harold Isherwood provided valuable assistance at the start of the project, particularly with the all-important clock. The LP & FC Section designed the multiple range receiver and plotter that was then manufactured by Barr & Stroud, while the firm was alone responsible for the PIL Unit. ARL devised the first clutch-brake motor. Elliott Brothers under Sir Keith Elphinstone introduced the air-motor, designed and made the other units and acted, in the modern sense, as the system integrator. Finally, the staff of *Excellent* performed its traditional role in testing and evaluating the prototype. Even without the gyro units, the AFCTs of 1927 were a great technical achievement which, with their elaborate plotting and automatic calculating mechanisms, were probably then the most advanced fire control system in the world; the United States Navy, for

example, did not reach similar levels of automation until the late 1930s.[83]

As we have now seen, after the Great War there was no 'adoption of both automatic rate and true-course plotters'.[84] Sumida also suggests that, after Dreyer returned as D of GD, 'the design process was well under way, but political circumstances [the presence of Beatty as First Sea Lord] were also such as to limit severely his [Dreyer's] powers of interference' and that, as ACNS, he 'had good reason to be circumspect in his remarks' because of the recent exposure by the Royal Commission on Awards to Inventors of 'the plagiarisation [*sic*] of the Argo Clock that had occurred in 1911'.[85] These interpretations might be justified if the Argo fire control system had been the basis for the AFCT Mark I, whereas, in fact, the influence was limited to the mechanical design of the variable-speed drives. Political circumstances did prevent Dreyer from influencing the Grand Fleet Committee, but their nature and timing were entirely different from those implied above: while, in 1922 and 1925, Dreyer's only declared concerns were about cost and the inclination plot. Naturally, he would not have objected to the reinstatement of rate-plotting: which allowed him to claim in his memoirs, not without some justification, that the AFCT 'was in fact only a rearrangement of my "Dreyer

Table'".[86] Thus Dreyer had no reason to interfere with the development of the Mark I, or to dissimulate his enthusiasm over the outcome; not a hint has been found that he did not give the new table his full support.

Epilogue

On 27 May 1941, HMS *Rodney's* AFCT Mark I was faced with the problem for which it had been designed–engaging an enemy capital ship with data obtained from optical instruments. After the action with *Bismarck*, *Rodney* continued on her way to the United States for refit; the work gave her gunnery officer–who retired in 1963 as Vice-Admiral Sir William Crawford, KBE, CB, DSC–time to complete a comprehensive set of reports on the gunnery aspects of the engagement. The author remains very grateful for the opportunity, in March 1995, to discuss these reports with Admiral Crawford; the following account is based on the wartime reports,[87] the notes from this interview,[88] and an earlier interview with Admiral Crawford recorded by the Imperial War Museum.[89]

Throughout the engagement with *Bismarck*, which began with *Rodney's* first salvo at 08.47, the conditions were very trying for visual observation. Although the visibility itself was good, a force 6 wind had thrown up a rough sea and heavy swell. Admiral Tovey in *King George V* (initially on *Rodney's* starboard beam) had chosen to

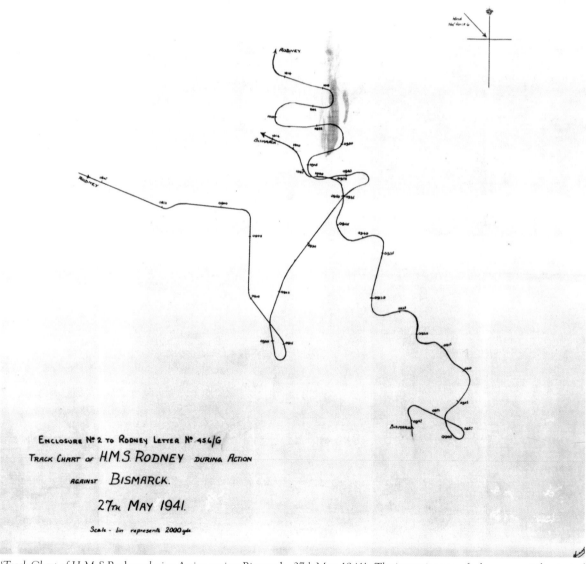

'Track Chart of H.M.S Rodney during Action against Bismarck, 27th May 1941'. The increasing rangefinder ranges at the start of the action gave the misleading impression that between 0850 and 0857, Bismarck had turned away onto much the same course as Rodney. The time marks on the courses are 0847, 0853, 0857 (Bismarck only), 0900, then at 5-minute intervals until 1010; the final marks are for 1014. ('Enclosure No. 2 to Rodney letter, ..'in ADM 1/11818)

engage from the westward to obtain the advantage of light and to prevent *Bismarck* from using smoke.[90] Consequently, throughout the engagement, their target was downwind from the British battleships, while, until she turned northward at 09.16, *Rodney* had to contend with a stern or quartering sea. Thus ranging and director laying, training and firing were all hampered by funnel haze and cordite smoke, and by severe and irregular roll and yaw; the smoke and fumes also interfered with spotting. Since her commissioning in 1927, *Rodney's* material to deal with the ship's motion had fallen behind modern standards. The vital duplex coincidence rangefinders in the Director Control Towers (DCTs), which were only 15-feet in length,[91] were unstabilised. Her directors had a prototype Time Interval Compensation (TIC) gear[92] that was too erratic to use; they also lacked the cross-levelling gear that corrected deflection errors caused by trunnion tilt.

Bismarck herself was a difficult target, veering erratically at unexpectedly slow speed as she attempted to keep her head to the sea. These course changes can hardly have helped her own gunnery; on the other hand, her material was still intact at the start of the action, and she was firing upwind. Her initial salvos were dangerously accurate:

> *Bismarck* opened fire at 08.49, engaging *Rodney* first. Her opening salvo was a four-gun salvo from 'A' and 'B' turrets which fell about 1000-yards short. A minute later, *Rodney* was straddled, one round falling just short and the rest over. Spread at first seemed to be good. In the next two minutes one salvo fell over and the one short followed by several overs....By 09.00 the enemy's fire which had been at the rate of 1-1.5 salvos per minute became slower and started to get erratic...[93]

Although, just before 09.00, *Rodney* found it necessary to turn away to avoid enemy fire. *Bismarck* was perhaps unlucky not to make a hit before she was overwhelmed.

In contrast, *Rodney* did not observe a straddle until her 18th salvo, fired at 08.59. Her opening range of 23,500 yards was an estimate. As firing began, some ranges were obtained from one of the rangefinders in her fore DCT but, by the 4th salvo, the gun-range was over 2000 yards below the rangefinder ranges, while the rangefinder plot indicated that the range was increasing. It is often stated that *Rodney's* third salvo made hits,[94] perhaps on the basis of post-action reports from the cruiser *Norfolk*. However, *Rodney's* control team saw no shots correct for line, let alone straddles; after the 4th salvo, they tuned up the gun-range by almost 3,000 yards to the mean rangefinder range, and also concluded (from the increasing range) that *Bismarck* had altered course 150 degrees to starboard. Until 08.56, the ranges from the DCT rangefinder continued to increase, providing misleading confirmation for what was almost certainly a mistaken conclusion, since no other reports describe a turn-away by *Bismarck*. With the wrong enemy course set on the AFCT, it is not surprising that, of salvos 5 to 16, only four were correct for line, and these were all overs. However, by 08.57, both the fore DCT rangefinders were showing the same rapid downward trend as the 41-foot rangefinder in 'B'-turret, so all rangefinder ranges were converging on the gun-range, which had been steadily reduced by a succession of 'down' spotting corrections. Like salvo 18 (range 20,000 yards), the next three were also spotted as straddles; this was the time (just after 09.00) when *Bismarck's* 'A' and 'B' turrets were damaged and her fore control put out of action.[95] Unfortunately, just as *Rodney's* gunnery team was getting into their stride, at 09.02, she began a large turn to port onto course 182 degrees:

Rodney, seen at anchor off Oslo, 29 June 1937. (CPL)

This course was a particularly difficult one for gunnery; with the sea on the Starboard quarter the yaw was very considerable and cordite smoke and funnel haze made rangefinding practically impossible, observation of fire very chancy and firing intervals long.[96]

Until the 18-point turn at 09.16, the gun-range, which continued to fall to 9100 yards, was a 1000 yards or more in excess of the rangefinder ranges, though these were few and without any consistent trend until after 09.11.

During the turn, the turrets and fore DCT had to slew from port to starboard but, when fire was reopened, for a time the conditions were much improved. A good plot of rangefinder ranges was obtained and consistent straddles were obtained from salvos 45 to 58 (the last fired at 09.27) as the range closed from nine to six thousand yards.[97] However, *Rodney* then turned further to the eastwards, which resulted in a worsening roll and more smoke interference. After 09.30 (when the 63rd salvo was fired) the whole gunnery team were tiring. From 09.36, they also had to cope with a succession of large turns as Captain Dalrymple-Hamilton, who could not slow to his target's speed because of the submarine risk,[98] zig-zagged *Rodney* back and forth across *Bismarck's* bows. Until salvo 90, the AFCT, operated by its team of Royal Marine bandsmen, had functioned faultlessly. But, at 09.49, a bandsman's boot dislodged a cover of the Range Correction unit, which then fouled the shafting between the units and sheered three couplings. The damage was too severe to repair immediately. For the remainder of the engagement, at an almost point-blank range of about 4000 yards, it was necessary to resort to range-keeping with a Vickers clock and Dumaresq.

This action illustrates vividly the problems of engaging in rough weather with optical instruments and guns that lacked gyroscopic stabilisation. As well as the difficulties of keeping on the target, there is little doubt that, in the first twelve minutes when the target was more than 20,000 yards distant, the rangefinder ranges were very inaccurate. Some of the errors may have been due to ranging through the temperature gradients produced by the funnel exhaust. However, the target was also indistinct and a number of the post-action reports insisted that stereoscopic rangefinders would have given more accurate opening ranges and, furthermore, that:

> ...the stereoscopic principle...has the additional advantage that one can sense the direction and possibly the amount of the error of splashes out of line [sic], thus giving one the opportunity, so often commented on about German and Italian fire, of correcting direct from an initial salvo one or two thousand yards over or short onto the target without wasting time on laddering.[99]

Unfortunately, the Royal Navy never overcame its tendency to see only the disadvantages of stereoscopic rangefinders. And, in *Nelson* and *Rodney*, ranging accuracy was further compromised by fitting them with coincidence rangefinders aloft that were less than half the length of those available to their opponents.[100] Observations of target bearings and inclinations were equally unsatisfactory:

> The bearing plot was of little assistance to the Central Rate Officer [in the TS]. The trace was very irregular as the yaw of the ship prevented the Director Trainer keeping on the enemy except when firing....No inclinations were received from the Inclinometers. No silhouette of *Bismarck* had been received...and the only length known was the overall length....On this account operators were instructed to concentrate on observing alterations of course of the enemy.[101]

Denied a good supply of accurate ranges, bearings and inclinations, even the elaborately engineered AFCT could provide only approximate indications of enemy course and speed.[102] At worst, as at the start of the action, the plot of false ranges suggested a seriously erroneous course, which was accepted for a time even though it was 'contrary to the observations of the Rate Officers'.[103] Perhaps this unnerving experience had its effect later in the engagement, when greater weight was given to spotting observations–which may have been either mistaken or misleading due to the aiming difficulties–than to good range plots.[104] There can be no doubt that, in the action with *Bismarck*, *Rodney's* AFCT Mark I was unable to function entirely as its designers had intended. The accidental breakdown was the final straw; as Admiral Crawford remarked many years later:

> Here we were with all this complicated machinery, where we opened fire on a guessed range and finished off with our fire control instruments back nearly forty years.[105]

At the end of the First World War, the Dreyer Table Committee had been well aware of the limitations of optical rangefinding. By 1941, these had not changed very much, especially when ranging at over 20,000 yards with coincidence rangefinders no longer than 15-feet. However, by 1943, improved radar sets had superseded optical rangefinders and radar ranging played a decisive part in the sinking of the *Scharnhorst* by the force under the command of Admiral Sir Bruce Fraser in *Duke of York*.[106] Indeed, probably only this sea-change in ranging finally realised the full potential of the Admiralty Fire Control Tables, which Fraser had helped to develop some twenty years earlier.

Acknowledgements

I am very grateful to Admiral Crawford for granting me an interview. Also to Mr Ron Bristow and Mrs Louise Jamison, past and present curators of the Elliott Archive, for their help in using this invaluable source: and to Marconi Corporation for permission to reproduce the photographs therefrom.

Notes

1   Frederic Dreyer, *The Sea Heritage* (London, 1955) pp. 208, 215, 233-4 and 238.
2   Bryan Ranft, *The Beatty Papers*, Volume I (Aldershot, 1989) pp. 528-531 and 536. Stephen Roskill, *Admiral of the Fleet Earl Beatty* (New York, 1981) pp. 260 and 282-3. Lord

Chatfield, *The Navy and Defence* (London, 1942) pp. 167 and 171. Navy Lists for dates of appointments.

3 The author's PhD thesis, *Fire Control for British Dreadnoughts: Choices in Technology and Supply* (University of London, 2001) describes the development and technical details of the Dreyer Tables. It concludes, inter alia, that they were not, as is now widely assumed, inferior to Pollen's Argo system.

4 William Schleihauf, 'The Dumaresq and the Dreyer' in *Warship International*, Vol. 38, 2001, Nos. 1 (pp. 6-29), 2 (pp. 164-201) and 3 (pp. 221-33). (Advanced copy gratefully acknowledged.)

5 For the 'electric follow-up gear', see *Handbook of Captain F.C.Dreyer's Fire Control Tables*, 1918, C.B.1456, pp. 51-4, Admiralty Library [AL].

6 Jon Sumida, *In Defence of Naval Supremacy* [*IDNS*] (London, 1989) p. 219; see p. 211 and Plate 5 for the Argo mechanism.

7 Schleihauf, pp. 28-9.

8 *Grand Fleet Gunnery and Torpedo Orders* [GFG&TO] 304. 'Full Calibre Firings...in third quarter, 1917', 20 November 1917, para. III/23 and 91, 'Full Calibre Firings...first quarter of 1918', 29 June 1918, para. 41, ADM 137/293, PRO. (A new numbering sequence for GFG&TOs was begun in May 1918.)

9 Admiralty, Technical History Section, *The Technical History and Index. A Serial History of Technical Problems dealt with by Admiralty Departments*, Part 23 'Fire Control in H.M. Ships', December 1919, pp. 28-9, AL. See also Admiralty, Gunnery Branch, *Handbook on Gyro Director Training Gear* (GDT) 1927, ADM 186/279.

10 Schleihauf, p. 24.

11 *Technical History*, p.30.

12 ibid. pp. 21-2.

13 'Notes on tactical exercises...24 February 1917' and 'Grand Fleet Battle Instructions', 1 January 1918 in *Beatty Papers I*, pp. 403 and 457.

14 Admiralty, Naval Staff, Gunnery and Torpedo Division, *Progress in Naval Gunnery* [PNG] 1914 to 1918, July 1919, pp. 50-1, ADM 186/238.

15 GFG&TO, 91 para. 28.

16 Enclosure with Admiralty to C.-in-C., 10 October 1916 in ADM 137/2027.

17 GFG&TO, 312. 'Rangefinder Errors', 29 December 1917.

18 GFG&TO, 105. 'Full Calibre firings...second quarter, 1918', 10 September 1918, paras. 31-2.

19 GFG&TO, 91 paras. 13 and 31.

20 GFG&TO, 123. 'Present position as regards Inclination...', 4 November 1918, para. 5 See also PNG 1914-18, pp. 32 and 42. GFG&TO, 105 paras. 7 and 26. *Technical History*, p.30.

21 Admiralty, Gunnery Branch, *Progress in Gunnery Material* [PGM] 1920, pp. 12-15 (ADM 186/244) and PGM 1922-23, pp. 14-25 (ADM 186/259). PNG 1923 (p.12), 1924 (pp. 3 and 12), 1926 (p.13) and 1927 (p.10), ADM 186/261, /263, /271 and /289.

22 'Excerpt from Admiralty Letter' and 'First and Second Interim Reports' in Admiralty, Gunnery Branch, *Reports of the Grand Fleet Dreyer Table Committee 1918-1919*, September 1919, pp. 4-5, ADM 186/241.

23 'Third Interim Report', *Dreyer Table Committee*, pp. 5-13; for the date, see 'Monthly Record of Principal Questions dealt with by Director of Naval Ordnance' [MR/DNO], Vol. 3,

January to June 1919, p. 1093, AL. The improved gyro-compass with mercury ballistic was introduced in 1919; A E Fanning, *Steady as She Goes* (London, 1986) pp. 218-228.

24 This cross-cut of inclination and speed-across gave the range-rate as well as the enemy speed.

25 'Third Interim Report', p.6 with their emphasis.

26 'Final Report of the Committee. Future Development of Fire Control Tables', *Dreyer Table Committee*, pp. 14-18. For its date, see MR/DNO, Vol. 3, p. 1114. For discussions between representatives of the Admiralty and the American Ford Instrument Company, see *IDNS*, pp. 314-5.

27 Beatty to the Secretary of the Admiralty, 7 February 1919, *Dreyer Table Committee*, pp. 18-19.

28 Dreyer, p.236. *Navy Lists*.

29 'Re-organisation of Naval Staff Division. 1917-1921', ADM 116/1803. Minute by ACNS (Dreyer), 1 December 1924 in MR/DNO, Vol. IX, July 1923 to June 1926, p. 3161.

30 Minute by DNA&T, 8 May 1919 in ' "Ford" Fire Control System...', MR/DNO Vol. 3, p. 1428 (copy courtesy Professor Sumida).

31 Capt. E T Wickam and H F Simes, 'Branch 5 of the Electrical Engineering Department of the Admiralty. Some Account of its History', September 1953, p. 1 in CLSN 5/3, Churchill College. In 1939, the Section was split between the Ordnance and Electrical Engineering departments (p. 6).

32 DNO's minute, 24 February 1919, MR/DNO Vol. 3, p.1123. 'List of Admiralty Committees and Committees in which the Admiralty is interested', September 1919, ADM 1/8568/259. *IDNS*, pp. 238-40.

33 *IDNS*, pp. 90, 106 and 314. See Crooke's service record (ADM 196/44/36) for his membership in 1912 of the 'Argo Range Clock Committee'.

34 Minutes of DNO and DNA&T and 'List of Committees', 1919 (op. cit.).

35 'Branch 5 History', Appendix I.

36 Hugh Clausen, 'Invention and the Navy - the progress from Ideas to Ironmongery', paper to the Institute of Patentees and Inventors, 30 January 1970 published in *The Inventor*, Vol. 10, No. 1, March 1970, CLSN 3/7. For dates - '1920-21' - see examination of Commander Isherwood in 'Minutes of Proceedings before the Royal Commission on Awards to Inventors....', 3 August 1925, pp. 5, 100 and 103, T.173/547, Part 10: and Pollen to the Secretary, RCAI, 28 July 1926, pp. 2-3 in T.173/90, PRO.

37' Final Report' p. 31 with President's Minute of 9 March 1920 in 'Fire Control Requirements Committee...Report, Admiralty remarks &c.' 1919-1921, ADM 116/2068.

38 *Navy Lists* for postings of committee members. 'List of Admiralty Committees and Committees in which the Admiralty is interested', 1 April 1922, ADM 1/8523/61. If the Fire Control Table Development Committee produced a report of their conclusions, it does not seem to have survived.

39 Richard Humble, *Fraser of North Cape* (London, 1983) pp. 81-4.

40 'Branch 5 History', p.4.

41 Admiralty, Gunnery Branch, *Handbook for Admiralty Fire Control Table Mark I (H.M. Ships "NELSON" and "RODNEY")*: Text, p.1, ADM 186/273. Diagrams in ADM 186/274.

42 Dreyer, p.261. *Navy Lists.*

43 DofGD's minute, 15 April 1921 in MR/DNO, Vol. VII, 1921, pp. 2275-6.

44 PNG 1921 (April, 1922) pp. 8 and 43, ADM 186/257.

45 IDNS, pp. 217 and 220.

46 Minutes, including the DNO's record of the meeting of 17 July 1923 in 'New Fire Control System', ADM 1/8654/12. See also the photographs showing 'General Progress on Tables as at 14 July 1923, negative numbers 1495 and 1496 in 1.24/5, Elliott Archives, Marconi Corporation [EA]. The PIL unit corrected ranges and bearings for the different positions-in-line of ships firing in concentration.

47 Clausen, 'Invention and the Navy'.

48 Fanning, p. 233.

49 PGM 1922-23, pp. 9-12.

50 *ibid.* p. 14-25.

51 The Elliott album 1.24/5 contains six photographs (N. 1418-23) captioned 'Links for Units E and F, Landstad's design'; the prints are stamped 'GKBE 4 Apr 1923'. While these suggest that Landstad may have continued working on the tables after 1921, the mechanisms finally used in Units E and F (the 'straddle and deflection units') were completely different.

52 As in the Dreyer tables, the error in bearing-rate had to be converted into an error in speed-across (using curves engraved on a drum) in order to set the speed-across suggestion-wire.

53 DNO's minute, February 1924, ADM 1/8654/12.

54 Hugh Clausen, 'A Report on Questions concerning the Gunnery Efficiency of His Majesty's Navy', n.d. but 1942, p. 4 in P. 1024, AL.

55 A clutch-brake motor, probably one of the first of its kind, was supplied to Elliotts by ARL in September 1923 - photo N. 1514 in 1.24/5, EA - although the motor used in the production AFCTs was differently constructed. ARL also devised an alternative design with a continuously-running motor and clutches - *Annual Report of the Torpedo School* [ART] 1923, pp. 189-91 (ART2, Hampshire Record Office). Their work was part of the development of the synchronous transmission system used in the new director sights (Type G) supplied by Elliotts for the 16-inch battleships and 8-inch cruisers - Admiralty, Gunnery Branch, *Director Gear...1929*, ADM 186/291 and PNG 1935, pp. 98 and 137, ADM 186/328.

56 *Handbook AFCT Mark I*, pp. 12-14.

57 Fraser to Clausen, 20 February (1954?). See also Humble, pp. 81-2.

58 *Handbook AFCT Mark I*, pp. 7-12.

59 Hugh Clausen, 'The Years of Achievement', *Naval Review*, August 1949, proof copy in CLSN 2/3.

60 Fanning, pp. 233-5. Balancer transmission had been first trialled in *Nelson* in 1931 and was planned for new (and possibly existing) cruisers: PNG 1931, pp. 82 and 86, ADM 186/309.

61 V W Baddely to Admiral Superintendent, Portsmouth, 28 June 1924 in ADM 1/8654/12.

62 Minutes by DNO (8 December), DofGD (11 December 1925), ACNS (4 January) and Controller (5, 8 and 12 January 1926) in MR/DNO, Volume IX, July 1923-June 1926, pp. 3180-8. At the suggestion of the DNO, letters of appreciation were sent to Fraser and Dove (plus two other officers of the DNO's and DTM's departments) and to Elliotts - Humble, pp. 83-4, though the date was 30 January 1926, not 1925.

63 M J Whitley, *Cruisers of World War Two* (London, 1995) pp. 83-94.

64 'Pamphlet on the Dreyer Table Mark IV* 1930' and '...Mark V 1930' in 'Guard Book for Pamphlets on Dreyer Tables', BR 938, AL

65 Functional descriptions from *Handbook AFCT Mark I* (the principal source for this section) pp. 5-6. For the SF7 inclinometer, see Admiralty, Gunnery Branch, *Director Firing Gear...1929*, p. 11, ADM 186/291.

66 A lever was rotated to an angle whose tangent equalled speed-across divided by range; even if the range was zero, the angle only reached 90 degrees. The follow-up motor set the rate of the bearing-clock and, at the same time, rotated a cam cut to the *inverse-tangent* function.

67 Range-rate can also be regarded as the apparent speed of the target along the line-of-bearing c.f. speed-across.

68 Hannibal C Ford, U S Patents 1,370,204 (*Range Keeper*, 1 Mar.1921, filed 4 Dec.1917) and 1,450,585 (*Range and Bearing Keeper*, 3 Apr.1923, filed 19 Jun.1918).

69 In direct fire, deflection errors were corrected by spotting without interfering with the plot of target bearing. In indirect fire, there was no way of knowing whether an opening error for line was due to incorrect target bearing (e.g. from an aircraft), deflection, or bearing-rate. The first two could be corrected by spotting the salvos into line; if they then drifted off again, the cause was incorrect bearing-rate.

70 'Branch 5 History', p.5. Baddeley to Adm. Supt. Portsmouth, 28 June 1924. PGM 1922-23, pp. 12-13.

71 Admiralty, Gunnery Branch, *Handbook for Admiralty Fire Control Table Mark II* (1927): Addendum No.1, Marks II and III (1928 and 1938) and Addendum No.2 , Marks IV and IV* (1933 and 1938); text in ADM 186/275, plates in ADM 186/276. The initial intention had been to fit *Leander* (the first of her class) with the table that was subsequently designated Mark IV*: PNG 1930, pp. 123-4 (ADM 186/304).

72 Admiralty Board Minutes, 10 November 1932 in ADM 167/85 and Board Memorandum 'Reduction in Fire Control Equipment of New Construction 6" Cruisers' 26 October 1932 in ADM 167/87.

73 Clausen, *Invention and the Navy*, p. 4. 'Recommendation of the Status Committee...12 November 1938....in respect of Admiralty Fire Control Clocks', CLSN 5/2. For an account of the AFCC-derived tables, clocks and boxes, see Allan G Bromley, *British Mechanical Gunnery Computers of World War II* (University of Sydney, Basser Department of Computer Science, 1984).

74 Photo N. 2727 in 1.25/7, EA. *Handbook for the Admiralty Fire Control Clock Mark I*, 1938, p. 39, ADM 186/350. Elliott ledgers 1.05/1, 2 and 3, EA: though no explicit references to *Warspite* and *Prince of Wales* have been found.

75 *Handbook of the Admiralty Fire Control Table Mark VII* (July 1939) with Addendum No. 1 (November 1939), ADM 186/357.

76 In the *Annual Report of the Torpedo School 1937*, p.71 (ART2, Hampshire Record Office) the tables for *King George V* and *Prince of Wales* were named Mark VIII: but PNG 1939, p.129 (ADM 239/137) designates the tables as Mark IX and describes a horseshoe layout and an inclination plot, as does

the *Handbook for the Admiralty Fire Control Table Mark IX* in the *Excellent* Historical Library.

[77] P Clarke, 'Visit to Admiral Sir F. C. Dreyer at Winchester, 10/2/49', 2/69/13 and Elliott ledger 1.05/3, EA.

[78] *Handbook for Admiralty Fire Control Table Mark 10*, 1951, *Excellent* Historical Library. *PNG 1938*, p.118 (ADM 137/349) and *PNG 1939*, p.132 refer to a Mark X table for new cruisers, but no other trace of this has been found.

[79] John Brooks, 'Percy Scott and the Director', *Warship* 1996, pp. 150-70.

[80] M M Postan, D Hay and J D Scott, *Design and Development of Weapons* (London, 1964) pp. 434 and 440.

[81] Fanning, pp. 218-28 and 233.

[82] This concluding section has benefited greatly from comments on the first draft by Sebastien Soubiran, whose doctoral thesis - 'De l'utilisation contingente des scientifiques dans les systèmes d'innovation des Marines françaises et britanniques entre les deux guerres mondiales; deux exemples: la conduite du tir des navires et la télémécanique', thèse de Doctorat, Université Denis-Diderot, Paris 7, Octobre 2002 - includes a description of ARL's role in the development of gunnery gyroscopes.

[83] Norman Friedman, *US Naval Weapons* (Annapolis, 1982) pp. 35-6 (reference courtesy Steve McLaughlin). Germany began development of a fully gyro-stabilised fire control system in 1926: Peter Padfield, *Guns at Sea* (London, 1974) pp. 282 *et seq.*

[84] *IDNS* p.331. However, a footnote on p.339 mentions the 'incorporation of rate rather than true-course plotting in the post-war British...system'.

[85] *ibid.* pp. 315-6.

[86] Dreyer, p.59.

[87] Appendices I to X with Commanding Officer, "Rodney" to Second-in-Command, Home Fleet, 26 July 1941 in ADM 1/11817; enclosed track-chart and plot of ranges and inclinations in ADM 1/11818.

[88] Notes with corrections and additional answers by Admiral Crawford, 7 April 1995.

[89] IWM 10673/1 to 3 (copy courtesy Admiral Crawford).

[90] Minute by Admiral Tovey, 15 November 1941 in ADM 1/11817.

[91] *Handbook for Naval Rangefinders and Inclinometers, Volume I*, BR 295, p.50, AL.

[92] This was supposed to compensate for roll velocity at the moment of firing.

[93] Appendix X, 'Enemy Gunfire'.

[94] For example, Correlli Barnett, *Engage the Enemy More Closely* (New York, 1991) p.312.

[95] Burkard Baron von Müllenheim-Rechberg, *Battleship Bismarck* (London, 1991) pp. 248, 250, 264, 269 and 276.

[96] Appendix I, '16-inch Narrative'.

[97] Salvos 41-44 were over because the straddle correction (the difference between the mean rangefinder and hitting gun ranges) from before the turn was kept on the table and was only cleared by down spotting corrections.

[98] Interview notes.

[99] Vice-Admiral A T B Curteis, 9 October 1941 in ADM 1/11817; he must have meant 'out for length' rather than 'out of line' (a deflection error). The French also used stereoscopic rangefinders 'to observe fall of shot': Jean Guiglini and Albert Moreau, 'French Light Cruisers...', *Warship International*, Vol. XXXVIII, No. 3, pp. 281-2.

[100] *Bismarck* had 10-metre rangefinders on the fore-top and aft directors as well as in the turrets (information courtesy Brooks Rowlett). Her gunnery 'radar had a shorter range and poorer bearing accuracy than the optical equipment': Müllenheim-Rechberg, p.38.

[101] Appendix II, 'Remarks on Control'.

[102] Some of this elaboration was perhaps necessary only *because* the target data was inaccurate: and nothing has been found to explain why *Rodney's* aloft rangefinders were not longer. On the other hand, more accurate bearings depended mainly on the power stabilisation of the DCT, but the necessary techniques were not developed (by ARL) until after 1935 (Postan *et al.* pp. 441-2).

[103] Appendix II, 'Remarks on Control'.

[104] Salvos 35, 40 and 61-4. Appendix I, '16-inch Narrative' and Enclosure 1, '16-inch Analysis'.

ARMSTRONGS AND THE ITALIAN NAVY

The financial constraints that restricted spending on the Italian Navy after the Battle of Lissa in 1866 began to reverse in the 1880s. These constraints had encouraged the building of a few high-quality designs. **Peter Brook** describes how the British firm of Armstrongs supplied cruiser designs that set a template for successive classes of protected cruisers, the first to enter service with the Italian fleet.

The Tyneside firm of Sir W G Armstrong Mitchell and Co built three cruisers for the Italian navy, *Giovanni Bausan*, *Dogali* and *Piemonte*. Four near-sisters of *Bausan*, *Etna*, *Stromboli*, *Vesuvio* and *Ettore Fieramosca* were built from slightly modified plans. In addition, Armstrongs built two trials gunboats, *Castore* and *Polluce* for the Italian army which were later taken over by the navy. Armstrongs also supplied heavy and medium ordnance from the 1870s for *Duilio* until the middle of the First World War.[1] Each of these contributions, all of which played a key role in the foundation of the modern Italian navy, will be looked at in turn.

GIOVANNI BAUSAN

Bausan was modelled on the Armstrong-built Chilean cruiser *Esmeralda* laid down sixteen months earlier but was ten feet longer in order to mount two broadside torpedo tubes. *Esmeralda* was the first modern light cruiser and was the product of a number of technological advances in the 1870s, the single most important being the production of cheap mild steel of consistent quality by the Siemens process. This allowed hulls to be lighter without loss of strength, while hull lines improved because of model tank experiments by the Froudes, father and son. Steel cylindrical boilers delivered steam at up to 150lbs pressure to the newly introduced compound engine, more economical and efficient than the simple engine, enabling ships to steam faster and longer thus making heavy masts and rigging unnecessary. Steel allowed the manufacture of breech-loading guns, stronger and of greater length which, in combination with slow burning gunpowder, pioneered by Armstrongs' Andrew Noble, gave higher velocities to improve range and accuracy. Thick external armour was abandoned to improve speed, and in place a complete underwater deck combined with cofferdams, transverse and longitudinal bulkheads and coal bunkers.

The first Royal Navy ships to incorporate most of these features were the 18-knot steel cruisers *Iris* and

GIOVANNI BAUSAN (Designed by George Rendel)

Yard	Laid Down	Launched	Completed
Low Walker	21 Aug 1882	15 Dec 1883	9 May 1885

Displacement	3082 tons normal (3131 tonnes)
Dimensions	280 x 42 x 18ft 6in
	(85.3 x 12.8 x 5.64m)
Armament	2 x 10in 30 cal BL
	6 x 5.9in (149mm) BL
	4 x 6pdr QF
	2 x 1pdr QF
	4 x machine guns
	3 x 14in TT
Armour	Deck 1 ½ in over machinery, ¾ in fore and aft, conning tower 2in.
Machinery	2 sets horizontal compound by Hawthorn Leslie
	4 double ended cylindrical boilers
	Trials IHP FD 6470=17.4kts.
Fuel	Coal 400 tons normal,
	600 tons maximum.
	Nominal radius = 5000 miles at 10kts
Complement	13/254 [2]

Weights (In tons and percentages of tons)		
Hull & fittings	1467	(47.6)
Equipment	215	(6.98)
Armament	320	(10.38)
Machinery	680	(22.06)
Coal	400	(12.9)
TOTAL	3082 tons[3]	

Mercury but they had no deck armour and carried a light armament. The Comus class had a flat deck covering machinery only and was fully rigged as were their successors the *Leanders*, which introduced the arched deck but again incomplete, being closed off at each end by thin bulkheads, highly vulnerable to raking fire. One year later *Esmeralda*, with all of the new features due to the technological advances outlined above, was laid down.[4]

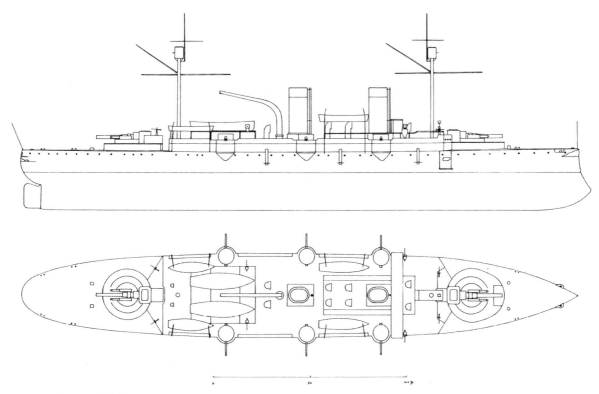

Giovanni Bausan. (IAS)

Giovanni Bausan, *lying in the Tyne after completion.* (Miss Elizabeth Rowell)

Giovanni Bausan, *after 1904 with reduced secondary armament, extended bridge and lying deeper in the water.* (Giorgierini and Nani)

In 1882, Italy's most modern cruisers were three 14-knot steel barque-rigged 14-knot corvettes; the decision was made to build up a fleet of modern cruisers of the *Esmeralda* type but, as well as that ships heavy gun armament, torpedo tubes were to be added. Because of the time that it would take to prepare a design, as well as a lack of construction expertise, Armstrongs were invited to build a prototype and to supply plans so that sister ships could be built in Italy.[5]

Armament

The main armament of two single 10in, 30 cal, 24 ton guns was mounted fore and aft, sixty feet from bow and stern, firing a 450lb projectile with a 230lb black powder charge to give a 2060ft/sec velocity. The breech and the men working it were protected by a two-inch thick loading chamber while the gun was run in and out by hydraulic presses; hydraulic power was used to train the gun to a maximum of 30 degrees abaft each beam. To load, the gun was laid fore and aft in line with a fixed armoured deckhouse into which ammunition was hoisted from below.[6] The 5.9in guns were mounted three on each side in Albini mountings which had been used in the *Tsukushi's* class secondary armament but were judged by the Royal Navy to be inferior to the Vavasseur mounting.[7] The Italian navy must have reached the same conclusion as *Bausan's* sister ships used Vavasseur mountings for their secondary armament. The 5.9in guns were 26

calibres long, weighed 4.15 tons, a 34lb powder charge giving an 82lb projectile a muzzle velocity of 1946ft/sec. The 14in torpedo tubes were mounted one forward underwater and one on each broadside above water, training through 50 degrees.

Protection

The armoured deck was complete from stem to stern, arched, with its crown a foot below the water line so that it could not guarantee buoyancy, stability or trim. Between this deck and the lower deck, four feet above, there were cellular spaces filled with coal and in addition side bunkers above and below the armour deck. There was also a cork belt extending from the waterline to four feet above. This was supposed to reduce the ingress of water after a waterline hit by swelling, but in practice was useless as the cork was blown out and would deteriorate quickly anyway.

Special Features

Bausan was quite unique in having a gooseneck crane immediately abaft the second funnel. Compared with her sisters her bridge was initially minimal, although it increased in size later. The Albini mounting shields were round-faced, unlike the flat shields of the Vavasseur mountings of the rest of the class. In 1899 the 5.9in were replaced by 6in QF, two of which were removed in 1904. In 1915 the 10in and two 6in were removed and later in the war *Bausan* was completely disarmed. The tops were of a distinctive shape.

Career

Bausan left the Tyne with an Italian crew on 21 May 1885 to become part of the Squadra Permanente (permanent squadron), the operational sea-going squadron of the Italian Navy. In 1887-88 she took part in the conquest of Eritrea, flying the flag of the flag officer commanding the Red Sea Squadron; she spent much time overseas, principally off North and South America. From 1905 to 1912 she was employed as a training ship for stokers and mechanics. During the war with Turkey in 1912 she was Flagship Cyrenaica, carrying out fire support bombardments, and was then used as a distilling ship. In the First World War she was used as a seaplane depot ship at Brindisi. Sold for scrapping 1920.[8]

Assessment

Bausan and her sister ships were, like many of the earlier Armstrong cruisers, over-armed for their size, while their heavy main armament was quite inappropriate for cruiser work. Both Rendel and Armstrong saw them as having a

ETNA, STROMBOLI, VESUVIO
(Designed by Rendel and Carlo Vigna)

Yard	Laid Down	Launched	Completed
ETNA			
Castellammare	19 Jan 1884	26 Sep 1885	2 Dec 1887
STROMBOLI			
Venice Arsenal	31 Aug 1884	4 Feb 1886	20 Mar 1888
VESUVIO			
Orlando, Leghorn	10 July 1884	21 Mar 1886	16 Mar 1888

Displacements	*Etna* 3474 tons (3530 tonnes) normal
	Stromboli 3395 tons (3450 tonnes) normal
	Vesuvio 3373 tons (3427 tonnes) normal
Dimensions	283ft 6in pp x 42ft 6in x 19ft
	(86.4 x 13.2 x 5.8m)
Armament	2 x 10in, 30 cal BL
	6 x 6in 32 cal BL
	5 x 57mm QF
	5 x 37mm QF
	2 x machine guns
	4 x TTs
Armour	Deck 1.5in max
Machinery	2 sets horizontal compound.
	4 double-ended cylindrical boilers
	Etna IHP 7480 =17.8kts
	Stromboli IHP 6252=17kts
	Vesuvio IHP 6820=17kts
Fuel	Coal 620 tons (630 tonnes)
Endurance	5000 miles at 10kts
Complement	12/296

potential role as battleship destroyers, using their speed to choose an advantageous range and position for the heavy guns to be at their most effective.[9] In practice their guns were slow firing and the cruisers' small size made them unsteady gun platforms. Too much was attempted on too small a displacement, resulting in a low freeboard, the protective deck being below the waterline, and cramped crew quarters.

ETNA, STROMBOLI, VESUVIO

Permission was given for the construction of a number of sister ships to *Bausan* provided that they were built in Italian yards and in consequence these three were laid down in 1884. They were three feet longer than *Bausan*, the draught was six inches greater and they displaced 300 tons more. From the outset their bridgework was more substantial than *Bausan*'s, the 6in gun shields were flat faced and the tops were shallower and wider.[10]

Armament

The main armament was the same as those in *Bausan* but the secondary armament was six 6in BL, 32 cal with a charge of 32lb of black powder firing a 100lb projectile with a muzzle velocity of 1940ft/sec. There were four TTs, one on the bow below water and three above water.[11]

Machinery

Machinery for *Etna* was made by the Tyneside firm of Hawthorn Leslie and on trials developed 6409 IHP =17.4kts. Machinery for *Stromboli* and *Vesuvio* were made by Ansaldo (Genoa) and Orlando (Leghorn) respectively. The latter's trial results were: 6480IHP=16.6kts; displacement 3427 tonnes.

Careers

Etna served initially with the Squadra Permanente from 1888 to 1893 and from 1893 to the end of 1895 in North and South American waters; she was stationed in the Red Sea, and then as part of an international force deployed during the Cretan uprising against the Turks of 1898. After service in the Far East she was disarmed in 1902 and from 1905 to 1907 was rebuilt with a poop and forecastle added along with a main armament of four 6in QFs, two each side in the waist, and two 4.7in QF fore and aft. From 1907 to 1914 she served as a training ship. During the First World War she was stationed in Taranto and flew the flag of the commander in chief. She was disarmed in 1920 and sold for scrap the following year.

Stromboli served in the Mediterranean with the First and Reserve squadrons until 1899 when she was posted to the Far East, taking part in the Taku forts action until

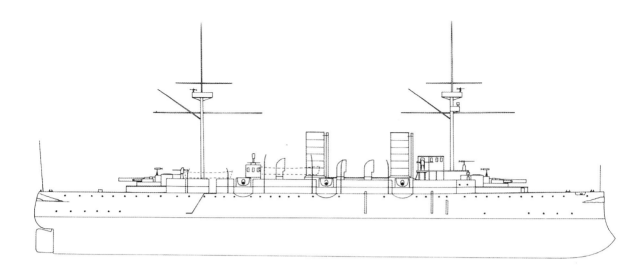

Stromboli.(Etna *class*). *As built.* (IAS)

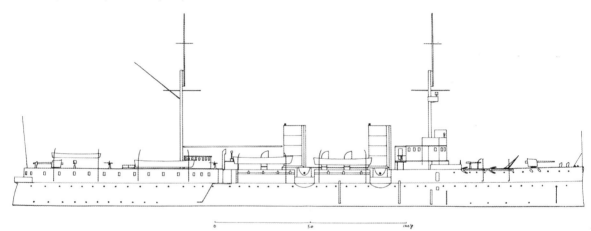

Etna.*After rebuilding.* (IAS).

Etna. *Built up fore and aft.* (Giorgierini and Nani)

Stromboli. *Victorian Livery.* (World Ship Society)

returning to Italy in 1901. After a period in reserve and acting as an ammunition storeship, she was struck off the navy list in 1907 and sold for scrap in 1911.

Vesuvio served with the Squadra Permanente until 1900 when she went to the Far East, taking part in the suppression of the Boxer Rebellion. After a second posting to the Orient from 1906 to 1909 she was put in reserve, struck from the navy list in 1911 and sold for scrap in 1915.[12]

ETTORE FIERAMOSCA

Fieramosca was almost identical to the three *Elba* class vessels but was seven feet longer and half a knot faster. By the time of her completion in late 1889 her design was hopelessly out of date, *Piemonte* having been completed three months earlier.

Career

Squadra Permanente after brief diplomatic missions to Portugal and Morocco. For most of 1899 she was stationed off the west coast of South America. In 1900 *Fieramosca*, in company with *Dogali*, *Calabria*, *Elba* and *Etruria* sailed for Chinese waters, to assist the internatioinal forces to suppress the Boxer Rebellion. She returned to home waters and in 1905 cruised off the east African coast and then crossed the Atlantic to fly the flag in Brazil, Argentina and Uruguay. She formed part of the

ETTORE FIERAMOSCA
(Designed by Rendel and Vigna)

Yard	Laid Down	Launched	Completed
Orlando, Leghorn	Dec 31 1885	Aug 30 1888	Nov 16 1889

Displacement	3538 tons (3595 tonnes) normal
Dimensions	290ft pp x 43ft 4in x 18ft 9in (35.95 x 13.2 x 5.7m)
Armament	2 x 10in 30 cal BL 6 x 6in 32 cal BL 6 x 6pdr QF 8 x 1pdr QF 3 x 14in TT
Armour	1.5in deck amidships; 0.75in at ends
Machinery	2 sets horizontal compound engines 4 cylindrical boilers Designed IHP 7000=17.5kts Trials at 3540 tonnes IHP=18 knots
Fuel	Coal 575 tons
Nominal radius	5000 miles at 10 knots
Complement	17/298

permanent American squadron serving mainly in the Caribbean and in North American waters until returning to Italy in 1909; she was struck off the navy list in July of that year.[13]

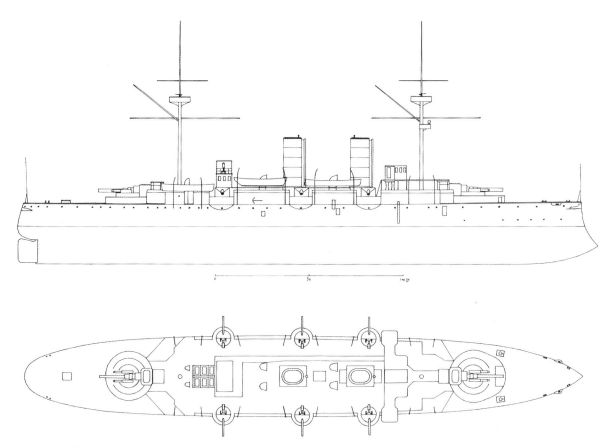

Fieramosca. (IAS).

Fieramosca. *Tropical Livery.* (Giorgierini and Nani)

DOGALI

Dogali was laid down as a stock cruiser. The Greek government had her under offer in December 1885 and thus given a Greek launch name (*Salaminea*) but the sale fell through. There was a Turkish bid in July 1886, but the sale never materialised; in January 1887 she was sold to the Italian government, renamed *Angelo Emo*, then renamed *Dogali*, the site of an Italian defeat in Eritrea in 1887. The long interval between completion and being taken over by the Italian navy in April 1887 allowed for repeated speed trials with different propellers to achieve maximum speed.[14] William White, Armstrongs' chief naval architect, was appointed Director of Naval Construction for the Royal Navy in 1885, leaving *Dogali* on the stocks. His first design for the Royal Navy, the 2800 ton cruiser *Medea*, was derived from *Dogali*.[15]

Armament

Dogali's 6in guns were mounted side by side on poop and forecastle and in large sponsons each side of the waist. Details are scanty about their characteristics but Giorgerini gives them as 40 cal 6 tons with a 50lb charge firing a 100lb projectile at 571m/sec (1873ft/sec); this last figure seems slow given the length of the gun and the size of the charge.[16] It seems more likely that they were the those of the *Etna* class, that is, of 32 calibre length.

Machinery

Dogali was the first cruiser to have triple expansion machinery; to keep the engines below the armour deck

DOGALI. ex SALAMINEA, ex ANGELO EMO.
Later *24 de* AUGUSTO; later MONTEVIDEO.
(Designed by William White.)

Yard	Laid Down	Launched.	Completed
Elswick	Feb 13 1885	Jan 28 1886	May 1886

Displacement	2050 tons (2085 tonnes) normal
Dimensions	250ft pp x 37ft x 14ft 6in
	(76.3 x 12.8 x 4.3m)
Armament	6 x 6in BL (4.2 ton)
	9 x 6pdr QF
	6 x machine guns
	4 x 14in TTs, above water.
Armour	Deck: slopes, 2in; flat,
	1in. 2in conning tower;
	4.5in shields to 6in guns
Machinery	Two sets horizontal triple expansion by
	Humphrys Tennant
	Designed IHP:
	normal draught 5000–17.75kts;
	full draught 7500=19.5kts
	Trials IHP:
	normal draught 5012=17.7kts.;
	full draught 7179=19.66kts
Fuel	Coal 200 tons normal. 480 tons max.
Nominal radius	4000 miles at 10 knots.
Complement	12/232
Weights	Hull & fittings 1005.2 (48.97)
(In tons	Equipment 136 (6.63)
and percentages	Armament 143 (6.97)
of tons)	Machinery 608.5 (29.64)
	Coal 160 (7.79)
	TOTAL 2052.7 tons[3]

Montevideo *ex* Dogali. (Jane's Fighting Ships, 1921)

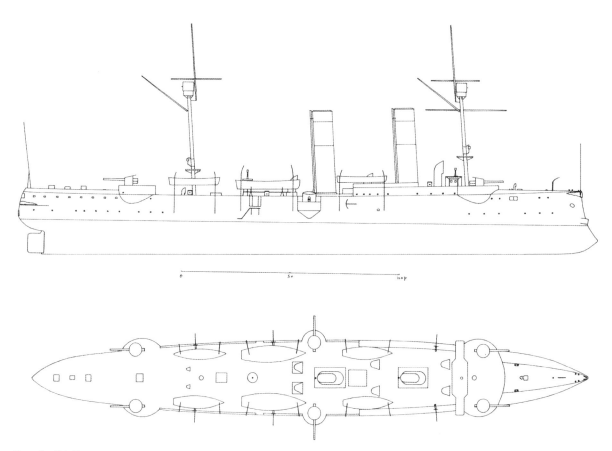

Dogali. (IAS).

Dogali. *Tropical Livery. May 1895, probably in the Red Sea.* (Author's collection.)

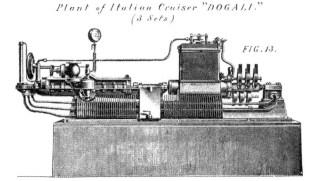

Plant of Italian Cruiser "DOGALI."
(3 Sets)

FIG. 13.

Parsons dynamo for Dogali. (Office of Naval Intelligence. Information From Abroad. June 1888. Washington. GPO. p210.)

they had to be mounted horizontally with the disadvantages looked at later. They had three cylinders, each being 32in, 45in and 73in with 33in stroke. The two engine rooms were each 26ft long. The four double-ended boilers worked at 150lbs pressure; each of the two boiler rooms were 34ft, giving a total length for machinery of 120ft.[17] Dogali was one of the first warships to be fitted with Charles Parsons shunt dynamos powered by a steam turbine; three sets were fitted, each delivering 125 amps at 80 volts powering 150 incandescent lamps and two searchlights. The Parsons dynamo set new standards for weight and space saving.[18]

Career

After a year in the Mediterranean and the Red Sea, Dogali took part in anti-slavery patrols off the west coast of Africa in 1888-89. She returned to the Mediterranean in March 1889, remaining there until May 1895 when she returned to the Red Sea for a year during the Italo-Ethiopian crisis, taking part in blockading operations. In April 1897 she sailed for New York City to represent Italy at the unveiling of the President Ulysses S. Grant Memorial. Most of the rest of her career was spent off the coast of South America including a record-breaking journey 2640 miles up the Amazon.[19] In Montevideo in 1908 she was sold to the Uruguayan government, renamed *24 de Augusto* on transfer and in turn renamed *Montevideo* in 1910, finally to be discarded in 1932.[20]

Assessment

Like all the early Armstrong cruiser designs, too much was attempted on too small a displacement. Freeboard amidships was only six feet and, with a short poop and forecastle, crew quarters were cramped. The large amidships sponsons coming down to near the waterline did not make for seaworthiness, making a wet waist even wetter. This might have mattered less in the Mediterranean, but in fact she spent most of her service in distant waters. However, *Dogali* was armed appropriately for a cruiser function.

PIEMONTE

More is known about *Piemonte's* design than any other Armstrong protected cruiser because of a paper presented by Philip Watts to the Institution of Naval Architects in April 1889.[22] What he did not reveal was that this epoch-making ship was laid down as a stock ship of an improved *Salaminia* type, but faster and with a designed armament of 2 x 8in BL, 4 x 6in BL and 4 TTs. A number of enquiries were made and on 30 July 1888 she was sold to Italy with a delivery time of six months, but this was not achieved as the Italians demanded an all quick-firing armament requiring the installation of sponsons and changes to the magazines. Trials were postponed until *Medea*, also fitted with vertical triple expansion engines, had her trials. Preliminary runs were made in February 1889 but although a speed of 21kts was reached, IHP was a full thousand short of contract; after adjustments to the motion bars, official trials in May were a resounding success. At normal draught IHP was 7040 over six hours with a mean of 20.4kts and with forced draught it was 12,600 with a mean of 22.3kts.[23] This made *Piemonte* the speediest cruiser in the world.

PIEMONTE (Designed by Phillip Watts.)

Yard	Laid Down	Launched	Completed
Elswick	1887	Aug 23 1888	Sep 8 1889

Displacement	2473 tons load (2515 tonnes)
Dimensions	310ft pp x 38ft x 15ft
	(94.6 x 11.6 x 4.6m)
Armament	6 x 6in QF 40 cal
	6 x 4.7in QF 40 cal
	10 x 6pdr QF
	6 x 1pdr QF
	4 x machine guns
	3 x 14in TTs (2 above-water training,
	1 above-water bow fixed)
Armour	Deck, slopes, 3-2 in, flat, 1 in;
	conning tower 3in;
	4.5in shields to 6in and 4.7in guns
Machinery	2 sets of 4 cylinder vertical triple expan-
	sion engines by Humphrys Tennant
	4 double-ended cylindrical boilers work-
	ing at 150lbs pressure
	Designed IHP, forced draught,
	12000=21.5kts
Fuel	Coal 200 tons normal,
	600 tons maximum
Nominal radius	13500 miles at 10 kts
Complement	12/245

Weights			
(In tons	Hull & fittings	1292	(49.75)
and percentages	Equipment	175	(6.74)
of tons)	Armament	258	(9.93)
	Machinery	672	(25.88)
	Coal	200	(7.7)
	TOTAL	2597 tons[21]	

Piemonte. *Running trials before armament mounted.* (Vickers)

Armament

Piemonte was the first cruiser to mount an all quick-firing armament. Small 3- and 6-pdr quick-firing guns had been introduced in the early 1880s with the projectile attached to a brass case containing the propellant and having a vertically sliding breech block: firing twenty or more shells a minute, they were highly effective against the torpedo boats of the day. There was no means of checking recoil apart from elasticity in the mounting.[24] In the mid 1880s William Armstrong turned to larger calibres. He began with a 4.7in gun mounted on a standard Vavasseur mounting using 'simultaneous loading', that is fixed ammunition with a 30lb projectile, then 36lb, 40lb and finally a 45lb one. Shell and cartridge were now too long and heavy to be combined and separate loading was used. Two further developments were a quick-acting conical breech block and the 'rocking slide'. The trunnionless gun barrel slid in a cradle, recoil controlled by hydraulic cylinders with the barrel being returned by springs. All were attached to the cradle which did not recoil and to which the sights were attached so that that the barrel recoiled in the line of fire; trainer and layer could keep their sights continuously on target. The final development was the substitution of a single-action handle in place of a three-action lever, trials of the 4.7in being most successful. In 1887 one gun firing 40lb projectiles mounted on the gunboat HMS *Handy* fired ten rounds in 48 secs while *Mastiff*, firing a 5in BL gun, took 6 min 16 secs to fire the same number of rounds. A major reason for the discrepancy was that the breech of the 5in gun had to be sponged after every round. The QF guns were also more accurate; five consecutive rounds each hitting a target six feet square at a range of 1300 yards in 31 seconds. Work was begun on a 70pdr 5.5in but was dropped for a 6in gun. This was not adopted by the Admiralty until 1890, when the introduction of cordite as a propellant, smokeless and needing a lighter charge than black powder, made a rapid-firing 6in gun a practical possibility.[25]

Figures for weights and performances of the 6in and 4.7in guns vary but the ones used below are from Giorgerini.[26]

	6in (152mm)	4.7in (120mm)
Weight of gun	5.7 tons	2.05 tons.
Weight of projectile	100 lbs	45 lbs
	(45.5 kilos)	(20.3 kilos)
Weight of charge	33 lbs	12 lbs
	(15 kilos)	(5.4 kilos)
Muzzle velocity	2291ft/sec	2116ft/sec
	(700m/sec)	(645m/sec)

The 6in guns were mounted one on the forecastle and poop and two each in the waist, in large sponsons extending down to about a foot above the water line and designed to give axial fire.

The 4.7in were mounted three each side of the waist in small sponsons. Two each of the 6 pdrs were under the forecastle and poop; two at the after end of the forecastle; two on the fore part of the poop, and two, together with two 1pdrs, were mounted on the topsides. The two heavy military masts each had two fighting tops, the lower ones with two 1pdrs and the upper ones had two 10mm Maxim machine guns. The 14in torpedo tubes were all above water, one fixed at the bow and two training on the beam. In the original design there were two more training aft of the machinery spaces and a fixed tube aft but the Italians did not want these fitted.[27]

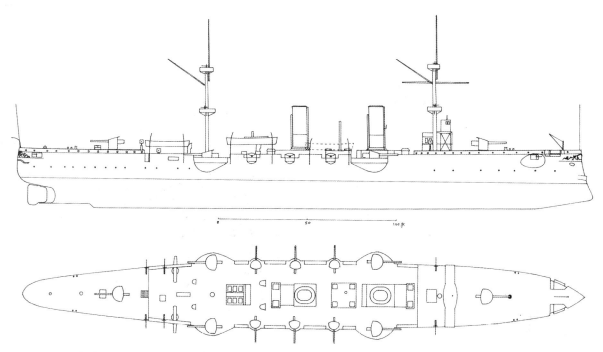

Piemonte. *As built.*

Piemonte. *As first completed.* (Cambridge University Library. Vickers Archive 2000)

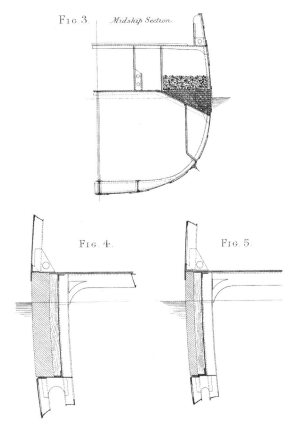

Piemonte. *Cross sections to show alternative armour arrangements. Figs 3,4,5. (Watts,*Piemonte,*Plate XXVII)*

Armour

The armour deck was 3-2in thick on the slopes and 1in on the flat, and was combined with a double bottom, omitted from the boiler rooms and the crank pits of the engine rooms. The machinery spaces were further protected by coal bunkers to the height of the upper deck and before and abaft the machinery spaces there were deck flats, 2-3 feet above the water-line, the spaces between them and the armour deck forming a raft body which could be filled with stores and patent fuel. Watts suggested stowing bricks of patent fuel in the angle formed by the ship's side and the deck slopes (Fig 3); the bricks would be less easily blown out or washed away through a shell hole. Watts calculated that if the flat deck was retained and the patent fuel not carried then a 10.5in armour belt with the same horizontal projection as the sloping deck could be carried (Fig 4). The sine of the 3in slopes was, together with the patent fuel, equivalent to 14in, giving an advantage of 3½ in. Retaining the patent fuel only allowed for a thinner belt (Fig 5). In addition sloping armour was more resistant than vertical for shot coming in nearly horizontally. The CT was 3in and the shields to the 6in and 4.7in were 4.5in thick. Openings in the armour deck which needed to be kept open in action were each surrounded by a cofferdam rising four feet above water.[28]

Machinery

The engines were four-cylinder vertical triple expansion, with the low pressure cylinder divided in two.

Piemonte. *After partial re-arming in 1900 and with military masts and sponsons removed. (Author's collection)*

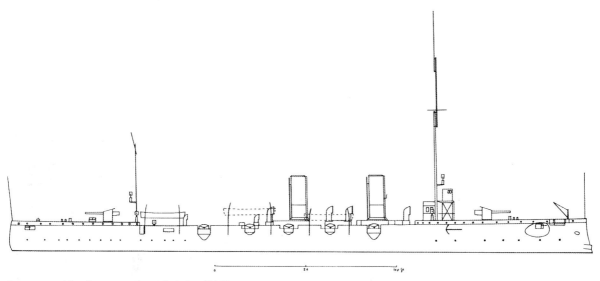

Piemonte. *After first re-arming and rigging.*(IAS)

Dimensions; 36in, 55in, 60in with a stroke of 27in. Four double-ended boilers gave steam at 155lbs. There were two boiler rooms each 36ft long and the engine rooms occupied a length of 40ft, the machinery spaces being 112ft long.[29] Watts summarised the advantages of the vertical arrangement as being more easily balanced, throwing less strain on the ship's structure, less subject to wear and tear, lighter than the horizontal arrangement, more accessible and taking less space longitudinally. The problem in small cruisers was to get the cylinder heads under the armour deck. *Medea* was fitted with glacis plates but these were heavy. Watts' first solution was to split the engines so that two operated in tandem on each shaft, but this meant extra weight and eventually Watts hit on the idea of a short stroke involving faster running engines, normal for torpedo boats but a daring innovation for cruisers. Another measure was to split the low-

pressure cylinder in two, resulting in extra weight but smoother running. *Piemonte* was the first warship to be fitted with four-cylinder VTE engines.[30]

Assessment

Watts could well be proud of *Piemonte*, his first Elswick design, powerfully armed and fast; but too much had been attempted on too small a displacement. She was over-gunned, the large sponsons were wet and the heavy military masts carried a quite useless armament. In 1900 4.7in were substituted for the beam 6in and the sponsons and military masts removed; in 1913 the remaining 6in guns were landed giving a final armament of 10x4.7in.[31] Freeboard was 8ft 3in and at full load was only 6ft 9in with the armour deck 6in below the waterline. The

Piemonte. *After final re-arming 1913.* (Jane's Fighting Ships, 1919)

steaming radius was wholly fictitious and in practice was about 4000 miles. A further design flaw was the incomplete double bottom.

Career

After service in the Mediterranean, Red Sea, and the Indian Ocean *Piemonte* was in South American waters and the Far East from 1897 to 1900. Following her return to Italy for modernisation, she was again in the Far East from 1902-1904. She then served in home waters, returning for a year to the Orient in 1909. During the war with Turkey in 1912 *Piemonte* helped to sink a number of small warships at Kundufu off the coast of Libya. During WWI she spent much time at Salonica as part of the Anglo-French Levant Squadron. Post-war plans to use her as a trials ship for torpedo work were abandoned and she was struck off the navy list on 15 May 1920 and scrapped soon after.[32]

CASTORE and POLLUCE

Surviving evidence leaves it unclear whether this unusual pair were laid down simply as trial gunboats to test the naval possibilities of the monster Krupp guns or whether they were intended as gunboats pure and simple. If the intent was the former, they did not need twin screws. They were ordered by the Italian War Ministry but were later taken over by the navy. They were built on Tyneside, disassembled, shipped to Italy and reassembled at the then-building Armstrong works at Pozzuoli on the western side of the Bay of Naples by a 27-year-old naval architect, Herbert Rowell, whose recently published diaries record the enormous difficulties he experienced with poor facilities, an untrained workforce and threats of violence. He always carried two revolvers in order to protect himself. Originally Pozzuoli was intended to have an ordnance factory and a naval yard but the Italian government vetoed the latter so that the two gunboats were a one-off.

CASTORE and POLLUCE

Vessel	Yard	Laid Down	Launched	Final Trials	Designer
CASTORE	Elswick	Feb 22 1887	September 1888	1889 (at Pozzuoli)	Philip Watts
POLLUCE	Elswick	Feb 22 1887	October 1888	1889 (at Pozzuoli)	and Herbert Rowell

Displacement	667 tons (678 tonnes)
Dimensions	115ft pp x 37ft x 9 ft 2in (35.1 x 11.3 x 2.8m)
Armament	1 x 40 cm 32 cal Krupp BL
Machinery	2 sets VTE by Wallsend Slipway and Engineering Company
	Designed IHP 350=8kts. Trials IHP 364=8.5kts.
Fuel	Coal 20 tons normal. 70 tons maximum.
Complement	42

Castore *and* Polluce. *Lying side by side after re-assembly.* (Author's collection)

Launch of Castore *by the Sindaco of Pozzuuoli October.1888.* (Miss E Rowell)

Polluce *firing the 120 ton Krupp gun.* (RO Morris collection)

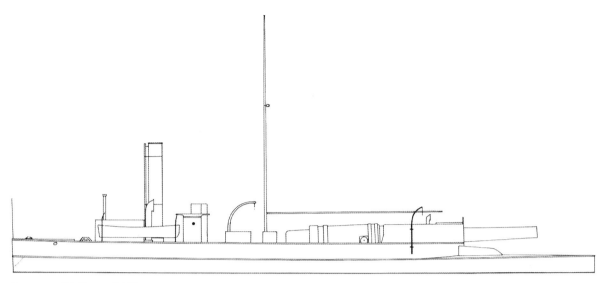

Castore and Polluce. (IAS)

Armament

The Krupp guns weighed 117 tons firing a 1980 lb shell with a muzzle velocity 1837 ft/sec and had a maximum elevation of 13 degrees. *Castore's* gun was removed in 1888-89 and *Polluce's* in 1899. Both re-armed with a single 4.7 in after rheir transfer to the Navy.

Careers

Castore was commissioned into the Royal Italian Navy as a gunboat in July 1891; disarmed and reclassified as a barge in 1899 and recategorised as a minelayer in 1904. From November 1915 she was employed as a torpedo testing craft, and was discarded on October 9 1925.

Polluce's career was the same as *Castore's* to 1899, but she was discarded in 1911.[33]

Acknowledgements
I am most grateful to Ian Sturton for his meticulous ship draw-ings which, as always, combine accuracy with attractiveness.

Notes

1 G Giorgierini & A Nani, *Gli Incrociatori Italiani 1861-1964* (Ufficio Storico della Marina Militare: Rome, 1964), pp. 151-391. A Giorgierini & A Nani, *Le Navi di Linea Italiani* (Ufficio Storico della Marina Militare: Rome, 1962), pp. 99-212.
2 P Brook, *Warships For Export. Armstrong Warships 1867-1927* (World Ship Society: Gravesend, 1999), pp. 56-57.
3 Brook, *Warships*, p. 47.
4 Brook, *Warships*, pp. 44~45.
5 Giorgerini, *Incrociatori*, p. 152.
6 Lord Armstrong, 'The Application of Hydraulic Power to Naval Gunnery', *Transactions of the Institution of Naval Architects* (Hereafter:Trans INA) 29, 1888, pp. 19~20.
7 *Manual of Gunnery for Her Majesty's Fleet 1885* (London, 1886), p. 68.
8 Brook, *Warships*, p. 57.
9 Tyne and Wear Archive Services, Rendel Papers, 31/3080, Undated, p. 4; W Armstrong, Presidential Address, Institution of Civil Engineers, Minutes of Proceedings, 68, 1882, p. 40.
10 Giorgerini, *Incrociatori*, pp. 159-160.

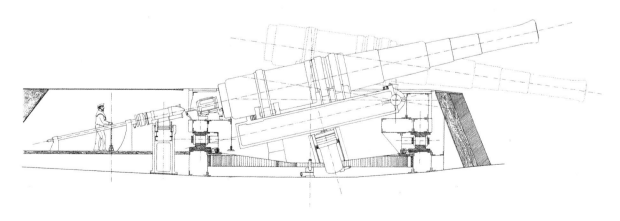

Barbette Mounting for Italia's *17 in BL.* (Armstrong,Hydraulic Power.,Plate 11.Fig 13.)

11 Admiralty Intelligence Department, London, Ship Reports, 1892: Italy, No 319 (Held at the Admiralty Library).

12 Giorgierini, *Incrociatori*, pp. 161-169.

13 Giorgierini, *Incrociatori*, pp. 207-212.

14 Brook, *Warships*, pp. 61-62.

15 N Rodger, 'The First Light Cruiser', *Mariner's Mirror*, 65, 1979, p. 227.

16 Giorgierini, *Incrociatori*, p. 178.

17 Armstrongs, Ships Particulars Book, Particulars of Machinery, p. 101 (National Maritime Museum, Brass Foundry).

18 Brook, *Warships*, p. 62,

19 Giorgierini, *Incrociatori*, pp. 180-182.

20 R Gray (ed.), *Conway's All The World's Fighting Ships 1906-1921* (London, 1979), p. 425.

21 Brook, *Warships*, p. 47, 68-69.

22 P Watts, 'The Italian Cruiser *Piemonte*', TransINA, *30*, 1889, pp. 286-308.

23 Elswick Yard Report Book, 1: 75, 79, 106, 102, 113, 116, 119, 129, 133, Vickers Archive, Cambridge University Library.

24 Manual of Gunnery, pp. 262-265.

25 Armstrongs, 'Simultaneous loading guns and their mountings by Sir W G Armstrong Mitchell and Co. nd ca 1886. NMM. Brass Foundry: Brook, *Warships*, pp. 225-226; A Noble, 'The Rise and Progress of Rifled Naval Artillery', TransINA, *41*, 1899, pp. 239-240; E Lloyd & A Hadcock

Artillery Its Progress and Present Position (Griffin, Portsmouth, 1893), p. 156.

26 Giorgierini, *Incrociatori*, p. 200.

27 Watts, '*Piemonte*', p. 200.

28 Watts, '*Piemonte*', pp. 201, 204.

29 Ships' Particulars Book, p. 102.

30 Watts, 'Elswick Cruisers', Trans INA, *41*, 1899, pp. 288-230.

31 A Fraccarolli, *Italian Warships of World One* (Ian Allan, London, 1970), p. 35.

32 Giorgierini, *Incrociatori*, p. 201-205.

33 E Rowell, *In Peace and War: Tyneside, Naples and the Royal Flying Corps: Memoirs of Herbert Rowell and Robin Rowell* (Privately Printed, 1996), pp. 62-94; Brook, *Warships*, pp. 39-40.

34 T Brassey, *The British Navy*, ii (Longmans, London, 1882), pp. 71, 90.

35 Giorgierini, *Navi Di Linea*, p. 111.

36 Giorgierini, *Navi Di Linea*, pp. 127-130.

37 Giorgierini, *Navi Di Linea*, pp. 117-119.

38 Giorgierini, *Navi Di Linea*, pp. 137-139.

39 Giorgierini, *Navi Di Linea*, p. 113.

40 Noble, Artillery, p. 243; Giorgierini, *Navi Di Linea*, pp. 149-151.

41 Armstrong, 'Hydraulic Power', pp 19-20.

42 Armstrong, 'Hydraulic Power', p. 13.

43 Manual of Gunnery.

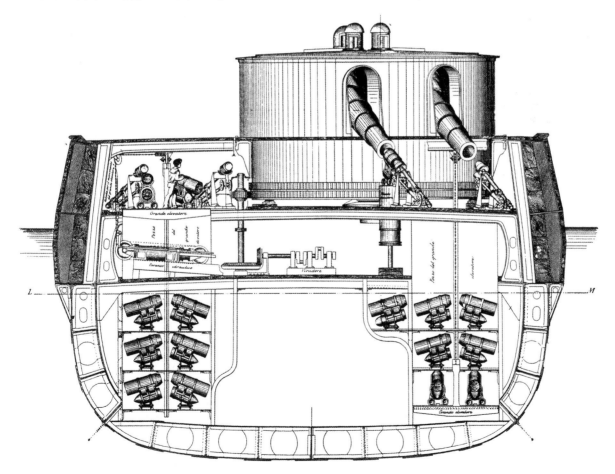

Loading Arrangements for 17 in ML gun on Duilio. (Giorgierini.Navi Di Linea.p111.)

GUNS AND MOUNTINGS

1. Muzzle Loaders

Calibre in.(mm)	Weight Tons	Length of Bore Calibres	Wt. Charge Pounds	Projectile Pounds	Muzzle Velocity Feet/second	Ships upon which Mounted
17.7 (450) See Note 1	102	20.5	551	2000	1700	*Duilio; Dandolo*

2. Breech Loaders

17 (431) See Note 2	104	29	900	2000	2018	*Lauria* class
17 (431) See Note 3	100	27.5	880	2000	1944	*Italia* class
13.5 (343) See Note 4	68	30	630	1250	2016	*Re Umberto* class
10 (25.4) See Note 5	30	40	300	500	2208	*Dandolo*
10 (25.4) See Note 6	30	40	? 77	450	2400	*Filiberto* class
10 (25.4) See note 7	25	30	230	450	2025	*Bausan* class
6.0 (152) See Note 8	32	5	49.8	100	1960	*Etna* class
5.9 (149) See Note 9	26	4.2	34	82	1846	*Bausan*

3. Quick Firers

6.0 (152)	40	5.7	33	100	2291	*Piemonte*
4.7 (120)	40	2.05	12	46	2116	*Piemonte*

Source: Primarily: W Laird Clowes, *Naval Pocket Book* (London 1896, 1907); supplemented by Giorgerini and Nani, .*Le Navi di Linea Italiani.*

Note 1. Built from an inner steel tube with wrought iron hoops shrunk on. Mounted in *Caio Duilio* and *Enrico Dandolo*. One of these guns burst on March 6 1880 using a 551lb charge.[34] Loading was done by training the guns to a fixed loading position where projectile and charge were raised and rammed home by hydraulic power.[35]

Note 2. Mounted in *Ruggiero di Lauria, Andrea Doria, Francesco Morosini*. The mountings were the same as the *Italia* class but were covered by a 25mm hood.[36]

Note 3. Mounted in *Italia* and *Lepanto*.[37]

Note 4. Mounted in *Re Umberto, Sardegna, Sicilia*. They were capable of all-round fire by means of a hoist containing powder and projectiles coming up to a working chamber immediately below the turntable and revolving with it. The shell and charge were transferred to a hoist attached to the centre girder of the turntable. This was the prototype of a system commonly used for many years. In Italian service the gun breeches were covered by a 100mm hood.[38]

Note 5. *Dandolo* was re-armed 1894-1897 with 40 cal 10in carried in Elswick hooded barbettes but it was concluded that the small increase in fighting power did not justify the expense especially since the speed remained low; *Duilio* was not therefore re-armed.[39]

Note 6. Carried in *Emanuele Filiberto* and *Ammiraglio di Saint Bon*. Details are from *Le Navi di Linea* but appear incorrect as the charge weight is too low. The mounting was the same as *Dandolo*'s with an elevation of 35 degrees; all round loading was achieved with a central powder hoist with projectiles hoisted from a revolving shell carrier in the barbette immediately below the gun chamber.[40]

Note 7. Carried on *Bausan* and her sisters.The mounting was first used in *Esmeralda*.[41]

Note 8. Vavasseur centre pivot mounting. *Etna* and sisters.[42]

Note 9. Mounted solely in *Bausan*.[43]

Armstrongs constructed many more guns and mountings for the Italian Navy until 1914, both at Elswick and from 1889 onwards at their armament works at Pozzuoli, but these are not listed here as they do not fall within the scope of this article.

Stern 10 in gun as mounted in Bausan. (The Engineer,10 Oct 1884.)

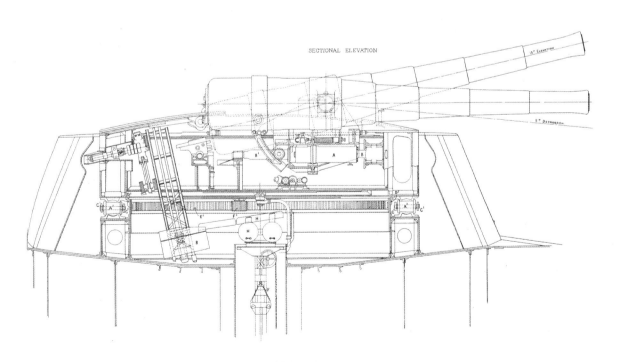

SECTIONAL ELEVATION

HIMS Re Umberto.*Mounting for a pair of 13.5 in 68 ton BL guns.* (Noble.Rifled Naval Artillery.Plate XL.)

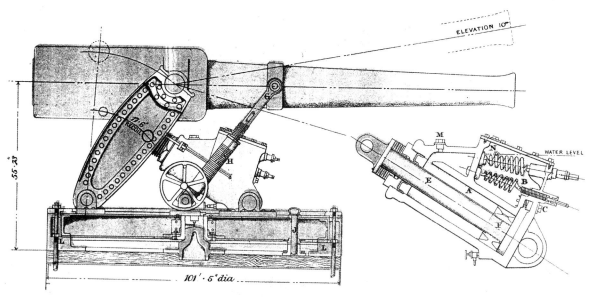

Bausan's *149 mm BL on Albini mounting*. (Manual of Gunnery 1885.

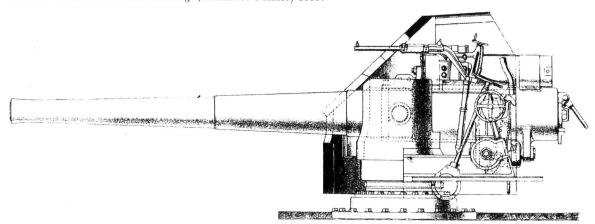

6 in QF on CP Upper Deck Mounting as in Piemonte. (LLoyd and Hadcock,p171.)

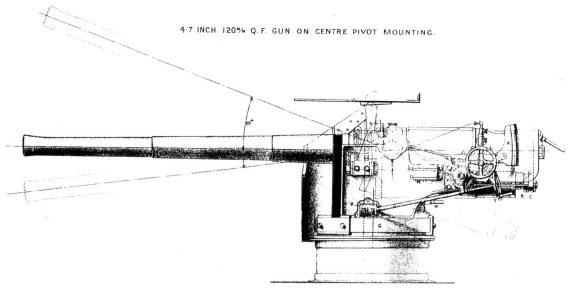

4.7 INCH 120ᵐ⁄ᵐ Q.F. GUN ON CENTRE PIVOT MOUNTING.

4.7 in QF on CP Mounting, Piemonte. (LLoyd and Hadcock,p155.)

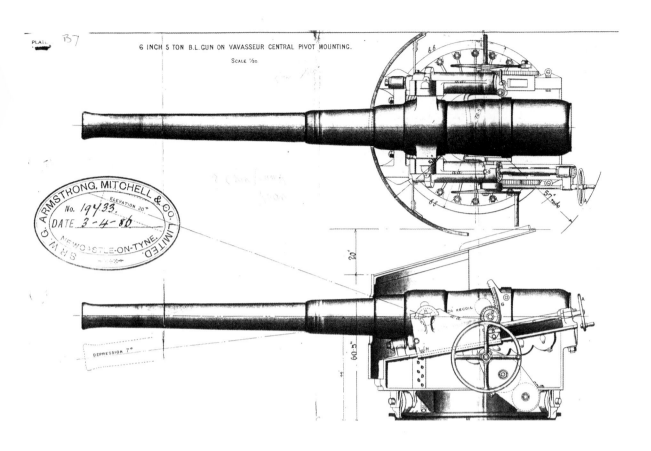

Six in BL on Vavasseur Centre Pivot Mounting. (Elswick Ordnance Plans.)

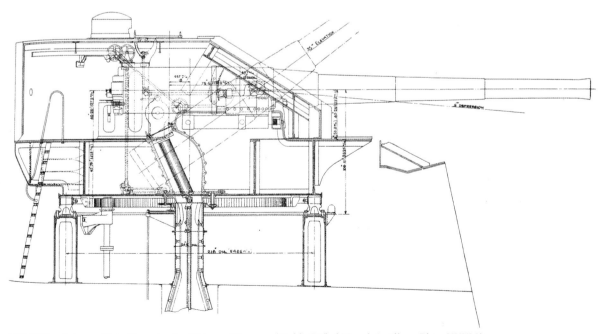

HIMS Dandolo *etc.Twin Mounting for 254 mm BL guns.* (Noble.Rifled Naval Artillery. Plate XXXV.)

AN ARGENTINEAN NAVAL BUILDUP IN THE DISARMAMENT ERA:

The Naval Procurement Act of 1926

The long rivalry between the so-called 'ABC' navies—those of Argentina, Brazil and Chile—spawned battleship programmes before 1914. The rivalry has persisted, as it was only recently that the old rivals engaged in competition to acquire aircraft carriers. **Guillermo J. Montenegro** looks at the expansion plans of the Armada Republica Argentina in the 1920s.

Introduction

This feature focuses on Argentinean naval expansion in the 1920s, and its roots in rivalries between Argentina, Chile and Brazil—referred to here as 'southern-cone' states—dating back to the late 19th and early 20th centuries.

A key element in Argentina's strategic outlook was the agreement among the political and naval leaderships that their security rested on a strong—even superior—naval power, and not on international agreements, which, it was claimed, did not offer effective guarantees of peace and stability. This viewpoint was held in spite of the ideas of pacifism, disarmament and collective security that came to light—or grew in significance, especially among the Great Powers of Europe—in the aftermath of the First World War.

As stated in the Executive's 'State of the Nation' reports to Congress between 1922 and 1928, Argentinean foreign policy intended to maintain friendly relations with all nations while keeping the necessary means for national defence. In addition, the Executive's instructions on arms limitation issues, as well as support for a reasonable degree of military readiness was in line with Argentinean contemporary military thought.

This similarity in viewpoints among civilian and military leaders was a good sample case of 'subjective control', as defined by Samuel Huntington in the 1950s in *Civilian Control of the Military: a Theoretical Statement.*[1] In Huntingtons's model, subjective civilian control of the military exists when the military forces are an integral part of society, embodying the dominant social forces and political ideologies of that society. In Huntington's words: 'In brief, in subjective civilian control, the military are at one with society. Civilian control, consequently, is the product of the identity of thought and outlook between civilian and military groups.'[2]

A southern-cone naval race in early 20th century

The Great Powers' naval race in early 20th century had its South American counterpart. Argentina had been already involved in a naval race with Chile, due to conflicting territorial claims in Patagonia. This issue was solved by several agreements signed in 1902, among which was a naval arms-control agreement.

In 1904 the Brazilian Government decided to launch a significant naval expansion programme, which took final shape in 1906. At the centre of this naval buildup were two dreadnought-type battleships (to be built in Britain) which would be named *Minas Gerais* and *São Paulo*. A third battleship was envisioned and actually ordered in 1910. Called *Rio de Janeiro* this ship was, however, sold to Turkey in 1913 before completion. There was another Brazilian attempt to build an even larger dreadnought, to be named *Riachuelo*, but the project was abandoned for financial reasons. In addition to the dreadnoughts, Brazil ordered two light cruisers and ten destroyers; these were

116

built in the United Kingdom and delivered to the Brazilian Navy.

Argentinean perceptions of Brazilian procurement plans were mixed. There was an important sector of influential public opinion which regarded Brazilian naval expansion as dangerous and aggressive, and favoured a hard line by way of a similar Argentinean naval buildup. Another sector saw no danger in Brazilian armaments policy and thought that Argentinean naval expansion would be extremely costly and harmful to national prosperity.

A heated debate followed—in Congress as well as in the Press—which delayed a decision, but in the end the upper hand went to the hardliners and led to the passing of the Armaments Procurement Act of 1908.[3] On the naval side, this Act authorised the acquisition of two battleships, six destroyers and twelve torpedo boats. It also stated that 'if necessary' the Executive could increase the former authorisations by one battleship, three destroyers and four torpedo boats.

The First World War

The First World War inevitably had a significant impact on Argentinean and Chilean naval acquisitions. Argentina actually ordered two battleships to be built in American yards and twelve destroyers to British, French and German yards. Except for some delays, there were no major troubles in the delivery of the US-built battleships, but only four destroyers were commissioned in the Argentinean Navy due to the outbreak of the war.

Chile had followed its South American neighbors, and in 1910 ordered two super-dreadnoughts to be built in Britain, derived from the *Iron Duke* class but armed with 14in guns. They were taken over by the Royal Navy at the outbreak of the War. One of them, *Almirante Latorre* served in the Grand Fleet as HMS *Canada*, fought in the British battle line at Jutland and finally was delivered to Chile at the end of the war, reverting to her former name. The second ship, whose intended name was *Almirante Cochrane*, was converted during construction into an aircraft carrier and became HMS *Eagle*. Chile had ordered six destroyers in British yards, of which two had been delivered before the outbreak of hostilities. The remaining four were taken over by the Royal Navy. Of these, three were handed over to Chile at the end of the War (one had been sunk in action). As compensation for HMS *Eagle*, Great Britain transferred five submarines to Chile (a sixth was purchased by the Chilean Government).

Besides the aforementioned disturbances in naval procurement plans, the First World War had another important effect on the navies of the southern cone: the relative obsolescence of recently acquired ships and the almost absolute obsolescence of naval units of pre-dreadnought vintage.

Southern-cone naval strategic views

Southern cone naval experts were deeply concerned about the balance of naval power in reference to their neighbors; a brief summary of their respective views demonstrates a distinct 'mirror-image' flavor.

In the 1910s and early 1920s there were several Argentinean naval officers who published their views on sea power, emphasizing Argentina's need for a strong navy, essentially centered on capital ships. Probably the best known and perhaps the most influential was Segundo R Storni, who, as a Commander, gave two lectures in 1916 which were published as a small book under

The Brazilian dreadnought São Paulo, built by Vickers and one of the vessels that started the naval arms race in South America in the early 20th century. At the time of her completion in 1910 she was amongst the most powerful battleships afloat.

The Chilean battleship Almirante Latorre, *which served in the Royal Navy from completion in 1915 until 1920 as HMS* Canada. *This photograph shows her towards the end of her career.*

the title *Intereses Argentinos en el Mar* (Argentinean Sea Interests).[4] This work had a definite Mahanian flavour, and covered all fields of current and prospective Argentinean sea power. In reference to the naval balance of power in the southern cone, Storni proposed a dictum that could be referred to as a 'One Power-Plus Standard': 'The Argentinean Sea Fleet should be strong enough to have superiority over any individual neighbor and should act to preclude their concentration in case of war'.[5]

Similar views were held in Brazil and Chile. Armando Burlamaqui, a Brazilian naval expert, complained of a perceived Brazilian naval inferiority in 1921.[6] On a later work the same author stated: '...Brazil needs to be strong enough at sea as to inspire serious fear in any squadron that might attempt to dictate laws to her[7] free maritime expansion....'[8]

In Chile, a naval officer, Luis Langlois, wrote a Mahan-inspired book about sea power and Chilean history, published in 1911.[9] When dealing with the dimensions of Chilean Sea Power, Langlois stated: 'In any case, to hold command of the sea is a need for Chile, both in a defensive war as well as in an offensive one. Any chance of war is going to be avoided if Chile maintains a naval power at least equivalent to any other South American country.'[10] These sentiments were echoed by the Chilean Minister Plenipotentiary in London, on 27 November 1913, on the occasion of the launching the *Almirante Latorre*: 'By modernising her naval forces, Chile has no other object in view but having enough power to prevent events that might threaten international South American peace and, by these means, to ensure the exercise of her[11] legitimate influence upon the American Continent's destiny, as

pointed out by history.'[12]

In summary, naval experts and statesmen in the southern cone strongly advocated naval superiority or at least naval parity for their respective countries.

The naval 'lessons' of the First World War

Southern cone navies kept a close watch on the naval side of the First World War, and post-1918 they also gave careful consideration to the massive amounts of information published in the naval, official and private works of the warring powers on all aspects of the conduct of the war at sea 1914-18.

In addition, with respect to the Argentinean Navy, several officers were sent to the United States to get both theoretical and practical training with the US Navy. A group was sent to the Battle Force, another to Naval Aviation, and a third group went to New London to be trained in submarines. As a matter of fact, the Argentinean Navy had submariners—qualified by the US Navy—several years before the commissioning of the first Argentinean submarines.

Even at the risk of oversimplification, it may be said that the perceived results of the First World War kept the traditional sailors' faith in surface actions between battle fleets. In spite of the submarine danger and the rise of air power, it was claimed that Allied naval superiority in capital ships had been an important factor—for some a decisive one—in achieving victory. In reference to the submarine menace, it was understood that the convoy system had kept it under control; new detection devices would make even more doubtful future submarine successes, and mine barriers appeared to be a promising anti-submarine system. Moreover, legal constraints would make it almost impossible to conduct future unrestricted submarine warfare—in the way Germany had done. Aircraft, the other newcomers to sea warfare, were still unreliable, had a restricted weapon-carrying capacity and short range, and were heavily constrained by weather conditions.

In short, the battle fleet was regarded as a well known, proven and efficient weapon system, and this view was fully accepted by southern cone national and naval leaderships.

Naval arms-limitation attempts

As already known, Collective Security and Arms Limitation became significant concepts at the end of the First World War. Collective Security first materialised in the League of Nations in 1919. In spite of taking part in the preliminary conferences, Argentina did not become a member because serving President Hipólito Yrigoyen (1916-1922) set as a necessary precondition to have the League open to membership by all nations with no exception. In spite of determined efforts by Yrigoyen´s successor, President Alvear (1922-28), Congressional obstruction kept Argentina out of the League until 1933.

In the wake of the Washington Conference of 1921-22, arms limitation in the American Continent was included in the agenda of an Inter-American Conference which took place in Santiago, Chile in March-May 1923.[13] The Chilean Government had recommended Arms Limitation in the agenda and received the full support of the United States. As Argentina, Brazil and Chile were the main South American naval powers, the success of the conference depended on the 'ABC' countries' perspectives on arms limitation. There were some promising discussions about naval arms limitation but, because of conflicting views on this subject—mainly between Brazilian and Argentinean delegates—no agreement was reached, in spite of determined efforts by the Chilean President Arturo Alessandri. Both Brazilian and Argentine representatives looked to maximize national interest in the matter of battleship tonnage. Argentina possessed two battleships amounting to 55,000 tons, while Brazil's pair totalled around 39,000 tons. The Brazilian position sought to have either high-enough limits or no limits for future battleship acquisitions—otherwise, with only 16,000 tons available to build a third battleship, they would have to decommission one to build another sufficiently large to be effective. The Argentineans supported an agreement based on a limit on battleship tonnage equal to their own (that is, the largest) battleship overall tonnage, and thereby would have only to support the cost of modernising their existing battleships.

Although no binding contract was signed, five agreements were accepted that set 'recommendations' in reference to peaceful solution of disputes, convenience of future arms limitation agreements, adherence to the Law of Armed Conflict, restriction of air operations against non-military targets, as well as adherence to the Washington treaties in respect to capital-ship tonnage, maximum gun calibres, submarine operations against merchant ships, and use of poisonous gases.[14]

Harold Peterson[15] summarised US views on the attitude of the Argentinean representatives: 'Throughout the conference, the Argentine representatives concentrated their fire on the Chilean proposal on arms limitation. By setting limits by which their government would not incur additional spending, they opposed land and naval arms limitation.'[16]

Regarding Brazilian views on the Conference, a Brazilian naval author stated in 1985: 'Without any doubt, Brazil's major concern in the Conference was not to accept limitations that could limit her freedom of action in the naval field, mainly when the future appeared to open promising perspectives and, once more, Baron de Rio Branco's dreams seemed to be close to fulfillment'[17]

The Naval Arms Limitation conference held in Rome in 1924—sponsored by the League of Nations—had the same inconclusive outcome for the southern-cone nations. And because of Argentina's non-membership of the League of Nations, the Argentinean representative was only able to act as an 'observer'.

As a consequence of the meager results of both conferences, each country kept for herself her freedom for weapons procurement, to be determined solely by her political will and her financial position.

The genesis of the Argentinean naval buildup in the 1920s

The interruption of the naval buildup authorised by the Weapons Procurement Act of 1908 was a great frustration for Argentinean naval leadership. There was an attempt to correct this state of affairs in 1918, when the Executive sent to Congress a bill asking for significant naval reinforcements which comprised cruisers, destroyers and submarines, among other types of naval and auxiliary vessels. Unfortunately for the Argentinean Navy, this bill was never enacted, which increased the previously mentioned sense of naval frustration.

In 1922, when a newly elected government took office in Buenos Aires, Admiral Domecq García, who had been an observer on board the Japanese Fleet during the Russo-Japanese War, was appointed Navy Minister. He believed—as did the naval leadership—that the Argentinean Navy was in a position of relative inferiority vis-à-vis the Brazilian and Chilean navies.[18] Their perception derived from a number of factors:

— The interruption of the 1908 building program because of the outbreak of the First World War.
— The modernisation of the Brazilian dreadnoughts in the United States and the establishment of an American naval mission in Brazil.
— The commissioning in the Chilean Navy of a super dreadnought, *Almirante Latorre* (ex-HMS *Canada*)

The battleship Moreno, *pictured after modernisation.*

armed with 14in guns, and updated by the Royal Navy during the war.

To make matters worse for the Argentinean naval chiefs, they received news of the further expansion of the Brazilian and Chilean navies.[19] Fortunately for the Argentinean Navy, the civilian leadership shared their views. Thus, the Argentinean Congress passed an act[20] in September 1923 authorising funds for battleship and destroyer[21] modernisation.

Plans for the dreadnoughts' update had been considered as early as November 1918, and there had been preliminary contacts between the Argentine Embassy and the US Government, followed by exchanges between the US Navy Department and the Argentinean Naval Commission in Washington DC.

Both battleships were modernised in 1924-25 in the United States, along the lines dictated by the lessons of the First World War:

Coal-fired boilers were replaced by oil-fired boliers.
Coal bunkers were converted into fuel or water tanks.
Direct-drive turbines were replaced by geared ones, which let an increase in SHP from 39,500 to 45,000.
A new fire-control system was installed.
The pole mainmast was replaced by a tripod one, although the fore cage mast was retained (which gave these ships a unique appearance).

As early as 1922, the Navy Minister had ordered the Navy Staff to undertake a study of Argentinean naval needs, given the current southern-cone situation. As may be imagined, the size of Brazilian and Chilean navies was of primary concern, especially with respect to first-line surface forces: battleships, cruisers and destroyers. The study also confirmed that in the future, the Argentinean Navy could only count on the 'new' ships of the 1908 program: the battleships and the four German-built destroyers. Consideration was also given to the difficulty of predicting rival buildups, because of the unpredictability of financial situations in the southern cone countries, where national economies rested almost exclusively on the export of primary products, the prices of which were subject to great volatility on international markets.[22]

The Argentinean study considered both 'acceptable' and 'desirable' expansions, although a 'minimum' programme dictated events. Two battlecruisers of 20,000 tons were included in the 'desirable' plan because frequent bad weather conditions around the southern tip of South America might inhibit scouting by light cruisers, flotilla leaders and destroyers.[23] Inevitably financial realities led to the enactment and actual execution of a naval expansion plan reasonably close to the 'minimum' programme.

The Naval Procurement Act

The Argentine Navy asked foreign yards for sketch designs and prices for several types of warships in 1924, in order to estimate the funds to be required from Congress. There was a considerable interest in foreign yards that submitted projects for cruisers, destroyers and submarines.[24]

The Naval Procurement Bill was sent to the Senate in mid-1925. It asked for a considerable amount of money:

170 million Argentinean pesos (or about £15,000,000), to be spent over ten years. By comparison, the contemporary naval budgets of first line naval powers—Great Britain and the United States—were around £60,000,000. Moreover, the significance of the required money can be compared with standard Navy Ministry budgets for 1922-28, which varied from 42 million to 54 million pesos.[25]

An explanatory submitting introduction by the Executive underlined the importance of what was regarded as a 'replacement' programme for updating Argentinean naval power. The Bill had a relatively easy passage in the Senate, but the issue became complicated in the House. As may be imagined, the amount of money requested by the Executive made a large group of representatives unwilling to let the Bill pass. In addition, Congress had passed an Act in late 1923 authorising significant funding for Army modernization. In spite of the full support of President Alvear enactment appeared doubtful because the Government party representatives were split among the President's supporters and a group which was absolutely loyal to former President Yrigoyen.[26] This last group was not willing to approve an increase in military expenditure, because the Socialist Party representatives were decidedly against a naval buildup,[27] and this issue could be successfully used in the coming legislative elections that were going to be held in Buenos Aires—an area in which the Socialist party had strong support.

Given this state of affairs, the Navy leadership decided to take advantage of the acquaintance of Captain (Supply Corps)[28] Francisco Senesi with former President Yrigoyen's physician. Captain Senesi found his way to

meet the former President and show him the importance, for the Navy, of the Naval Procurement Bill. Yrigoyen accepted the Navy viewpoint and agreed to instruct his supporters in Congress to vote in favour of the Bill.

The Bill was enacted in late 1926,[29] after a long and heated debate in which Socialist representatives made determined efforts to defeat it. The situation demanded the attendance of Navy Minister himself to the House in various occasions, and further appeals to former President Yrigoyen to ensure a favorable outcome. In addition to improvements in shore facilities, the authorised ships included three cruisers, six destroyers, six submarines and two surveying vessels. There was a considerable interest from foreign yards, which submitted tenders for cruisers, destroyers and submarines.

As a result of the tender selection process, two cruisers[30] were ordered from Italian yards, as well as three destroyers from British yards[31]; two Spanish-built destroyers[32]—based on a design very similar to the destroyers ordered in Britain—were purchased, and three submarines[33] were taken on by Italian builders—the first submarines to be commissioned into the Argentinean Navy.

Moreover, the approved funding allowed further development of base facilities, acquisition of updated communications equipment, and first steps towards the development of naval aviation.

The reaction to the Argentinean naval procurement programme had a tone of alarm and disappointment in Brazil. By contrast, in Chile the press asked its Government to follow Argentina's example, mainly not for fear of Argentina but because of strained relations between Chile and Peru. In fact, Chile achieved a sub-

The British-built cruiser La Argentina.

The destoyer Mendoza after launching at J Samuel White's yard in Cowes, Isle of Wight. (Courtesy of Whites Archives, Cowes Maritime Museum)

Mendoza *after completion. She was one of three destroyers ordered from Britain in the late 1920s. (Courtesy of Whites Archives, Cowes Maritime Museum)*

stantial naval expansion by extensively modernising the battleship *Almirante Latorre*, and by ordering in Britain six destroyers and three submarines. *Brassey's 1927* gives a cost of £11,000,000[34] for the Chilean naval programme, which underlined a substantial financial effort, especially if compared with the £15,000,000 Argentinean buildup.

Brazilian political and financial troubles in the 1920s precluded a significant naval improvement as envisioned by her civilian and naval leaders. In spite of the efforts of the US naval mission, the only significant achievements in these years were the modernisation of cruisers *Bahia* and *Rio Grande do Sul*, and the acquisition of an Italian-built submarine.

Coming back to the Argentinean Navy, the remaining allowances of the Naval Procurement Act let to an order for seven destroyers from British yards in the mid 1930s.[35] Moreover, additional Congress authorisations resulted in the commissioning of a British-built light cruiser[36], and the construction of nine minelayers/minesweepers in Argentinean yards. The fulfillment of this procurement programme gave the Argentinean Navy a significant margin of superiority in the southern cone up to the end of the Second World War.

Conclusion

During most of the 20th century, Argentinean leadership considered that a strong balance of military power in the southern cone—naval power included—was essential for national security. And the ship acquisitions and refits authorised in the 1920s were key to the increase in Argentinean naval strength deemed instrumental—from an Argentinean viewpoint—to achieve and maintain this balance of power.

Bibliography

Arguindeguy, Pablo E. *Apuntes sobre los buques de la Armada Argentina (1810-1970)* Vol. 4. Buenos Aires: Departamento Estudios Históricos Navales, 1972

——. *Apuntes sobre los buques de la Armada Argentina (1810-1970)* Vol 5. Buenos Aires: Departamento Estudios Históricos Navales, 1972

Bagnasco, Erminio y Rastelli, Achille. *Le Costruzioni Navali Italiane per L'estero. Centotrenta anni di Prestigiosa Presenza nel Mondo.* Roma: Rivista Marittima, 1991

Barber, Jr., James A. 'Britain and France: the Officer Corps and Civil-Military Relations'. *Naval War College Review* Vol XXII, No. 4 (December 1969): pp. 17-28.

Belot, Raymond de. *La Mer dans un conflit futur. Evolution de la stratégie navale.* Paris: Payot, 1958.

Boletín del Centro Naval. 1903-1930

Brassey's Naval and Shipping Annual 1920-1930.

Breyer, Siegfried. *Battleships and Battlecruisers, 1905-1970* Garden City, N.Y.: Doubleday & Co., 1973

——. *Grosskampfschiffe Bd.3: Mittelmeeranlieger, Russland/Sowjetunion, Niederlände und ABC Staaten Südamerikas.* Munich: Bernard & Graefe Verlag, 1979

Burlamaqui, Armando. *A situação naval sul-americana em 1921.* Rio de Janeiro: Imprensa Nacional, 1922.

——. *Esboço da Política Naval Brasileira.* Rio de Janeiro: Imprensa Nacional, 1923.

Chesneau, Roger, ed. *Conway's All the World's Fighting Ships 1922-1945.* London: Conway Maritime Press, 1980.

——, and Eugene M. Kolesnik, eds. *Conway's All the World's Fighting Ships 1860-1905.* London: Conway Maritime Press, 1979.

Conference on the Limitation of Armament. Washington. November 12, 1921 - February 6, 1922. Washington: Government Printing Office, 1922.

Conferencias Internacionales Americanas 1889-1936. Washington, D.C.: Dotación Carnegie para la Paz Internacional, 1938.

Diario de Sesiones de la Cámara de Diputados Año 1923 Tomo IV. Buenos Aires, Cámara de Diputados, 1923.

Diario de Sesiones de la Cámara de Diputados Año 1923 Tomo V. Buenos Aires, Cámara de Diputados, 1923.

Diario de Sesiones de la Cámara de Diputados Año 1923 Tomo VI. Buenos Aires, Cámara de Diputados, 1923.

Diario de Sesiones de la Cámara de Diputados Año 1926 Tomo II. Buenos Aires, Cámara de Diputados, 1926.

Diario de Sesiones de la Cámara de Diputados Año 1926 Tomo III. Buenos Aires, Cámara de Diputados, 1926.

Diario de Sesiones de la Cámara de Diputados Año 1926 Tomo V. Buenos Aires, Cámara de Diputados, 1927.

Diario de Sesiones de la Cámara de Diputados Año 1926 Tomo VI. Buenos Aires, Cámara de Diputados, 1927.

Diario de Sesiones de la Cámara de Senadores Año 1923 Tomo I. Buenos Aires: Cámara de Senadores, 1925.

Etcheparaborda, Roberto. 'Notas sobre la Presidencia de Marcelo T. de Alvear'. Revista *Administración Militar y Logística* 459 (Marcch 1976): pp. 115-151

——. *Historia de las Relaciones Internacionales Argentinas.* Buenos Aires: Pleamar, 1978.

Gallardo, Angel. *Memorias para mis hijos y nietos.* Buenos Aires: Academia Nacional de la Historia, 1982.

Ghisolfo Araya, Francisco. "Situación Estratégica Naval". In *El Poder Naval Chileno*, Vol 2. Edited by Claudio Collados Núñez (Valparaíso: Revista de Marina, 1985., pp. 605-612.)

Gray, Randal, ed. *Conway's All the World's Fighting Ships 1906-1921.* Annapolis: Naval Institute Press, 1985.

Hunt, Barry. 'The Outstanding Naval Strategic Writers of the Century'. *Naval War College Review* 305 (September–October 1984): pp. 86-107.

Jane's Fighting Ships. (several issues)

La Prensa (Argentine periodical - Buenos Aires). September, October and December 1926 files.

Lagos, Manuel J. *El Poder Naval como garantía de la soberanía y prosperidad de la Nación.* Buenos Aires: L. J. Rosso, 1921.

Langlois, Luis. *Influencia del Poder Naval en la Historia de Chile, desde 1810 a 1910.* Valparaíso: Imprenta de la Armada, 1911.

Martins, Helio Leoncio. 'Almirante Julio Cesar de Noronha - Uma Grande Figura Naval'. *Revista Marítma Brasilerira* Vol. 116, N° 1-3 (January - March 1996): pp. 23-31.

Memoria Anual del Ministerio de Marina 1922-23. Buenos Aires: Ministerio de Marina, 1923.

Memoria Anual del Ministerio de Marina 1924-25. Buenos Aires: Ministerio de Marina, 1925.

Memoria Anual del Ministerio de Marina 1925-26. Buenos Aires: Ministerio de Marina, 1926.

Memoria Anual del Ministerio de Marina 1926-27. Buenos Aires:

Ministerio de Marina, 1927.

Memoria Anual del Ministerio de Marina 1927-28. Buenos Aires: Ministerio de Marina, 1928.

Memoria Anual del Ministerio de Marina 1928-29. Buenos Aires: Ministerio de Marina 1929.

Mendonça, Lauro Furtado de. 'A Agitada Carreira do Encouraçado Rio de Janeiro e suas Dramáticas Conseqüencias.' *Revista Marítima Brasileira* Vol. 111, Nº 4-6 (April–June 1991): pp. 57-62.

Montenegro, Guillermo J. 'The Character and Extent of Mahan´s Influence in Latin America'. In *The Influence of History on Mahan.* Edited by John B. Hattendorf, pp. 87-98. (Newport, R.I.: Naval War College Press, 1991.)

——. 'Acorazados norteamericanos para la exportación: los "dreadnoughts" argentinos'. *Revista de la Escuela de Guerra Naval* Nº 47, (June 1998): pp. 105-120.

Monthly Information Bulletin. 1921-1931. Washington, D.C.: Office of Naval Intelligence.

Naval War College. *International Law Documents. Conference on the Limitation of Armament. 1921.* Washington D.C.: Government Printing Office, 1923.

——. *International Law Documents. International Agreements. 1924.* Washington, D.C.: Government Printing Office, 1926.

Noronha, Júlio César de. *Programa Naval de 1904 (Subsídios para a História Marítima do Brasil Vol. IX).* Rio de Janeiro: Imprensa Naval, 1950.

Papers Relating to the Foreign Relations of the United States 1927, Vol 1. Washington, D.C.: United States Government Printing Office, 1942.

Peterson, Harold F. *La Argentina y los Estados Unidos 1810-1960.* Buenos Aires: Eudeba, 1970. Spanish translation by Patricio Canto and Denise Rivero of: *Argentina and the United States 1810 –1960.* New York: State University of New York, 1964.)

Peck, F. Taylor. 'Latin America enters the World Scene, 1900-1930'. Chapter 7 of *Latin American Diplomatic History,* Davis, Harold Eugene; Finan, John J., y Peck, F. Taylor, pp. 146-190. Baton Rouge, La.: Louisiana State University, 1977

Potash, Robert A. *El ejército y la política en la Argentina 1928-1945 De Yrigoyen a Perón.* Buenos Aires: Sudamericana, 1971. Spanish translation by Aníbal Leal of: *The Army and Politics in Argentina.* Standford: Standford University, 1969.

Presidencia Alvear 1922-1928. Compilación de Mensajes, Leyes, Decretos y Reglamentaciones. Tomo I. (Mensajes de Apertura del Honorable Congreso);Tomo III (Relaciones Exteriores); Tomo VII (Marina). Buenos Aires: Pesce, 1928.

Quinta Conferencia Internacional Americana. Actas de las Sesiones de las Comisiones de la Conferencia. Santiago de Chile: Imprenta Universitaria, [1923].

Roskill, Stephen W. *Naval Policy Between the Wars. 1: The Period of Anglo-American Antagonism 1919-1929.* Londres: Collins, 1968.

Sabsay, Fernando L. y Etchepareborda, Roberto. *El Estado liberal democrático.* Buenos Aires: Eudeba, 1987.

Scheina, Robert L. 'Latin American Navies: Who Needs Them?'. *U.S. Naval Institute Proceedings* Nº 900 (February 1978): pp. 61-66.

—— 'Lateinamerikanische Dreadnoughts'. *Marine Rundschau* Nº 9/79 (September 1979): pp.571-580.

——. *Latin America: A Naval History 1810-1987.* Annapolis: Naval Institute Press, 1987.

Senesi, Francisco A. *Hipólito Yrigoyen y los armamentos navales de*

1926. Buenos Aires: [...........], 1947.

Silva, Carlos. *La Política Internacional de la Nación Argentina.* Buenos Aires: Ministerio del Interior, 1946.

Silva, Hernán Asdrúbal y Güenaga de Silva, Rosario. 'La Conferencia de Santiago y los poderes nacionales en el Cono Sur de América'. *Investigaciones y Ensayos* 16 (January - June 1974). Buenos Aires: Academia Nacional de la Historia, pp. 407-439.

Solveira, Beatriz. *La Argentina y la Quinta Conferencia Panamericana.* Córdoba: Centro de Estudios Históricos, 1993.

Storni, Segundo R. *Intereses Argentinos en el Mar.* 2nd ed. Buenos Aires: Platt, 1952.

Vanterpool, Alan. 'O Encouraçado Brasileiro Riachuelo'. *Revista Marítima Brasileira* Vol. 115, Nº 7-9 (July–September 1995): pp. 37-40.

Viana Filho, Arlindo. *Estratégia Naval Brasileira.* Rio de Janeiro: Biblioteca do Exército, 1995.

Vidigal, Armando Amorim Ferreira. *A Evolucão do Pensamento Estratégico Naval Brasileiro.* 3a. ed. Rio de Janeiro: Biblioteca do Exército, 1985.

Zeballos, Estanislao. 'Los armamentos navales del Brasil'. *Boletín del Centro Naval* 253 (Deceber 1904): pp.581-590

——. *Diplomacia Desarmada.* Buenos Aires: Eudeba, 1974.

Unpublished Sources

'Antecedentes sobre pedido de precios–Año 1924' (6 pages). Domecq García Collection. Departamento Estudios Históricos Navales. Buenos Aires.

Apuntes sobre antecedentes Ley 11378. Domecq García Collection. Museo Naval de la Nación. Tigre (B.A.)

Ayuda Memoria del Ministro Domecq García. Domecq García Collection. Museo Naval de la Nación. Tigre (B.A.)

Files from Archivo General de la Armada (Navy Archives) Buenos Aires.

Estudio comparativo sobre Poder Naval Sudamericano 1923. Domecq García Collection. Museo Naval de la Nación. Tigre (B.A.)

Recopilación de notas relaciondas con la ejecución de la Ley 11378. Domecq García Collection. Museo Naval de la Nación. Tigre (B.A.)

Resumen de las Sesiones Secretas del Congreso - Ley de Armamento - 1926. Domecq García Collection. Museo Naval de la Nación. Tigre (B.A.)

Trama, Gustavo Adolfo. 'Incidencia de los tratados de desarme de Washington de 1922 y de Londres de 1930 y 1935 en el desarrollo de la Armada Argentina'. Master in International Relations dissertation. Buenos Aires: Universidad de Belgrano, 1991.

Notes

[1] Huntington, Samuel. 'Civilian Control of the Military: a Theoretical Statement', in *Political Behavior: a Reader in Theory and Research,* Heinz Eulau et al., eds. (Glencoe Illinois,: Free Press, 1956), quoted by Barber, James A. In 'Britain and France: the Officer Corps and Civil Military Relations', p. 19.

[2] Huntington, quoted by Barber, p. 19

[3] Act Nr. 6283, 19 December 1908.

[4] Storni, Segundo R. *Intereses Argentinos en el Mar.* 2d. ed. Buenos Aires: Platt, 1952. This is a reprint of the orginal text of 1916, with the addition of an updated introduction

by the author.

5 Storni, *Intereses...*, page 105.

6 Burlamaqui, Armando. *A situação naval sul-americana em 1921*. Rio de Janeiro: Imprensa Nacional, 1922.

7 i.e.: Brazilian.

8 Burlamaqui, Armando. *Esboço da Politica Naval Brasileira*. Rio de Janeiro: Imprensa Nacional, 1923, page 64. A contemporary report by the US Naval Intelligence about ABC navies, states: 'Brazil makes no secret of the fact that she regards Argentina as her most probable enemy. The two countries do not compete seriously in an economic sense, but each is jealous of the political leadership in South America assumed by the other.' (Office of Naval Intelligence, *Monthly Information Bulletin* Nr. 6–1922, 15 June, 1922, p. 3.)

9 Langlois, Luis. *Influencia del Poder Naval en la Historia de Chile desde 1810 a 1910*. Valparaiso: Imprenta de la Armada, 1911.

10 Langlois, *Influencia...*, page 11.

11 i.e.: Chilean.

12 Ghisolfo Araya, 'Situación Estratégica Naval', pages 607-608.

13 There had been a significant previous arms limitation achievement in the Western Hemisphere: the Central American Convention for the Limitation of Armaments, signed in Washington, DC on 7 February, 1923.

14 *Conferencias Internacionales Americanas 1889-1936*, pp. 284-286

15 Peterson, *Artgentina y los Estados Unidos*

16 Peterson, *Argentina y...*, pp. 419-420 and note 27. (This quotation is a re-translation of the Spanish version. Actual wording in English may differ).

17 Vidigal, *A evolução do pensamento*, p. 69.

18 US Naval Intelligence reported on 15 April 1922 that the Argentine Navy was number one in the ABC Navies, followed by Chile and Brazil. However, this report assesed that there was ample evidence that Brazil was prepared to challenge this state of affiairs. (Office of Naval Intelligence) *Monthly Information Bulletin*, Nr 6–1922, p. 6.

19 For Brazilian plans, see Scheina, *Latin America...*, pages 134-137. For the Chilean buildup, see Gardiner (ed) *Conway's 1922-1945*, pages 422-423.

20 Act Nr. 11222, 20 September, 1923..

21 i.e.: the four German-built destroyers commissioned a little before the First World War.

22 *Estudio comparativo sobre Poder Naval Sud-Americano 1923*, page [89]. This is the final document of the study started the previous year. (Pages in this document are shown in brackets because they appear to have been hand numbered by an achivist)

23 *Estudio Comparativo*, pp. [9a], [10], [12] and [116].

24 'Antecedentes sobre pedidos de precios - Año 1924'.

25 Figures in British pounds and Argentine pesos refer to the contemporary rate of exchange.

26 In spite of belonging to the same party—Unión Cívica Radical—both President Alvear and former President Yrigoyen headed their own 'wings'.

27 In fact, Socialist representatives based their opposition on grounds that the current political situation in the southern cone did not deserve an increase in military readiness.

28 At that time, supply officers had diferent titles for their ranks. Senesi's actual rank was 'Contador Inspector', that could be translated into English as 'Inspector Paymaster'.

29 Act Nr. 11378.

30 Names given were *Almirante Brown* and *25 de mayo* (A reduced version of Italian *Trento* class.)

31 *Mendoza*, *La Rioja* and *Tucumán* (a modified version of British *Scott* class.)

32 *Cervantes* and *Garay*

33 *Santa Fé*, *Santiago del Estero* and *Salta*

34 *Brassey's Naval Annual 1927*, p. 49.

35 Similar to British 'G' class.

36 *La Argentina*.

DEFEAT IN THE ATLANTIC?

Anti-Submarine Warfare 1917-19

For many historians and laymen, the battle to defeat the U-boats in the First World War is a closed book. Some claim that the victory was a close one, with the likelihood that a resurgence of U-boat attacks in 1919 would have put the Allies and Associated Powers in a desperate situation. **Eur Ing David K Brown RCNC** demonstrates that the battle was won decisively in 1918 (after a near defeat in the spring of 1917), tying together all the complex factors which made the victory possible.

Introduction

It is often said that the U-boat was not defeated in the First World War and that the outcome of the campaign was stalemate.[1] This article will show that the U-boat was indeed defeated by 1918 and that the chance of any resurgence in 1919 was slight.

During the war the U-boats had three primary objectives:

- Weakening the Grand Fleet to reduce it to the level of the High Seas Fleet;
- Defeating the UK by starvation;
- Preventing the US Army reaching France.

They failed in all three, although the margin by which they were defeated in the war against merchant ships was small.

The result of the first of these objectives is clear; no dreadnought of the Grand Fleet was sunk or damaged by submarine attack. The only losses from submarine attack were two light cruisers.[2] Much of the North Sea was a 'no-go' area due both to mines and submarines which could only be entered in full strength and for good reason. The Grand Fleet's superiority grew.

The third case is even more clear-cut: two million US troops were carried to France, 62 per cent in British ships, with the loss of one ship and about 100 men. In addition, there were some sixteen million crossings of the Channel by British troops only a few miles from German submarine and destroyer bases in Flanders.

In order to understand the time of crisis in 1917 and the subsequent victory, it is necessary to outline both pre-war anti-submarine warfare studies and the history of the earlier war years. The war against trade was a much closer fought campaign and will be considered in more detail. Figures are essential in judging the ebb and flow of the conflict but the tables have been kept short to reduce indigestion.

It is important to realise that an organisation like the Admiralty is rarely united in its outlook though there was a generally healthy tradition of closing ranks to outsiders once a decision had been taken. Letters to the newspapers were usually from retired officers often unaware of then-current thinking. The Royal Navy's attitude to the submarine both in the capability of the new vessel and in countermeasures against it before the First World War is usually misrepresented.[3] It was to the disadvantage of the country to render obsolete the fleet in which the UK had such a large superiority, particularly since British industry could quickly overtake any temporary lead elsewhere.

Early Days

From 1882 onwards the RN (Royal Navy) had sought for means to locate submerged submarines and for weapons to destroy them when located. Brief notes on such early work are included in later sections. By the turn of the century both France and the United States had completed submarines of real potential. The USN had purchased Holland's design VI and the RN was easily persuaded to purchase five similar craft to be built under licence at Barrow.[4] The reasons for their purchase were to assess their capability and to devise anti-submarine measures.[5] The first of these was ready for trials in January 1902 and the next year was spent learning how to operate these unstable craft.[6] By this time, however, the bigger and much improved A class was under construction.

The Controller who ordered the 'Hollands' was A K Wilson, usually remembered for his advocacy of hanging submarine captains captured in wartime. Lambert has shown that Wilson's well-reasoned paper of January 1901 did not exactly say this.[7] Wilson discussed unrestricted submarine attack on trade and suggested 'enlisting the moral sense of nations' to allow for the 'sternest measures' against captured crews. He also suggested that the RN should not encourage improvements to submarines that might be used against us.

Early Notions about Anti-Submarine Warfare

An 'anti-submarine committee' was set up in secret in the spring of 1909. The committee was strengthened in 1910 and several old submarines were allocated as targets including A1, which was given a mechanical control system so that she could manoeuvre to some extent without a crew—it failed and she disappeared.

In November 1913 Admiral Sir John Fisher circulated a paper 'The Oil Engine and the Submarine' whose main object was to kill any thoughts of steam-powered fleet submarines. This paper is, however, better known for Fisher's forecast that in war submarines would sink unarmed merchant ships without warning. Fisher's views were taken seriously and both the technical and ethical issues were fully discussed. Churchill, Battenberg, Jellicoe and Keyes were all sure that no civilised power would attack merchant ships without warning. They were wrong but it was not an ill-considered view in that civilised era. Even in October 1914, Hugo von Pohl (German Chief of Naval Staff) rejected a proposal from for an attack on trade as a violation of international law as expressed in the German Naval Prize Regulations.

Fisher's views were echoed by Sir Percy Scott in two letters to *The Times* in 1913. His main point was that the battleship was very vulnerable both at sea and also in harbour. However, Scott also pointed out that the chief purpose of the Navy was to protect the food supply. Scott's letters drew the expected replies from retired admirals but the modern historian Peter Padfield is wrong in saying that the official view was opposed to this, indeed Fisher's 'flotilla defence' was very similar.[8]

By 1914 the Admiralty thought that submarines would pose little threat to a battle fleet, with escorts, moving at speed in open waters, and this view seems to have been correct. They thought, too, that a submarine presence effectively ruled out a German invasion of the UK. On the same basis, a close blockade of German ports was ruled out, although a distant blockade closing the English Channel and the northern route to Germany was planned.

In 1914 international law on war at sea affecting blockade, 'stop-and search', contraband etc. was confused, almost non-existent, in fact—although there was some consensus on what was acceptable in practice. Blockade was a long-standing operation of naval war and an attempt had been made to set rules in the Declaration of Paris in 1856.[9] The series of conferences at the Hague from 1899 aimed at humanising the conduct of war—culminating in the Peace Conference of 1907—set a background but were not specific concerning war at sea.[10]

Immediately after the Hague conference, the UK set up a body of international lawyers to set rules of blockade and to define 'contraband'. This led to the Declaration of London in 1909 though none of the participants ratified it.[11] This defined categories of contraband and also stated that blockade should only apply to enemy coasts, prohibiting the distant blockade that the RN intended to

Destroyers screening the Grand Fleet at sea in 1917. The vessels in the foreground are Kempenfelt, Mystic, Marne *and* Prince, *while beyond are battleships of the* Iron Duke *and* Royal Sovereign *classes, together with further destroyers.*

apply. The British procedure of intercepting ships on the 'distant line' and sending them into port for examination, which was usually followed by purchase of dubious cargoes, involved no loss of life and drew little more than formal protest from neutrals. The United States was the most powerful neutral state and the warring powers were concerned to avoid driving her to military action.

None of the declarations envisaged merchant ships being sunk at sea. They could be stopped, searched and, if necessary, taken by a prize crew to land where the legality of the seizure would be tested before a court. Perhaps the clearest formal statement of these rules was in the German Prize Regulations which were to be obeyed by all vessels, submarines as well as surface. The difficulty of following such rules from a submarine was clear before the war and was a principal factor in seeing a submarine war on trade as 'unthinkable'.

The Early Years of War

When war broke out the German Navy had twenty-eight U-boats in service. Of these, the four oldest were suitable only for training. *U-5* through *U-18* were handicapped by smoky and unreliable Korting paraffin engines.[12] *U-19* through *U-28* were very satisfactory boats with powerful

U-1, the first German U-boat. She served as a training vessel during the war. Drawing at 1:550 scale.

and reliable diesel engines and sixteen similar boats were nearing completion with eleven more ordered in the first month of the war.[13] This latter design was developed during the war, forming the basis for all mainstream U-boats —and the Type VII of a later war.

Operations in 1914 were directed against warships, firstly to protect the Heligoland Bight against the expected RN close blockade which never materialised and then in unsuccessful attempts to locate and attack the Grand Fleet. Several older ships were sunk with grievous loss of life. The RN learnt that the later U-boats had a much greater endurance than expected; at least twice that of the British 'E' Class.[14] They also learnt that chivalry is dangerous, particularly stopping to pick up survivors when the submarine is still there. The Germans lost five U-boats in the five months of 1914, three by accident and two rammed on the surface.

The sinking of the cargo ship *Glitra* on 20 October

The small minelaying U-boat UC-5, pictured at Temple Bar Pier. In 1916 she ran aground off Harwich and was captured.

The famous photograph of the doomed Lusitania, probably the last ever taken of the ship, heading out on her final voyage. It ended with her being torpedoed by U-20 off southern Ireland, with the loss of over a thousand lives. While controversy has surrounded several aspects of the sinking to this day, there is little doubt that the fact that 123 Americans were amongst the dead was an early factor in turning the then neutral United States against Germany.

The sinking of U-8 on 4 March 1915 by British destroyers in the Dover Straits. She was one of the first U-boats to be sunk during the war.

1914 marked, almost unintentionally, the beginning of a war on trade. The captain of *U-17* took great care to ensure the safety of the *Glitra's* crew and though he was in technical breach of Prize Regulations he was close to their spirit. During the same month a senior officer of the U-boat force, Korvettenkapitan Bauer, proposed an all-out attack on British trade. The Commander-in-Chief, von Ingenohl, supported Bauer but von Pohl, Naval Chief of Staff, turned the proposal down as contrary to International Law. However, on 2 November the British declared the whole of the North Sea to be a war zone and began to confiscate cargoes carried to Germany in neutral ships. This was seen by Germany as a breach of the Law and on 1 February 1915 the Kaiser agreed to allow U-boat attacks on ships within a declared war zone. Neutral ships would be spared if recognised as such.

The First Offensive, February–September 1915

This campaign lasted until September when it was stopped following energetic protests from the USA over the deaths of American citizens in the sinkings of *Lusitania* and *Arabic*. There was also a shortage of U-boats as fourteen had been lost in 1915 up to September and two U-boats had entered service. In addition, seventeen small UB-boats had entered service (two lost) as

well as fifteen UC-minelayers (one lost). Anti-submarine measures were generally ineffective, although a vast auxiliary patrol service was set up

The Q-ships scored some early successes.[15] The concept was simple; an innocent looking merchant ship would, if attacked by a U-boat on the surface, unmask a heavy armament while dropping any false flags and hoisting the White Ensign. By April 1915 there were four Q-ships in service and many more were to follow. The best estimate is that there were 184 conversions and one purpose-built Q-ship. They sank five U-boats up to the end of 1916 and six in 1917 (none in 1918), 8 per cent of the total U-boat sinkings. In addition two U-boats were sunk by RN submarines working with a trawler decoy. Nineteen Q-ships were sunk, mostly in 1917. By that date slow merchant ships, sailing independently, were a cause for suspicion. It seems probable that Q-ships should have been given up by the end of 1916. Their main success was in forcing U-boats to attack submerged, using their few torpedoes, rather than the gun. The perceived brutality of such methods was an important factor in bringing the USA into the war.

The first of the small UB submarines became operational in April. Initially, they were confined to the Hoofden, as Bauer believed that the Straits were impassable, but from June onwards they transited without difficulty. The UC-minelayers became operational in May carrying twelve mines externally.[16] They laid numerous

Crewmen manning a 4-inch gun beneath a dummy hatch on board the 'Q' ship Baron Rose.

Q-ships were converted from merchant vessels and sailed the seas as decoys. When attacked, they revealed their armament and, it was hoped, blew the German submarine out of the water. The collier SS Vitoria was converted in 1916-17 into a Q-ship that went under various names, such as Pargust and Pangloss. On her first cruise she sank the UC-29, but was badly damaged in the process.

small fields of six or twelve mines off the French coast and in the approaches to English ports in the southeast. From May to September they laid 420 mines in forty-six fields causing serious disruption as well as sinkings.

During the 1915 campaign 327 merchant ships were sunk, totalling 773,000 tons, about one-third being offset by new construction. For the first three months there were, on average, 5.6 U-boats at sea (maximum 12) increasing to an overall average of 7.3 at sea. (Losses amounted to 15,000 tons per month per U-boat at sea.) There were, however, too few U-boats for a decisive effect, and the restrictions imposed upon them were impractical, leading to incidents which irritated rather than placated neutrals.

Second Offensive, February–April 1916

By the end of 1915, Germany was feeling the effects of the British blockade. Some 743 neutral ships carrying supplies for Germany had been stopped by British patrols and their cargoes either confiscated through the Prize Court or purchased. It was clear that there was worse to come as Germany was running very short of fertilisers which would lead to a marked reduction in the size of future harvests.

German shipping experts had examined Allied resources, noting the 20 per cent of merchant shipping allocated to military use. They were also aware that ship-

yard capacity had been reduced by the number of men called up for military service, and further reduced in terms of merchant shipping by the naval building programme. They believed that British yards would only build some 650,000 tons of merchant ships in the whole of 1916—the actual figure was 542,000 tons. In the previous campaign, thirty-five U-boats had sunk 80,000 tons per month and the German planners took the simplistic view that seventy U-boats would sink 160,000 tons month. Over a full year the losses would accumulate to nearly two million tons and, allowing for new building, the British merchant fleet would be reduced by about 1,270,000 tons. Admiral Holtzendorff, Chief of Admiralty Staff, believed that such losses would lead to the collapse of Britain.

Holtzendorff suggested that all merchant ships in the original War Zone should be sunk with the sole exception of passenger liners. This led to a prolonged debate between the Staff and the Chancellor which eventually led to the Kaiser issuing a compromise directive that all enemy ships should be destroyed in the War Zone and armed steamers anywhere. Passenger liners, armed or not, were not to be attacked anywhere. Admiral Tirpitz, Naval Secretary, who favoured an unlimited campaign, resigned in protest.

The big U-boats from Heligoland had been fairly inactive since the end of the previous campaign in September but the smaller Flanders boats had been busy. The UB-boats sank seventeen ships of 5034 tons in the Hoofden whilst the UC-boats laid 842 mines in eighty-seven fields off south-east British ports and along the northern coast of France. These sank seventy-eight ships of 44,843 tons. New submarines of the UB II and UC II[17] classes, bigger and more capable than the earlier boats, were entering service. By March 1916 Germany had fifty-two U-boats of all types ready for operations. However, twelve of these were in the Mediterranean and four in the Baltic. For the offensive in UK waters there were only sixteen large boats at Heligoland while the Flanders flotilla had twelve UB and eight UC boats. During the period April to August 1916 another thirty-eight boats would enter service including ten of the big minelayers of the UE class.[18]

Once again, the offensive was opened by a single U-boat, *U-32*, which sank her first victim on 4 March 1916 in the Southwestern Approaches.[19] At this date, Heligoland boats were routed round the north of Scotland. From 26 February to 29 March eight U-boats reached the SW Approaches followed by five more in April. There were only sixteen boats that could reach the SW Approaches, five less than the number found inadequate before. Two of the new, bigger UB II class operated from Heligoland, working in the Firth of Forth.

During March and April they sank fifty-seven ships of 157,009 tons, to which one may add the first success of the UE-minelayers off the Firth of Forth. In addition, the Mediterranean boats sank 26 ships of 76,483 tons (Plus one of 5350 tons in the Black Sea) and the Flanders flotilla sank 66 ships of 106,199 tons, a global total of 347,843 tons. However, Holtzendorff's target of 160,000 tons per month referred to British tonnage alone and his boats had achieved only 120,000 per month. This was

more encouraging (to Germany) than it sounds as thirty-eight big U-boats were due to be completed in the next five months. UC-boats laid 710 mines in their usual areas, sinking thirty ships of 46,383 tons.

On 24 March *UB-29* sighted a ship about to enter Dieppe and observing that her deck was crowded he assumed her to be a troopship and therefore a legitimate target. She was, in fact, the *Sussex*, a French passenger ship carrying 325 people including fifty US citizens, some of whom were among the fifty casualties. The US Press and government took the sinking as a deliberate challenge and amid their protests the submarine offensive was abandoned on 24 April. From October 1915 to April 1916 there were seven U-boat losses, including four from accidental causes and one unknown.

There was an interlude from May to August 1916 which included the unsuccessful U-boat operations in support of what became the battle of Jutland.[20] It also saw the only U-boat success against the Grand Fleet itself when two light cruisers were sunk. Nine U-boats were lost in this 'quiet' time; the cause being unknown for four of them.

The Third Offensive; October 1916–January 1917

In October 1916 the Germans had thirty-six U-boats in the High Seas Fleet and twenty-two smaller boats in the Flanders Flotilla, together with fourteen in the Baltic and twenty-four in the Mediterranean.

The Royal Navy had begun to introduce hydrophones

The famous U-35, seen here entering the harbour of Cartagena in June 1916.

A U-boat towing a lifeboat and crew from a sunken steamer, a sight that became increasingly rare as the war went on.

to listen for submarines (discussed later). Some were shore-based installations to protect harbours etc. while others could be used from ships. The latter could only be used when the ship and its machinery were stopped and did not give direction, just a vague warning that there was a submarine nearby. At this date hydrophones were of little operational value but they were an important first step.

The main British anti-submarine tactic was still 'offensive patrolling'. This was ineffective, however; in September 1916 three UB-boats in the English Channel sank thirty ships without encountering any one of the 570 patrol vessels in the Channel.

Date	Aux. Craft in service
Jan 1915	827
Jan 1916	2595
Jan 1918	3301

This vast force sank about fifteen U-boats during the war. By November there were a total of 2994 patrol vessels but from the outbreak of war till January 1917 offensive, patrolling (including Q-ships) had accounted for a mere fourteen U-boats.

The arming of merchant ships was more useful, as can be seen from figures from the last quarter of 1916:

	Number of attacks	No. Sunk	No. escaped
All ships	206	98	108

Of the escaping ships, eighty were armed, twenty-eight unarmed.

By September 1916, 1749 British merchant ships were armed and by February 1917 this had risen to 2899. This (and the threat of Q-ships) forced the U-boats to attack submerged, using the limited number of torpedoes and risking the wrath of neutrals.[21] It was usual for a U-boat attacking submerged to fire only one torpedo. A more vigorous use of zigzagging would have forced U-boats to use salvoes much reducing the number of victims.

Once again there was an attempt to create a barrage across the Straits of Dover. A German report was recovered from a sunken U-boat in 1917 listing 190 transits mainly at night between 23 December 1916 and 6 June 1917. Of these, only eight reported touching a net and another eight were forced to dive in order to avoid patrol vessels. From December 1916 Bauer lifted the ban on Heligoland boats using the Straits, shortening their route to the SW Approaches by 1400 miles. From May to July 1917 the western end of the barrage was removed and the mines swept. The nets were then relaid, with stronger moorings, to the south west of the original position, clear of any unswept mines, and yet the barrage was still ineffective.

The Flanders boats had begun the offensive in September and the increased endurance of the UB II boats enabled them to extend their operations to the west end of the English Channel and even as far south as the Gironde. By the end of January 1917 they had sunk 289 ships (104 neutrals) of 289,558 tons. In particular, ships carrying coal to France were heavily hit.[22]

The UC-boats also did well, benefiting from the increased endurance of the UC II class. They continued laying small fields from the Thames estuary to

Flamborough Head, from Boulogne to Nieuport and could now reach along the south coast even as far as Swansea Bay. With just under 1,000 mines they sank sixty ships (thirteen neutrals) of 82,379 tons.[23]

The big U-boats entered the campaign in October operating mainly in the SW Approaches but ranging down to the Spanish and Portuguese coasts. *U-53* sailed for the coast of the USA on 17 September and refuelled in Newport. She then sank five ships (two neutral) of 20,388 tons off the Nantucket light vessel but outside US territorial waters. Though her actions were in accordance with international law they caused grave offence in the USA and the President summoned the German Ambassador who was told that it must not happen again. It is unclear why this mission was planned; one submarine would not deter the USA but would, as happened, irritate.

The losses of British, Allied and neutral shipping for the four months makes grim reading.

Force	No. sunk	Neutrals	Tonnage
Heligoland & Flanders	253	-	446,306
Mediterranean	154	-	506,656
Baltic	12	-	2,319
TOTAL	768	500	1,535,863

Monthly losses were 307,172 tons, much higher than in the previous offensives.

Offensive	Ton/month	U-boats*	Tons per U-boat
First	114,580	30	3819
Second	173,921	52	3345
Third	307,172	96	3200

* Available at the start of each offensive; about one third would be on patrol suggesting some 9,000 tons per boat at sea.

The tonnage sunk each month per boat is remarkably constant suggesting that the standard of training of new commanders, officers and men was good. *It also suggests a plentiful supply of targets*.

The U-boat threat to the United Kingdom had suddenly became serious. In addition to the million-and-a-half tons sunk, 178 ships of 788,595 tons had been damaged, needing lengthy repairs which competed with new construction for scarce shipyard labour. It is said that reports of U-boat activity had caused delays in sailing equivalent to a reduction in capacity of 30 per cent, though there seems little evidence for this claim. The new offensive was beginning to scare off the neutrals; in the first quarter of 1916 3,442,000 tons of neutral shipping cleared UK ports but by the last quarter this had fallen to 959,000 tons of which 723,000 was Norwegian.

Sir John Jellicoe, First Sea Lord from 5 December 1916, wrote to his minister warning that if losses continued it might be necessary to negotiate peace, inevitably on unfavourable terms, by the summer of 1917. He said that the rate at which U-boats were being sunk had actually fallen to 0.73 per month, far below the estimated building rate of 2.56 per month. At this date, Jellicoe saw

Admiral Sir David Beatty, who rose to command the Grand Fleet, advocated using submarines against U-boats.

the introduction of convoy as impossible because of a shortage of escorts and difficulty of maintaining station. There was also the difficulty of unequal speed of ships, inability to zigzag and tendency to straggle. A further argument against the convoy was the belief that concentrating targets would increase losses. All these were wrong. Jellicoe's solution was to build even more ineffective patrol vessels.

By October 1917 a more effective hydrophone was coming into service. The Nash fish had a limited directional capability and could work while towed at slow speed. Considerable numbers were fitted in motor launches and auxiliaries, which were formed into hunting groups. Once again, the sheer size of the ocean had been forgotten and the Nash fish was too limited to detect distant or quiet targets and these hunters accounted for only one U-boat. The submarines soon found that they were inaudible at low speeds—2 knots—and they had better hydrophones. In May 1917, 1108 new A/S vessels were ordered—97 destroyers, 10 P boats, 34 sloops, 114 minesweepers, 486 trawlers, 215 drifters, 36 Q-ships, 56 motor launches and 60 submarines. Hunting forces of destroyers and P boats were set up to work on submarine transit routes following up D/F bearings. Admirals Beatty and Duff attached great importance to 'sub v sub' work. Success was rare but there may well have been a moral effect, with the U-boat never feeling safe, at least on the surface.

U-boat sinkings from October 1916 to January 1917 totalled ten.

Unrestricted Warfare:
February to April 1917

This was indeed the crisis of the U-boat war and must be considered in more detail. The Allies so nearly lost before they finally snatched victory. It should be appreciated that many of the new procedures and technical developments, which were used successfully in 1917-18, had been in development in earlier years.

The successes of the German Army in the latter half of 1916 eliminated the fear of Holland and Denmark entering the war on the Allied side and the German Army high command team of Hindenberg and Ludendorff both supported the submarine campaign. Peace overtures were rejected by the Allies in late December and a new proposal was put forward by Holtzendorff on 22 December with greatly revised figures. He put the strength of shipping needed to supply and support Britain at 10 million tons—six million British, 900,000 prizes and three million neutral. He set a target of sinking 600,000 tons a month and of scaring off 1.2 million tons of neutral shipping. After five months he expected to have reduced British shipping by 39 per cent, which would be intolerable for Britain. He attached considerable importance to swift action so that available shipping would be severely reduced before the harvest in August, which would otherwise alleviate the situation.

A Council with the Kaiser was held at Pless on 9 January 1917 at which the case was presented.[24] The risk of US intervention was dismissed as her armed forces were seen as negligible, while it was expected that Britain would starve before any significant number of trained US troops could reach France. It was also thought that the U-boats would inflict very heavy casualties on US troopships crossing the Atlantic. (In fact, one ship and 100 men were lost from two million). Meanwhile, the British blockade had inflicted great suffering on the German people during the winter, particularly affecting the poorer people who could not afford Black Market prices. Food was short, fuel for heating was short; after freezing and soaking in food queues, housewives returned to cold houses. It is not surprising that there was strong popular support for an unrestricted submarine war.

The Kaiser sent a telegram to Scheer to launch the unrestricted campaign on 1 February. All Allied and neutral shipping was to be sunk without warning in the English Channel, the western half of the North Sea and the western coasts of Ireland, Scotland, England and France extending about 400 miles west into the Atlantic. Only hospital ships were exempt and even they were to be targeted in the Channel from a mistaken belief that they were used to carry troops.[25]

Bauer amplified this direction in orders of 27 January in which he particularly emphasised the need for energetic and rapid action. The use of the Straits of Dover was compulsory (with few exceptions) both to reduce the distance to reach the operational area and also to reduce weather damage, too frequent off the north of Scotland. Commanders were urged to make sure of using-up their munitions before return. Short cruises were a waste of resources and the aim should be for a U-boat to be at sea

Generals Hindenburg and Ludendorf of the German High Command.

fourteen days in each month. There is an implication that some commanders were lacking in aggression. Leave was reduced as was maintenance. In partial return, rations were increased for U-boat crews. Venereal disease was seen as a serious problem and to be tackled ruthlessly. There were detailed instructions on the use of gunfire without incurring risks from Q-ships—basically attack from astern.

At the beginning of February 1917 there were forty-six U-boats in the High Seas flotilla and twenty-three in Flanders, as well as ten in the Baltic and twenty-six in the Mediterranean. This total of 105 which grew to 117 in March and 120 in April. In February orders were placed for six large U-boats and forty-five smaller UB III coastal boats. Seven *Deutschland* 'merchant submarines' were to be converted to U-cruisers with two 5.9in guns (4.1in some originally) and two 19.7in torpedo tubes (18 torpedoes). It was argued that since the U-boats were to win the war in five months a bigger programme was unnecessary and more orders might actually delay completion of the earlier boats—as seems to have been the effect in 1918.

Sinkings rose rapidly:

Month	No. sunk	Tonnage	U-boats at sea	Tons/U-boat
Feb	254	500,573	36	13,904
Mar	310	556,775	40	13,919
Apr	413	873,754	47	18,591
Total	977	1,931,102		

More than half the sinkings—about one million tons—came from Heligoland boats, particularly those operating in the SW Approaches, while the UB-boats claimed 349,000 tons and the mines of the UC-boats accounted for 127,300 tons. The twenty-three boats operating in the Mediterranean scored 422,498 tons. In addition, 321,000 tons were damaged (270,000 British) and since

Three views of U-35, operating in the Mediterranean during April-May 1917. The small UB type submarine coming alongside is possibly UB-42. Under her commanders Wilhelm Kophamel and then Lothar von Arnauld de la Periére, U-35 had a phenomenal record in both the Mediterranean and the Atlantic. De la Periére went on to become the most succesful U-boat commander of all time, and all the while operating within the rules of engagement.

repair yards were already busy, repairs were going to take a long time. Neutral shipping was indeed scared off, reduced to about one-quarter of the previous year. But the USA declared war on Germany on 6 April 1917, partly because of the U-boat campaign, partly the Zimmermann telegram.

Attacks: Feb-Apr 1917

Weapon	Attacked	Sunk	Damaged	Escaped
Torpedo	516	374	31	111
Gun	216	154	6	105

The figures show a surprising number of gun attacks for that date. The cost of this slaughter was not great to Germany; only nine submarines were lost.

May-July 1917

The United Kingdom was facing defeat. One estimate suggested that British-controlled shipping would be down to under five million tons by the end of the year which would barely suffice for food supplies. The USN Commander in European waters, Admiral Sims, met the First Sea Lord, Jellicoe, on 10 April and was horrified both by the atmosphere of gloom and by the actual figures produced at the meeting. Jellicoe made it clear that the UK could not continue the war if losses remained at April levels or worse.[26] Destroyers and other patrol craft were doing their best but it was not good enough.

The Admiralty proposed three new measures: to increase drastically the tonnage of new-construction merchant ships, to mine the Heligoland Bight and to experiment with convoys. A Ministry of Shipping Control was set up under Sir Joseph Maclay which initiated a programme of building standard types of merchant ships (discussed later). The steel allocation for merchant ships was increased from 13,000 to 20,000 tons weekly and 35,000 extra men found for the yards. This involved withdrawing men from the army, already desperately short of men, and suspending work on three battle cruisers (*Hood* class) and five light cruisers. Many neutral ships were purchased and old ships brought back into service—even sailing ships used as hulks. All these measures together added 1,163,000 tons to the register in 1917, roughly one quarter of the tonnage lost.

Admiral Scheer, commander in chief of the German High Seas Fleet, pictured here with Prince Henry of Prussia.

Vice Admiral William S. Sims of the United States' Navy, pictured here in the garden of Admiralty House, Queenstown, Ireland. Sims, who commanded the US ships in European waters, had made his reputation as a gunnery expert. In this role he played a major part in the instigation of convoys, the use of American destoyers as escorts, and the building of submarine chasers.

Month	No. sunk	Tonnage	U-boats at sea	Tons/U-boat
May	285	589,603	47	12,544
June	286	674,458	55	12,264
July	224	545,021	41	13,293

The fifty-eight boats from Heligoland accounted for almost half the total, once again primarily in the SW Approaches. The first of the U-cruisers (*U-155*) cruised off the Azores for 104 days sinking ten steamers and seven sail of 52,000 tons, mainly by gun and explosive charge. Her voyage spanned 10,220 miles (620 submerged). This cruise was of limited direct value but was a distraction to patrols.

Both sides now began to feel concern as they looked at the statistics, The British looked at the weekly loss-rate of thirty-one ships—some 1600 in a full year—compared with a mere 1300 ships available for imports. Only 300 would be built in the year. The German view was less pessimistic but they were beginning to realise that victory would not come as quickly as they hoped. Many of the neutrals who had left the trade had been persuaded to return and this was now only 20 per cent below the peak. As a partial consequence, British shipping was not being sunk as quickly as planned and Holtzendorff was now expecting two million tons sunk instead of the target of three million.

The rate of sinking achieved was still roughly proportional to the number of U-boats at sea and hence a big building programme of U-boats was planned. It was decided to plan for U-boats to complete up to January 1919, and 95 new boats were ordered to complete from mid 1918 onwards.[27]

U-boat Sinkings May-July 1917

	In period	Cumulative
TOTAL	15	72

Within the German Navy there was some concern that the number and tonnage of ships sunk per U-boat lost was falling:

First quarter	86.3	194,524
Second	53	124,570

However, the fifteen U-boats lost were comfortably exceeded by twenty-four new construction boats. On the other hand, losses per boat at sea had remained fairly constant at just over 4 per cent.

For the quarter August-October, 12,098 ships were convoyed of which only forty-nine were sunk against 221 independents. However, the monthly average had dropped to 400,000 tons, which, though grievous, was well short of that needed for a German victory.

Month	No. sunk	Tonnage	U-boats at sea	Tons/U-boat
August	186	509,142	46	9257
Sept.	158	338,242	55	6149
Oct.	159	448,923	56	8016
Nov.	126	289,905	39	7433
Dec.	160	382,060	48	7960

One of the three big 'U-boat cruisers' of the U-139 class with its two 5.9-inch guns prominent.

Monthly sinkings per U-boat were little more than half the April figure; for the British the worst was over.

Convoys forced the U-boats to come to the escorts and Allied successes rose. The German counter should have been the Wolf Pack, as in the Second World War, where a large force of submarines could overwhelm the escort. Bauer claims to have proposed something of the sort in 1917. Radio was inadequate for shore control so he suggested using the ex-*Deutschland* boats as HQ-ships (with elaborate radio)—and as tankers to replenish the attack boats. He hoped that these HQ boats could track convoys using direction finders and inform U-boats of their track. He does not seem to have envisaged a concerted attack. It is probable that British direction finders would have located these HQ boats quite quickly and sent a hunter unit after them (as with the 'milch cows' of the Second World War).

During the last five months of 1917 thirty-seven U-boats were sunk, an average of 7.4 a month—approaching the New Build figure of 8.8 per month that was bound to fall in 1918. There were several reasons for this, of which the performance of the H.II mine was probably the most important. The mechanical efficiency of this mine was enhanced by the use of intelligence in placing the fields. The 'exchange rate' of merchant ships sunk per U-boat lost had dropped from eighty-six to twenty-one.

Britain was not yet home and dry, however. In May it had been calculated that the absolute minimum tonnage of shipping was 4.8 million while in April there were 8.4 million available. In the following nine months 2.9 million had been lost and only 0.9 million of new construction had been added. This left 6.4 million at the end of the year but of that nearly a million was damaged, leav-ing some 5.4 million—all too close to the minimum value of 4.8.

U-boat Sinkings: August to December 1917

	In period	Cumulative
TOTAL	37	109

Introduction of Convoys

When the Grand Fleet went to sea, some twenty battle-ships were escorted by seventy-plus destroyers. It might seem obvious that similar protection could be given to merchant ships in convoy but many reasons were given which seemed to make convoy impossible. First was the number of escorts required: twenty battleships needed seventy escorts and, at first sight, it might appear that twenty merchant ships would need the same. This ignores the fact that the seventy destroyers were needed to fight off a massed attack by a similar or greater number of German destroyers. There were many other reasons quoted, few of which stand up to examination.

The reasons for the Navy's hostility to convoy went back nearly a century and were ingrained by 1914. During the Napoleonic and earlier wars very large con-voys of merchant sailing ships operated without too much difficulty despite great differences in sailing per-formance, and it was well documented that the risk of capture was far less in convoy than when sailing inde-pendently—a point made clear by the insurance premi-ums.[28] The introduction of the steam ship was thought to have changed all this. It was claimed that steam mer-

The American tanker SS Illinois *sinking in the English Channel after being stopped and fired upon by a U-boat, 18 March 1917. The Channel was then part of the unrestricted warfare zone.*

chant ships could not keep station and hence there would be large numbers of stragglers and collisions.

During the 19th century a considerable number of papers were written by naval officers, naval architects and others, almost all of which stated that convoy was impossible in the steam era. Most of these papers were discussed at institutions such as RUSI and the INA with little or no dissent.[29] It was believed that a convoy would be easier to find than a single ship, which was true, but a convoy of twenty ships was much less easy to find than twenty single ships. Once found, it was thought that a raider could sink numerous ships in a short time using guns and the ram. Experience would make it clear that sinking of a single merchant ship with guns was not quick whilst a single ramming would severely damage the raider. Above all, it was thought that the role of the Navy was to attack enemy warships and that escort work was merely defensive.

During the early years of the war a number of additional objections to convoy were raised but these were not critically examined because every sailor 'knew' that convoy was impossible. Somewhat illogically, major troopship convoys were always escorted.

It was claimed that a convoy would be much more conspicuous than a single ship, aiding the hunter. In fact, the opposite was true. The chance of a convoy being seen from a submarine was little greater than the chance of seeing a single ship. In reasonable visibility, a single merchant ship could be seen from a surfaced submarine at about ten miles whilst a convoy of twenty ships, two miles across would be seen at about eleven miles from its centre.[30] Thus ten convoys of twenty ships were as easy to find as twenty single ships but the convoys represented 200 ships. As several U-boat commanders noted, the sea suddenly emptied of ships. In fact the advantage of convoy was even greater than suggested as independently routed ships tended to follow close to pre-war shipping lanes and use the same landfalls, offering a stream of targets for the waiting U-boats.

Diversionary routing of independents was difficult as some had no wireless and few kept a 24-hour radio watch. On the other hand, it was comparatively easy to divert a convoy, incidentally providing a very effective counter to minelaying.

In June 1916 the steamer *Brussels* was captured on the Holland route and her master, Captain Fryatt, executed. The next month another steamer, *Lestris*, was captured. Action to protect ships on this very exposed route was swift; on 16 July 1916 it was decided to use ships of the Harwich Force to protect vessels on this route. Initially the organisation was loose but was soon formalised into convoys, running each way at six to seven day intervals. Between July 1916 and November 1918 there were 131 convoys comprising 1861 ships of which only six were lost (and those in the early days). After June 1917 there were no losses. The overall loss rate on this route was 0.32 per cent but this lesson was ignored.

A little later the French coal trade demonstrated the

same lesson. To make good for the loss of coal fields in north-east France, the French required two million tons of coal each month from Britain but by December 1916 shipments had fallen to about half that figure. There were two linked causes, one the direct loss of colliers to U-boat attack, the other being reluctance to sail for fear of the submarine threat.

On 7 February 1917 a series of 'controlled sailings'— the word convoy was not politically correct—was instituted on four routes:

Mount's Bay to Brest,
Weymouth to Cherbourg,
Weymouth to Le Havre,
Dover/Folkestone to Calais/Boulogne,

Convoys sailed at 24-hour intervals. The reduction in losses was immediate; in March only three out of 1500 colliers were lost and by the end of the war only fifty-three were lost out of 39,352 convoyed. Contrary to expectations, the escort force needed to achieve this result was tiny. Initially, the two Weymouth routes had a total of fifteen trawlers and by the end of April the total escort force only amounted to thirty trawlers for 4000 crossings per month. It does not seem to have been noticed that such a great reduction could be achieved by running convoys with only a weak escort—their main protection was invisibility.

On 3 April 1917 a conference decided to institute convoys on the Scandinavian route. This route had suffered from surface attack as well as submarines and a stronger

escort was clearly needed. Initially convoys were small, six to seven ships but this was soon increased to twenty to twenty-five ships escorted by two destroyers and four or five auxiliaries. Once again, losses fell dramatically. In May and June 1917, 1871 ships were convoyed for the loss of only six and four of these were between Lerwick and the Humber.

When Jellicoe took the post he asked Sir Maurice Hankey to prepare a paper on convoy. Hankey wrote in his diary, 11 February 1917 (Sunday): 'Had a brain wave on the subject of anti-submarine warfare, so ran down to Walton Heath in the afternoon to formulate my ideas to Lloyd George [the Prime Minister] who was very interested. I sat up late completing a long memo on the subject. My memo was an argument for convoys, but contained a great number of suggestions.'[31]

Again from his diary, 13 February 1917: 'Breakfast with Lloyd George, Carson [Sir Edward Carson, First Lord of the Admiralty, December 1916 to July 1917], Jellicoe and Duff[32], the Admiral in charge of anti-submarine warfare, to discuss my theories as regards the adoption of convoys. They resisted a good deal but I think the discussion did good. They admitted they were convoying transports, and agreed to enquire about the results of a big convoy of transports coming from Australia…'.

Roskill points out that Hankey's brainwave could have been self generated from his interest in history but was very probably inspired by a leak from Commander R G H Henderson. The evidence is clear that in early 1917 both the RN and the merchant navy were still strongly opposed to convoy. There were a few who felt that con-

The German merchant submarine Deutschland, which in 1916 had symbolically broken the British blockade by making two trading voyages to the United States. Together with six of her seven sister vessels (the eighth was too badly damaged during her maiden voyage) she was later converted into a straightforward U-boat, but the advantage gained from her long range (13,000 miles) was considerably negated by slow speed and light armament.

voy should at least be given a fair trial. Henderson was one and Norman A Leslie of the Ministry of Shipping was another (he had worked in the Transport Dept of the Admiralty). It was these two who showed that the interpretations of statistics on merchant ship movements were wrong. It seems very likely that these two 'leaked' their views on convoy to Hankey in the hope that they might reach the War Cabinet.

This would be seen as 'disloyalty' by the admirals of the day. Roskill quotes letters from Lady Duff recalling her husband's resentment over Henderson's action in passing on the statistical error without Duff's knowledge. Roskill also studied Leslie's papers: 'Leslie had no confidence in Duff'. None of these prove that Henderson was the source of Hankey's brainwave but make it probable. One has the hilarious situation of the two most likely instigators of convoy action busy concealing their tracks whilst all those not directly involved claimed the credit. There is more direct evidence in a letter to Hankey by Churchill in 1937 'I well remember how you played an essential part in saving the country over the convoy system, and how when young officers came to you and told you the truth, against service rules, you saw that the seed did not fall on stony ground…'. Churchill also wrote,[33] 'A junior officer, Cdr R G Henderson, working in the anti-submarine department and in close contact with the Ministry of Shipping broke up this monstrous and tamely accepted obstacle.' Roskill takes the 'obstacle' as objections to convoy but the text would fit better with the statistical error.

On 23 February 1917 Jellicoe chaired a meeting of the naval staff with a number of merchant-ship masters whose ships happened to be in the London docks. He claimed that the masters came from every type of merchant ship from liner to tramp.[34] Jellicoe gave an outline of the requirements in terms of station keeping, such as communication from bridge to engine room. They were quite certain that they could not keep station due to the inexperience of both deck officers and engineers together with the lack of communication between bridge and engine room and that collisions would be likely. They thought that no more than two or three cargo ships could keep in company.

There remained one apparently insuperable objection to the general introduction of convoys. A study in March 1917 had produced figures showing that 5000 ships entered and left British ports each week, clearly far too many to escort.[35] Commander Henderson with the help of Leslie re-examined these figures. They discovered that the 5000 movements included coasters making several calls each day. The correct figure for ocean going ships was about twenty arrivals and twenty departures per day. They seem to have leaked these figures to Ministers, probably through Sir Maurice Hankey, a move very unpopular with their senior officers. At this level, convoy became practical. The figures also showed the situation was far more grave than had been thought and convoy was not only possible but essential. To lose fifty ships each week out of 5000 movements was painful but fifty losses from 120 was the way to rapid defeat.

Things began to move quickly. On 25 April, Duff for-warded a very detailed paper to Jellicoe proposing the introduction of convoy.[36] He recommended that all vessels making for the UK with a speed of less than 15 knots should be convoyed. They would form up at one of four depots—Gibraltar, Dakar, Louisbourg and Newport News and would be escorted by Q-ships for the first part of the voyage. While still well clear of the danger zone they would be met by an escort of destroyers and guarded to a UK port. Duff thought that twenty-six vessels would pass through the danger zone each day and would require forty-five escorts.

Duff also advocated large convoys, pointing out that if all trade could be concentrated into one convoy it would only be possible for a single submarine to make one attack. This was contrary to belief of the day that thought small convoys to be safer. The virtue of very large convoys was not fully recognised until well into the Second World War.

Jellicoe was not convinced but he did authorise a further study. However, on 27 April[37] Jellicoe wrote to First Lord Sir Edward Carson saying '…supremacy (on surface) will be quite useless if the enemy's submarines paralyse us as they do now our lines of communication.' All that Jellicoe could suggest was a reduction of the number of routes to be protected and limits on the quantity of imports.[38] On the same day, however, he approved Duff's paper.

Lloyd George visited the Admiralty on 30 April and was to claim credit for implementing convoy. This claim is clearly unjustified though the warning of his impending visit may well have prompted Jellicoe's belated approval of Duff's scheme. On 29 April SNO (Senior Naval Officer) Gibraltar was notified that a north-bound convoy was to sail in ten days time under the following conditions:

Convoy not to exceed twenty ships
Ships to have speed of at least seven knots, not exceeding eleven knots
Each ship was to have a telephone from bridge to engine room
Each ship to have fog buoys, and an RNVR signalman was to travel in each ship

Sixteen ships were selected for this first convoy and there was a conference on 7 May addressed by the convoy commander who also commanded the escort of two Q-ships. They sailed in the evening of 10 May in three columns 1200 yards apart. On 18 May they were met by eight destroyers off the Western Approaches and a 'Large America' flying boat. Station keeping was reported as excellent, there were no losses and Masters said they had had more sleep than for months. They arrived in the Downs on 22 May.

On 3 May the Admiralty proposed that six US destroyers due to sail to Queenstown should escort a convoy across the Atlantic. The USN raised all the familiar counter arguments, in particular the 'risk' of numerous targets assembled together. They suggested that small groups of four cargo ships with two escorts should be adopted. The Admiralty were at first prepared to accept this but on 22 May, presumably as a result of the success of the Gibraltar convoy, they changed their mind.

A convoy of twelve ships sailed on 24 May from Hampton Roads under the escort of the elderly cruiser *Roxburgh*. Quite soon, two ships could not keep up and turned back for Halifax. One, the *Highbury*, was torpedoed on the return, tragically illustrating the value of convoy. On the passage, the convoy steamed in three columns, two of four ships and one of two but approaching the danger zone they changed to five columns of two. On crossing the 20 degrees W meridian on 5 June they began to zigzag in formation. The next day they were joined by eight destroyers and on 9 June the main convoy anchored, without loss, off the Isle of Wight. The Captain of *Roxburgh* praised the seamanship of the merchant ships and said that he would happily escort a convoy of thirty ships across the Atlantic.

Four more convoys left Hampton Roads in rapid succession on 4, 12, 19 and 25 June with twelve, eleven, eighteen and twenty ships respectively. Of these sixty-one vessels, only one was torpedoed and she was able to reach harbour. sailing independently, one would have reasonably expected fifteen sinkings. The majority of these ships were tankers, as previous losses had caused a severe shortage of oil.[39]

On 15 May an Atlantic Trade Convoy Committee was set up to supervise convoy organisation, even before the first Gibraltar convoy had reached England. Home-bound convoys would assemble at New York, Hampton Roads, Dakar and Gibraltar and it was planned to run two convoys every eight days alternately to UK east and west coast ports. Ships in convoy were to be able to steam at least eight knots and not more than twelve. It was planned to provide fifty-two cruisers or armed merchant cruisers for ocean escort and fourteen flotillas of escorts for the last stage. By the end of July 1917, 244 ships had reached the UK from North America in thirteen convoys with the loss of only two ships, one of which was a straggler. The convoy system was extended to the South Atlantic from 11 August. The speed with which these actions were implemented is remarkable.

By September 1917 the U-boats were concentrating their attacks on the unescorted outward bound shipping. From 13 August, outward-bound convoys assembled in Devonport, Queenstown, Lamlash/Buncrana, Falmouth and Milford Haven. Scheduling was precise so that the outward escorts would meet an inward convoy at sea for the return trip. The main U-boat offensive then moved back into coastal waters where ships, which had been safely convoyed across the Atlantic, dispersed to make their way to port. Only in June 1918 was convoy extended to east-coast and Irish Sea shipping.

Stowinng a torpedo abourd a U-boat.

Convoys at sea escorted by American destroyers. The top photograph shows the troop ships George Washington, America, *and* Dr. Kalb, *all converted liners, on 18 May 1918.*

Defeat of the U-boats

The defeat of the unrestricted U-boat campaign can only be demonstrated in figures. The problem with statistics is not in the mathematics, though this is quite simple if well taught,[40] but in asking the right question. For example, the object of the anti-submarine forces was not to sink U-boats but to get sufficient cargoes across the Atlantic, although sinking U-boats might be an important means to that end.

German planning assumed that they would need to sink about 600,000 tons of shipping each month to defeat the United Kingdom. The table below shows that from the introduction of convoys they fell further and further behind that target. Germany believed that they could reach this figure again in 1919 due to the very large building programme which was in hand (149 U-boats under construction were scrapped after the Armistice).

Month (1918)	Sunk	Tonnage
Jan	123	302,088
Feb	115	318,174
Mar	169	244,814
Apr	112	273,355
May	112	294,019
June	101	252,637
July	95	259,901
August	104	278,876
September	79	186,600
October	52	112,247
November	3	26,857

Forty-five U-boats were sunk in the last seven months of the war; the German Navy had no answer to the convoy.

The rate of monthly sinkings per submarine at sea needed to be roughly constant, so that double the number of submarines at sea would double the total sinkings. Tables in an earlier section show that this figure had halved since the peak of nearly 19,000 tons in April 1917. This reduction was largely due to the difficulty of finding and then attacking a convoy, although there were other factors. Losses of merchant ships due to mines had been greatly reduced as it was comparatively easy to divert convoys away from hazardous areas.

It is probable that the training of U-boat crews was failing to keep up with the number of new boats entering service. Experienced men were used to leaven the inexperienced crews of the new boats entering service. In particular, training of commanding officers was reduced whilst the greater number of submarine sinkings involved the death of experienced captains. There was another effect; the transfer of the best officers from the High Seas Fleet to submarines reduced the efficiency of the surface ships and is held to be a factor in the mutinies of 1918.

Admiral Spindler points out that during the war some 13,000 men served in U-boats of whom 5087 were lost.[41] In particular, 75 commanders and lieutenant-commanders were lost, presumably commanding officers, together with 160 lieutenants, potential commanders at least. These losses amount to half the lieutenant-commanders and one-third of the lieutenants killed during the war in the German navy. Spindler also says that supporting services, dockyards etc. employed 113,000 men.

Aces

There were about 400 commanding officers of U-boats during the war and, of these, twenty were responsible for 3,720,000 tons of sinkings. Few of these outstanding officers were at sea when the war ended, others were dead[42] or no longer fit for service.[43] One can only quote the old saying 'There are old Captains and bold Captains but there are no old, bold Captains'. It would have been wise to have withdrawn a considerable proportion of the best captains and put them on training the next generation.

The greatest of all the U-boat commanders was von Arnauld de la Periére with 400,000 tons claimed (and still operational at the end of the war), a total not exceeded by any of the Second World War aces. It is also worth pointing out that only one of the top-twenty commanders figures in the list of those accused of war crimes.

A convoy, with its escort, represents a 'concentration of force' which could only be countered by a concentration of U-boats, the Wolf Pack of a later war. One attempt was made to make a concentrated attack (though falling well short of a Pack) but this was a failure mainly because the radio of the day was inadequate. Night surface attacks were increasingly frequent but by single boats only and these were ineffective.

Between April and October 1917 some 22 per cent of attacks were at night, on the surface; in the same months of 1918 this figure had increased to 38 per cent. Of fifty-one attacks on convoys between October 1917 and July 1918 there were eighteen attacks from between the columns of which ten were at night.[44] There was no sign of a successful breakthrough in tactics, however.

Other than some rather strange designs for U-cruisers, there was no great change in technology; indeed, the Type VII and Type IX of the Second World War differed little from the U-boats of 1918.[45]

Convoy Statistics

The significance of convoys can be demonstrated in figures and these are overwhelming. The problem is that there are so many important figures that their significance may be lost. The French coal convoys started in February 1917 and from then to the end of the war 257 ships in convoy were sunk[46] out of a total of 84,000 ships in convoy, a loss rate of 0.3 per cent. Some 1,500 ships sailing independently were sunk for a loss rate of 5.9 per cent—85 per cent of all losses were of ships sailing independently.

Taken area-by-area or quarter-year by quarter one always finds a similar disparity. Convoys represent a concentration of force and U-boats were compelled to attack at their quarry's strong point. Much of the problem of searching for submarines disappeared when they were forced to come to the killing ground. For ships sailing in convoy, the exchange rate was one U-boat sunk for every nineteen merchant vessels sunk, while the exchange rate for independents was 1:140.

In April 1917 Bauer wrote a paper suggesting that U-boats should be co-ordinated and concentrated on homeward-bound convoys by a headquarters submarine (converted *Deutschland*) using radio. It would monitor Allied radio signals and sighting reports to build up a concentration of force against a convoy. It was a big step towards Doenitz's Wolf Packs of the Second World War but the proposal was turned down. Allied radio interception and direction finding was very good by this date and it is likely that the life of the HQ ship would have been brief.[47] It seems probable that Wolf Packs needed shore-based control with high-frequency (HF) radio, not then developed.

Doenitz made a personal contribution to the precursor of a Wolf Pack attack in October 1918. Night attacks on the surface were common by then and he agreed with another commanding office to a joint attack but the other boat was delayed and Doenitz's submarine was sunk, he being captured. In his memoirs, Doenitz claims that this was the origin of mass attacks on the surface at night. One can draw a parallel with destroyer attacks at night that also became effective only with the introduction of HF radio and radar.

The table below shows the way in which U-boats were sunk during 1918 and for the whole war. The increased effectiveness of mines and depth charges in 1918 is clear. It is likely that many of those lost to 'unknown' causes were also due to mines.

U-boat Sinkings: Jan-Nov 1918

Cause	Sunk	Cumulative
Rammed, warship	3	16
merchant ship	3	5
Gunfire, merchant ship	1	1
Unknown	13	37
Accident	1	19
Explosive sweep	0	1
Paravane	1	2
Q Ship	0	11
Submarine	6	18
Small craft, guns	3	6
depth charge	10	11
Mines	19	34
Destroyer depth charge	9	14
Bombed	0	1
Indicator nets	0	1
Mine nets	0	1
TOTAL	**69**	**187**

Intelligence[48]

There are two main aspects to intelligence work: the first involves the gathering and analysis of material, the second is the dissemination of the information in such a way that it can be used in the direction of operations and evaluation of technology. To a considerable extent these two aspects are contradictory as the more people who see the information, the more likely it is that the source will become apparent and closed down.

In the ASW campaign of the First World War the main sources of information were:

- Interception and decoding of messages
- Radio direction finding
- Inspection of wrecks by divers
- Interrogation of prisoners
- Spies

Few official papers became available until after the Second World War and unofficial reports were discouraged, though by the late 1930s there was a general awareness of all these sources. On the other hand, there was a considerable amount of disinformation, particularly during the war, usually suggesting that spies were the main or even the only source. It will be suggested that the Admiralty was very good at gathering information and by 1918 had an effective system for using it.

Interception and Decoding

By a combination of good luck and assistance from Russia, the RN had code books for all three main German naval codes by the end of 1914.

On the outbreak of war the main German telegraph cables were cut leaving radio or letter as the only means of communication with distant ships. The Post Office and amateur radio enthusiasts began to pick up these messages but there was no code-breaking organisation. The Admiralty was quick to react and within ten days had set up a decryption service in Room 40, Old Block of the Admiralty under Sir Alfred Ewing, Director of Naval Education. He was able to recruit a number of mavericks and with the aid of the captured code books and some intuitive deciphering by Paymaster Commander Rotter they were soon able to read German signals.

There were numerous problems at first; the code breakers were not familiar with 'navalese' and came up with some bizarre interpretations. This added to the suspicions of these strange civilians in the minds of the more hidebound naval officers. Churchill, in a well-meaning attempt to preserve secrecy issued rules on distribution which prevented full information reaching those who needed it.

British code breakers were helped by the Germans who did not change the SKM code until May 1917. They changed the cipher key frequently but were prone to sending out the same text in both the old and new versions. The chart grid used to give positions was not changed until July 1918. The new grid was soon recovered from a sunken U-boat. By the spring of 1915 many signals were read, by 1916 the majority in the Bight area, and by 1917 all were read.

Early in 1915 Room 40 knew the strength of the U-boat force, the rate at which it was growing, the number of U-boats at sea and in port, losses and, in general terms, the level of the threat in each area. What they could not do was to locate individual U-boats sufficiently quickly and with sufficient accuracy for them to be attacked.[49]

Members of the crew of a German U-boat, strain quite clearly visible in their faces.

Ewing left in Oct 1916, with Room 40 coming directly under Admiral Sir William R Hall—making it more integrated with other intelligence agencies. For about three years Fleet Paymaster Thring had been trying to track and record the movements of U-boats but was not allowed access to Room 40 material. In May 1917 Room 40 became ID 25 of naval intelligence and Thring was given access. Plots of submarine locations were kept from 1917. In June 1917 a convoy section was set up. There was poor collaboration with the French at least until 1917, though liaison was good with Russia. It was often possible to track an individual U-boat from its call sign even if the full message could not be deciphered.

Radio Direction Finding

In early 1915 a Captain Round of the Marconi Company, who had worked with the Army in France, set up a direction-finding service. Trials at Chelmsford were unsuccessful and the first station was set up at Lowestoft. Many others followed, including Ireland, giving a wide base line. Some were intercept as well but control was independent of Room 40. Beesley suggests an accuracy of a twenty-mile radius in the North Sea and fifty in the southwestern approaches. Doenitz, writing after the war, thought that British direction finding could, at best, locate a transmitter to within thirty miles, though other accounts suggest that it was more like three miles close to the receivers. French direction finders were numerous and effective, although Anglo-French liaison was not all it might have been.

Divers

Grant says there were five visits to U-boat wrecks in 1917 and fifteen in 1918. Typically, visits produce up-to-date ciphers, log books, minefield maps, and personal details that might be of value in the interrogation of prisoners. It must be realised that for a diver in a 'brass-helmet' diving suit to venture inside a wrecked submarine, usually with poor visibility, called for considerable bravery and skill.[50]

Interrogation of Prisoners

This usually followed the now familiar pattern: an officer speaking fluent German (frequently Major Trench RM) would politely ask a number of questions. If these were not answered, he would supply the answers himself demonstrating that he knew so much that further secrecy seemed meaningless. A good deal of information on new equipments, routes etc. came this way. Personal details would aid the questioning of later prisoners. Familiarity with life at the base suggested a vast network of spies.

Spies

It is likely that some information was received from spies, including mercenaries working in neutral countries. Much of the information from this source was low-key but included personal details, useful as background during the interrogation of prisoners.

By the Armistice, the movements of U-boats and their general pattern of operation were sufficiently well known to route convoys clear of known U-boats and minefields. Sometimes sighting reports from a U-boat could be intercepted and the convoy diverted. The movements of individual U-boats were often known sufficiently well to set up a search but these were always unsuccessful as decrypting took long enough for the submarine to move a considerable distance. Asdic would have enabled some of these contacts to be prosecuted successfully.

The converse was that U-boat routes became well known and effective mines laid.

Technical Development—Putting it together

Technical developments will, inevitably, be discussed topic by topic. However, by 1918 these separate developments were coming together in such a way that each enhanced the performance of others. For example, convoy while valuable in itself as discussed earlier, also conferred the ability to use intelligence in altering course to avoid U-boats or minefields. In 1917-18 intelligence was, on several occasions, able to forecast the movements of individual submarines but there was no way to localise such information sufficiently to attack; by 1919 such attacks should have been possible using Asdic.

In turn, Asdic should have greatly enhanced the effectiveness of depth charges, and even more the howitzer and bomb thrower. Anti submarine mines, including the new magnetic and acoustic devices, could be laid on information from intelligence.

All these developments would have led to more U-boat sinkings in 1919, exacerbating the German problems of training and of bottlenecks in the submarine-building programme. On the other hand, the massive programme of merchant-ship-building, particularly in the USA, made the U-boats' task more difficult—they were chasing a rapidly moving target,

Credit for this integration of tactics and technology

U-42 prepares for transfer of supplies at sea.

must lie with many individuals—and even a touch of luck—but one must remember the leaders on operations and research, Duff and Merz.[51]

First, a brief description of the enemy, the U-boats.

U-boat Construction

The Types VII and IX of World War II were similar in most characteristics to the later boats of the First World War showing that there was no prospect of a technical breakthrough in the design of the submarine affecting a war in 1919.[52]

German machinery was much superior to that of RN submarines[53]; most had six cylinder diesel engines either MAN 4-stroke or Germania 2-stroke. (There were a few other variants.) The MAN had brief teething problems but very soon became reliable even when uprated. The Germania took much longer to become reliable. The MAN engine was always preferred and mainstream U-boat production was largely governed by the rate at which engines could be supplied. Most gave about 200 bhp per cylinder but some of the later ones gave 300 bhp. British boats had an elderly Vickers design[54] giving about 100 bhp per cylinder which meant many more cylinders for a given power. The German engines were smaller and lighter making weight and space available for other purposes. German boats do not seem to have had the comprehensive telemotor (Hydraulic) system[55] used in later British designs to operate the planes, vents, valves etc. In turn this may have forced German designers to use rather small planes. Postwar, RN submariners were not impressed by the handling of submerged U-boats and preferred that of their own.

Some of the advantages given by the superior machinery was lost by poor hull design, in particular, badly aligned and shaped appendages such as the ballast keel and two side keels intended to keep the boat upright when sitting on the seabed. The British 'J' class were much the same size as *U-127* and both had about 3,600 bhp but the 'J's were about 3 knots faster on the surface. (19 1/2 v 17) However, the 'J's needed three engines with 36 cylinders to equal the power of two German 6-cylinder engines. Similarly, the 'L' class were 1/2-1 knots faster than *U-161* of similar size and power. The difference was relatively greater submerged due to bridge screens, guns

and shields, net cutters, riding wire etc. The speed of German submarines was greatly exaggerated by Britain during the war leading to demands for faster British boats.

Building Programmes

To increase the rate at which merchant ships were sunk, it would be necessary to increase the number of U-boats or to increase the effectiveness of each one. The number of U-boats entering service each year was:

Year	U-boats completed	Ordered
1914	3	
1915	62	272
1916	95	
1917	103	273
1918	81	220

From 1916 onwards completion rates seem to have levelled out at about eight per month while the rate at which boats were ordered was about twice the rate at which they were built. During 1918 losses were equal in number to those completed. At the end of the war there were 208 uncompleted boats which were broken up under the terms of the Armistice and also 212 projected boats which had not been started.

During and before the war Germany completed about 390 submarines, a monumental task.[56] Before the war there were two yards building submarines, the Imperial Yard at Danzig and Krupp-Germania at Kiel. During the war four additional major yards and some smaller ones learnt the difficult task of building submarines.[57] The German admiralty adopted a central ordering system for fittings such as pumps, blowers, compasses etc allocating them as needed and this system seems to have worked well.

Arrears in the building programme began to accumulate in the autumn of 1916 as labour was diverted to surface ship repairs following Jutland. (A bonus point not recognised in accounts of Jutland.) These arrears were never caught up and were exacerbated by the decision of the Pless conference to build U-cruisers in place of medium boats with effect on the 1917 campaign.[58] The medium boats took about 18 months to build, roughly the same as a British 'E'. (Johns quoting Persius says twenty-four months initially, later more than thirty for an 800-ton boat; others say 7-10 months.) The cruisers started in 1916 were unfinished 24 months later.

The first UB Is were completed in 100 days (re-erection took a fortnight) and all seventeen were delivered in seven months. The 30 UB II boats were also completed in seven months while the bigger UB III took 12-18 months. Johns points out these times were quite comparable with British yards, one of which completed six 'E's in 13 months, the first in 8 months from order; the first 'K' was delivered in 15 months and the six 'J's in 15-18 months. Note Bethlehem Steel who completed 10 'H' class in 6-7 months.

It was hoped to complete on average some 30 sub-

Particulars of representative German Submarine Classes[1]

Class	U-23	U-161	UA-139	UB	UB II	UB III	UC	UC II	UCIII	UE-71	Cargo U-151
Dspt(s) tons	669	821	1930	127	263	516	168	417	474	755	1512
Length m	64.7	71.6	92.0	28.1	36.1	55.3	34	49.4	56.1	56.8	65
bhp	1800	2400	3300	60	284	1100	90	500	600	900	800
speed s	16.7	16.2	15.3	6.5	9.2	13.6	6.2	11.6	11.5	10.6	12.4
Endurance /@ 8	7620	8500	12630	1650[2]	6650[2]	9040[3]	780[2]	9430[4]	9850[4]	7880[4]	?
bhp	1200	1230	1780	120	280	788	175	460	770	900	800
speed sm	10.3	8.2	7.6	5.5	5.8	8	5.2	7	6.6	7.9	5.2
Tubes/torp	6	6/12	6/24	2-	2/6	5/10	-	3/7	3/7	2/4	2/18
Guns	1-88	1-105	2-150 2-88	-	1-50	1-105	-	1-88	1-88	1-88	2-105 2-88
Mines	-	-	-	-	-	-	12	18	14	150	-
Cost 1000mark	2808	6752	10817	712	1290	3276	?	1729	(3300)	3510	5741

[1] For full details see E Groner. *German Warships*, Vol II. London 1991

[2] at 5 kts

[3] at 6 kts

[4] at 7kts

marines a month in 1919. In October 1918 13 were completed (average over the year was 8) and it was hoped to reach 22 by April 1919, 33 by August, 37 by December and 33 a month in early 1920. By August-September 1918 men were being released from the army to speed U-boat production. Note that the back-up labour force for 1917-1918 numbered 113,000 and presumably would more than double have had to have the 1919 building programme was to be achieved.

The UF-boats were of simple design and it was planned to build them in yards not previously involved in the submarine programme. However, it is likely that these new yards would have drawn on the same sources for equipment—pumps, periscopes, etc.—as the mainstream U-boats, leading to production bottlenecks in all classes of U-boat.

Even had the building programme been achieved it is hard to see how the new U-boats would have been crewed. Even in 1918 experienced crews were being broken up to provide a nucleus for new crews whilst they were replaced by new men with a very minimum of training. The shortage of commanding officers would have been the most serious difficulty since the German command was reluctant to withdraw successful ones from operations to train new men. The resulting lack of skill and experience—there does not seem to have been any loss of determination—must have led to a marked reduction in sinkings per U-boat at sea.

Costs

Johns quoting Persius gives for a medium U-boat:

1914	4110 marks per ton (Probably surface)
1915	4450
1916	4850
1917	6070
1918	9000

while for UB (Constructor Schuerer):

Early UB	0.6M	4700 per ton [Use % above for real increase]
Middle UB	1.4M	5030
1916 UB	3.3M	6350
1918 UB	5-6M	9500-11500 per ton

These figures are generally similar but not identical to those deduced by Groener. It is less certain what they mean. Since the technology of the medium U-boat did not change greatly it is tempting—and probably correct—to attribute the changes in cost per ton by Persius entirely to inflation. This invalidates Johns comparison with British costs, also subject to inflation.

Cost-Effectiveness

The medium-size U-boats bore the brunt of the battle; they were effective and not too demanding in production. Occupation of the Flanders ports, close to important British routes gave a splendid opportunity for small submarines with both torpedo and mine. It is suggested that both the UB and UC opening batches, though successful, were too small. Batch three boats, on the other hand, were unnecessarily large. Boats akin to UB II and UC II seem about right and this size was chosen for the UF.

It would be of interest to compare the effectiveness of the UC-minelayers with that of the UB-boats but figures have not been found. It is likely that torpedoes were more effective than mines in sinking ships; but the disruption caused by minefields and the diversion of resources in sweeping were a bonus for the UC-boats. Some figures are available for 1918 but, by then, the convoy system had greatly reduced the effectiveness of mining. In 1918, 11 ships of some 22,000 tons were sunk by mines against 529 ships of 1,670,000 tons by submarines.

The cruisers were demanding in resources and,

designed to operate in distant waters where targets were few, had few successes. They did, however, force the dispersal of AS vessels. It is possible that a small number would have been worth while for their nuisance value but no more.

Location

The location of a submerged submarine may be divided into two phases that may overlap. The first is the early warning that a submarine is nearby with an indication of its distance and bearing. The second phase involves locating the target submarine precisely enough for the successful launch of a weapon, most of which having a very small lethal radius. The need to know the target's depth makes the whole problem a three-dimensional one. There are two qualifications in relation to First-World-War operations; initial sightings were usually visual, of a surfaced submarine, and if the attack could be launched quickly there was reasonable certainty that the submarine would still be close to the surface. In addition, much of the campaign was fought in shallow water, again reducing the need for accurate determination of depth.

The earliest RN reference to submarine location occurs in the report of the Torpedo School, HMS *Vernon*, for 1882. Captain C A McEvoy had devised an induction balance which could detect the minute currents caused by metal objects in sea water forming an electric cell. There is no later mention of this device.[59] However, McEvoy did not give up and the following year he devised a hydrophone to pick up the sound of approaching craft.[60] His hydrophone was stationary, resting on the seabed and was intended to be unmanned, ringing a bell when a significant noise was heard. Similar hydrophones were developed at *Vernon* with ranges of 200-700 yards till 1903 when the work was abandoned. It seems that the requirement for the hydrophone to give an automatic warning, without a watchkeeper, was the stumbling block.

The problem was examined from the other direction by the Submarine Committee of 1910 whose main role was to develop submarine tactics and design but which also examined A/S methods. In 1911 the *Holland No 2*, already obsolete, was used in tests of primitive weapons—including hand grenades. Even this primitive craft seems to have been quite difficult to sink. In 1912 trials were carried out to see if submerged submarines could be seen from seaplanes. Some success was obtained in the Mediterranean but UK waters were usually too 'opaque'. In 1909 another committee was set up to consider underwater sound signalling and their work was to interact with detection.

Science

It is tempting–and almost true–to say that there wasn't any. There had been very few attempts even to establish the basic parameters such as the speed of sound in water. The sinking of the *Titanic* led to many proposals for

underwater sound detection of objects such as icebergs and these merged with earlier studies by Trinity House and others for sonic beacons to augment lighthouses. The leader in such work was the US Submarine Signal Company (and its British subsidiary) with Prof. Fessenden as consultant. From about 1901 underwater bells and Fessenden oscillators were installed in some lightships and a few warships including the Royal Yacht, *Victoria and Albert*.

This brief account brings the subject up to the outbreak of war. While it is true to say that nothing of value had been achieved it was not for want of trying. The technology of the day was not up to it.[61]

Wartime

The first significant advance was due to a naval officer, Cdr (later Capt) C P Ryan.[62] He had left the Navy in 1911 and went to the Marconi Company. Working at Inchkeith, initially as a freelance, but soon winning Admiralty support, he began to develop successful hydrophones. His theoretical knowledge was negligible but on the other hand, as a lieutenant in 1902, he was praised for his sound judgement and inventive genius while the following year he received the appreciation of their Lordships for his work on wireless. In December 1915 he and his work was transferred to Hawkcraig in Aberdour on the north side of the Firth of Forth close to Beatty's house; Beatty was a supporter of Ryan.[63]

Shore-based Hydrophones

In February 1915 the Admiralty encouraged Ryan to go ahead with the development of a shore-based system with hydrophones on the sea bed. Initially, he used equipment based on that of the American Submarine Signalling Company, and later changed to that of the Automatic Telephone Manufacturing Company. There were problems from interference by sea noise and also physical damage by minesweepers. These problems were slowly overcome and a prototype station was laid out off Oxcar in March 1915. Ryan's Standard Station Hydrophone was adopted for service in January 1917 and 400 sets were produced. By the end of 1917 there were 21 stations in home waters and others supporting the Otranto barrage. There were about eight hydrophones at each station and the operator would listen to each in turn. Some idea of the position of a noise source could be obtained by noting which phones were detecting it. The effective range was three miles in calm weather and about half a mile in rough. Experienced operators could distinguish the type of machinery. Range could be increased by increasing sensitivity but this also increased background noise and was not effective. Listening was exhausting and two-hour watches were normal. They were laid in water from 50-100 fathoms deep and were non-directional. Ryan's personal contribution was great; he would select the site, supervise the installation, train the operators and sort out later problems.

Ryan also developed a system of mines controlled from shore on information from hydrophones and electromagnetic induction. The first such minefields were laid in mid-1916 but they were not effective until 1918 when UC-78 was a probable victim. The last submarine to be sunk in the war, UB-116, also fell to a controlled mine involving both the use of hydrophones and an electromagnetic loop.

Shipborne Sets

Ryan's main effort remained on submarine detection and he adapted his shore-based, non-directional set into the so-called 'drifter' set—it was mainly used from drifters. It was lowered over the side of a stationary ship and the operator would listen for a submarine. It went into service in large numbers (4,500) from the end of 1915. Its range was of the order of 200 yards against a moving submarine and ineffective against a stationary, bottomed submarine. However, it was a worthy first step in removing a submarine's invisibility.

Ryan also developed by 1917 a Portable Directional Hydrophone (PDH) Mk I soon followed by the Mk II. These became available during 1917 and were used initially by fast hunting flotillas of US-built Motor Launches (ML). They were fairly successful in finding U-boats but they carried too few charges for successful prosecution. By the summer of 1918 there were 15 units (155 ML) round the coast.

The Board of Invention and Research (BIR)

A J Balfour succeeded Winston Churchill as First Lord of the Admiralty and soon realised that research work in both the naval and military sides was not well co-ordinated. In particular, the innumerable suggestions from the general public were not being considered properly and the few that might be of value were not followed up. After consultations with Hankey the formation of the Board of Invention and Research (BIR) was announced on 5 July 1915. A similar panel was set up for the Ministry of Munitions—the Munition Inventions Department.

The BIR was to have a central panel of three very distinguished scientists and engineers.[64] There was a consulting panel of twelve scientists and engineers with a naval secretariat. The BIR worked through six panels of which Panel II dealt with submarines and W/T. Admiral Lord Fisher was the chairman of the BIR. It would be hard to find a less suitable man for the job. The chairman's main task was to reconcile opposing views and clashing temperaments while Fisher had never heard the word compromise. The BIR met outside the Admiralty and this separation was a major cause of the suspicion with which it was viewed by the Admiralty.[65]

Panel II, a distinguished body, was led by the Duke of Buccleuch with Prof. W H Bragg, Mr W Duddel FRS, Prof. Sir E Rutherford FRS, Dr R T Glazebrook FRS and Mr C H Merz. Very soon, the BIR and its panels began to

see themselves as much more than a vetting organisation and more as directors of research.

This author has spent much of his career—and even his retirement—in attempting to direct research. It is a very difficult task; the first problem is whether to see 'Research' as an entity where one may trade off electronic warfare with seakeeping or whether seakeeping is part of the design process and funded as such. The simple word 'priority' causes confusion as it may mean importance or urgency. A trivial task may be urgent whilst something of great importance is not necessarily urgent. The innovative man is always single minded, often intolerant and sometimes plain awkward and does not respond well to direction. A compromise, observed for many years, was to allow successful groups to freelance for about 10 percent of their time, often following up a promising line after funding for the primary objective has run out.

The BIR had a commendable wish to try everything—rejecting dowsing but only after a trial. Their most famous failure was the use of circus sea lions to track submarines. This was not as silly as it may sound; the animals were quickly trained in a swimming pool to associate submarine noises with food and in sea trials they could locate sounds up to three miles distant while swimming. However, they were too easily distracted, preferring to play or chase fish, and were soon 'returned to their legitimate business'.[66]

Co-ordination was never going to be easy; there were already a number of organisations involved in R & D activities related to ASW. There was HMS Vernon, the Torpedo School, and, from late 1916, its offshoot, the Mining School. The main task of these two naval establishments was training and research was very much a part-time occupation for the enthusiast. There was Ryan's establishment at Hawkcraig, the Ordnance Research department at Woolwich and, increasingly, a number of university departments.

Rutherford was convinced that Ryan needed scientific support and appointed two of his bright young men to Hawkcraig–Dr A B Wood and H Gerrard.[67] They joined in November 1915 and a few day's later Sir Ernest Rutherford came to see how his men were getting on—they were horrified that Ryan had never even heard of Rutherford! Hawkcraig had now been allocated a number of trials vessels—the submarine B3, drifters Tarlair and Hiedra and the yacht Nyker.[68] The use of these vessels was one of the many sources of friction between the naval and scientific groups at Hawkcraig. The latter was strengthened by the appointment of Prof. W H Bragg as Resident Director of Research in May 1916 with a considerable number of other scientists.

By the end of the year clashes had become too severe and Bragg left to found a new research establishment at Parkestone Quay followed by most of the scientists.[69] Hackmann sees the conflict between Ryan and the scientists as a general problem with the Navy but I suspect it was more one of personalities. The Froudes got on very well with the Navy as did many other scientists. The uniformed Navy of the era was well accustomed to incorporating new technology (e.g., Marconi).

However, relations between the BIR, the Admiralty and with and within Hawkcraig remained difficult. The Admiralty was sponsoring numerous research contracts about which the BIR knew nothing while funding for the scientists at Hawkcraig came from a different source from that of Ryan. A meeting at the Admiralty in March 1916 seemed to reconcile many of these points but at mid-management level there were still serious problems. In August 1917 a new experimental station was opened at Weymouth, moved to Portland in April 1918 and taking its name from the attached drifter, *Sarepta*. This was quite small, providing relatively deep-water sites not readily available elsewhere.

A particular example of friction came in May 1917 when the Admiralty cancelled an order for 200 BIR portable directional hydrophones Mk I and ordered 700 Ryan Mk II instead, purely on Ryan's opinion and without comparative trials. Experience would show that they were complementary and both were needed. Sir Eric Geddes became the first civilian Controller of the Navy in May 1917 and soon saw the need for changes in the working of the BIR. Geddes backed Fisher's idea's on reorganisation. When Geddes became First Lord of the Admiralty in July 1917, he set up a committee to look into BIR.[70]

They took a month to look at Admiralty research establishments and other government laboratories such as the NPL (National Physical Laboratory) and the Royal Aircraft Factory. The author is surprised that they did not study the Admiralty Experiment Works, Haslar (Ship Tanks) where for forty years a civilian scientist, Edmund Froude, had led a team of naval constructors and draughtsmen working with a blend of basic and applied research in harmony with the uniformed Navy.

The Holland-Skinner report recommended that the BIR should be abolished and replaced by a Director of Experiment and Research (DER) within the Admiralty and that DER should control a single Central Laboratory, on the model of the NPL.[71] The recommendation for a DER was accepted, but setting up a single laboratory was too ambitious for wartime though the report had some effect later. The first Director was C H Merz, a well known electrical engineer who had devised the National Grid. Fisher was quietly eased out.

The arguments for and against a large establishment are closely balanced. There is a fair amount of evidence that the best work is done in establishments numbering 2-300. At this size there is only one level of management between the superintendent and the researcher on the bench and the chief can know everyone by name. On the other hand, a small laboratory may well lack specialised knowledge—eg, a specialised maths group, library— while separate book production teams, police and security may be wasteful. One solution is to group a number of almost independent laboratories on a single site with common services—including the canteen and bar where most useful co-operation takes place.

The new Director was in charge of all the old, diverse and feuding establishments as well as teams in many universities. Two local groupings of universities achieved useful results, apparently without acrimony. The Lancashire Anti-Submarine Committee was based at Manchester and were to lead on Silent Propulsion, while the Clyde Anti-Submarine Committee requisitioned the Hydro at Shandon on the Gareloch which was later used by the Lancashire Committee and was to become the early base for postwar research.

Towed Hydrophones

The early hydrophones could only work with the ship stationary and machinery shut down, making the ship a perfect target for the submarine. Many attempts were made to design a hydrophone which would work with the ship moving. This involved eliminating or shielding machinery and propeller noise from the ship and also noise from the flow of water over the hydrophone body.

The first successful device was due to G H Nash[72] of the Western Electric Company backed by the ASD (Anti-Submarine Division).[73] Trials in July 1917 were successful and a first order for 136 sets was placed at an estimated cost of £25,000. His 'fish', mainly of wooden construction, held one bi-directional and one uni-directional hydrophone, the former being used for initial detection. With a bi-directional set there was a chance of getting the inverse bearing, 180° out.

Ryan came back with his 'rubber eel', a tiny fish only 18in long and 3in in diameter. It was towed 1-200 yards astern of the ship at a depth of 20-30ft and at speeds of about 8 knots with a range of up to 4 miles. At higher speeds there was interference from the towing ship and at 10 knots the range dropped to $1\frac{1}{2}$ mile. It was non-directional and usually used in pairs with an estimate of direction obtained binaurally.

Ryan then developed a larger unit, the Porpoise, with a PDH Mk II in a 5ft wooden body. It had a slightly longer range than Nash's fish and was preferred in a single-ship hunt though the Nash was better in a two-ship operation.

ASDIC[74]

The ASDIC means of submarine detection did not enter service until just after the war but a prototype had been successfully tested and the first production order placed. Given the wartime sense of urgency it seems almost certain that it would have been operational in small numbers had the war continued into 1919.

A B Wood, himself a pioneer in underwater acoustics, has made clear the origin of the word Asdic.[75] ASD stood for Anti-Submarine Division whilst -ic was a suffix meaning 'pertaining to' and roughly as in physics or dynamics.[76] Similarly, since the use of quartz was seen as highly secret it was always referred to as ASDIVITE.

The loss of the *Titanic* on her maiden voyage in 1912 led to many suggestions for detecting icebergs and at least one involved the use of echoes from ultrasonic sound waves. This idea remained a dream until 1915 when Paul Langevin and M Chilowski,[77] working in Toulouse, produced high-frequency sound using mica. They eventually achieved a signalling range of 3 kilometres and obtained echoes at 100 metres.

In August 1916 the BIR became interested in detection by high-frequency sound and the Canadian professor R W Boyle was put in charge assisted by W F Rawlinson and J Anderson working at AES Parkestone Quay from 1917. It soon appeared that the best oscillator would be one made from quartz using the piezoelectric effect discovered by Pierre and Jacques Curie in 1880. Some tentative work had been done by Sir Ernest Rutherford in 1915 but was not proceeded with. Langevin, too, had used quartz in a receiver in combination with a valve amplifier.[78] Langevin was very helpful and visited England several times to pass on his work.

It was decided to proceed with quartz oscillators but a great deal of theoretical and experimental work was needed to find the most efficient slab, the choice of thickness and voltage, and the mounting of the slabs. In the autumn of 1918 the cutting and testing was supervised by J Anderson[79] at the Geological Survey Museum (Jermyn Street). The actual cutting from large crystals was carried out by Farmer and Brindley, a firm of tombstone makers in Lambeth, and units were assembled at Callender's Cables of Erith. It was all very secret; hence code names such as Asdic.

It was soon found that the device worked best if the oscillator was mounted in a dome below the ship so that it was surrounded by still water. It could be turned manually in the horizontal plane and could also be tilted. 'Sea' trials began on a barge in the River Stour and from the drifter *Hiedra*.[80] The destroyer *Melampus* was also used for trials. A 700-ton surface ship, stern on, could be detected at 1,400 yards. A surfaced submarine would be detected at the same range, a little less if submerged. In October 1918 the trawler *Ebro II*,[81] which already had Walser hydrophones, became the trials ship. She had a retractable canvas dome tested by Froude in the ship tank at Haslar. Much of her fish hold was occupied by the gear. Sea trials continued until the new year when she was transferred to Shandon. Excellent echoes were obtained at 600 yards.

The Admiralty (ASD) were delighted and ordered 20 sets in June 1918 and installation drawings prepared for trawlers, sloops, 'K' class destroyers, P and PC boats. The first fitting was in *P59*[82] followed by the whalers *Icewhale* and *Cachalot*. By early 1919 the two whalers were achieving echo ranges of 1100 yards in ideal conditions. *P55* completed in early 1919 and her installation was developed into the first standard set, Type 112, by the end of the year and a flotilla of P-boats had been fitted by early 1920.[83] By 1922 the submarine *H32* had a prototype set but this is well clear of the First World War. Wartime urgency would have seen numerous ships fitted in 1919. Asdic work was moved to Dartmouth about July 1918 and to Shandon in 1919.

A/S Weapons: High Speed Sweep

The 'modified' sweep consisted of a loop of wire some 200ft long with charges (usually nine) attached at inter-vals. The upper leg was supported by wooden floats while the lower leg was held down by a 'kite'. It was towed behind a destroyer when a submarine had been sighted, but since it took 20 minutes to deploy—and twice that to reel in—the submarine had plenty of time to get away. It could be used at speeds up to about 8-10 knots and severely restricted manoeuvrability.[84]

The complicated system of wires, floats and charges was always getting tangled and was most heartily cursed by the operators. If the sweep was fouled a needle would flick over and the man at the electric firing key would explode all the charges. It worked—once. On 4 March 1915, *U-8* was sighted by *Viking*, the only six-funnelled destroyer, in the Straits and the destroyer opened fire. The submarine dived and *Viking* deployed her sweep which was fired over the spot without effect. Later *Maori* saw a periscope and, five hours after the first sighting, *Ghurka*'s sweep caught on an obstruction. The charges were fired and *U-8* surfaced. She surrendered, but her sea cocks were opened and she sank. Her crew was rescued.

Lance Bombs

This consisted of a charge weighing some 20-30 lbs on the end of a stout ash staff like a broomstick, which could be thrown at a U-boat close alongside.[85] 'Taffrail' tells the story of how, on 24 April 1916, the drifter, *Gleaner of the Seas*, saw a periscope close ahead and Skipper Hurren ran to the bow and hurled his bomb at the forepart of a submarine which was clearly visible. Oil and air bubbles came to the surface and more bombs were dropped and the position buoyed. Later, a destroyer fired her sweep over the spot.

Depth Charges

The idea of the depth charge originated at the end of 1914 and by January 1915 four simple devices were available in very limited numbers.[86] All were fired by a lanyard attached to a float on the surface which pulled the trigger when the charge fell below the pre-set length of the lanyard. The charge was of guncotton; 32½lbs in the A and B versions and 100lbs in the E type. The C and C* were dropped from aircraft and had charges of 35 and 65lbs respectively. It was hoped that the E type would cause serious damage at 70ft and the smaller charges at about 20ft. Very few were issued and there are no reports of them causing damage but it was a start.

The design of the first effective anti-submarine weapon was completed in June 1915 and the first were issued in January 1916.[87] The Type D charge had 300lbs of TNT which could be set to fire by a hydrostatic pistol at either 40ft or 80ft. Contemporary accounts say that the explosion had to be within 14ft to sink a U-boat but at 28ft the submarine might be disabled and forced to surface.[88] Second World War figures for similar charges are 20ft and 40ft against much stronger hulls with some shock protection. U-boat hulls were generally sound but some classes had external framing so that pressure or shock would put the rivets in tension, forcing the plates away from the frame. This was a bad feature but there was worse; at least one class had frames which were external in the upper part of the hull and internal on the lower part. This discontinuity would seriously weaken the frame ring under explosive loading.

Owing to the shortage of TNT only two charges were allocated to each ship. The chance of lethal damage with only two charges and no means of location other than the diving spot was remote. There was also a D* charge with 140lbs explosive for use by slower vessels which could not get out of the danger area of the bigger charge in time. The first success was by the Q-ship *Farnborough* against *U-68* on 22 March 1916. The Germans became aware of it after unsuccessful attacks in April.

Initially depth charges were rolled over the stern as the hunting vessel followed what was thought to be the submarine track. The lethal radius of about 20 feet—a distance traversed by a submerged submarine in less than 2 seconds—allowed little margin for error and it was soon realised that a means was required to throw a depth charge to each side of the track. Thornycroft began development of a depth-charge thrower based on a bomb thrower in December 1916 and it entered service in August 1917. The charge sat in a cradle across the barrel into which a stem projected. The charge was projected about 40 yards to the side of the ship. Initially, there was one thrower each side but later two or even three were installed.

Howitzers and Bomb Throwers

For most of the war the only way to locate a submarine was to see it on the surface, usually when the submarine was on the point of diving. It was soon found that the guns mounted on ASW vessels, mainly 4in or smaller, were ineffective against the thick and well-rounded pressure hull of a U-boat.[89] There were many experiments with a variety of guns, howitzers and smooth-bore bomb throwers.[90] Jellicoe says that 30 bomb throwers were on order by the beginning of 1917 and by April designs had been approved for seven types and 1006 were on order.[91] By the end of 1917 about 400 had been completed.

Most of the howitzers had a 7.5 inch bore and these could either fire a 100lb bomb (43lb burster) to 2100 yards or a 500 lb (250lb burster) to 300 yards.[92] The fuse could be set to contact or two-second delay which should explode at 20ft. The bomb thrower had a 3½-inch 'stick' which went down the bore carrying a bomb. The 200lb bomb (burster 98lbs) had a range of 1200 yards; the 350lb bomb (burster 250lb) ranged 650 yards.

The weapons fired forward (the howitzer had a limited amount of training) and were mounted forward where possible. Many fishing trawlers had 7.5in howitzers usually mounted over the fishing hold while those fitted with hydrophones had a bomb thrower on the forecastle with a 12pdr gun aft.

There is no record of any success with these weapons, but in principle they were a sensible response to the problem.[93] They would have been very much more effective fired using target data from Asdic, though Second World War experience would not rate the chance of success from a single charge very highly.

Mines

British (and USN) mines need only brief coverage here.[94] By the end of 1916 the H2 mine had been designed with a firing mechanism based on the German Hertz horn and with the other faults of earlier mines corrected, such as inadequate sinkers. Production was initially slow, probably because of a national shortage of TNT,[95] but by September 1917 laying in numbers was possible. U-boat sinkings increased rapidly.

A lot of magnetic mines had been laid off the Flanders coast, but their susceptibility to countermining made them ineffective. This problem had been solved by the Armistice and they would have become effective in 1919. By the war's end several thousand acoustic firing mechanisms were available for attachment to the H2 moored mine. Trials had been carried out and they, too, should have been effective. As pointed out earlier, the improved use of intelligence added to the effectiveness of mine laying.

Aircraft in ASW: Introduction[96]

Bleriot's heroic flight across the Channel took place in 1909 but in 1914 flights over water were still hazardous. Engine failure was a serious problem: most aircraft had a single, unreliable engine. Though reliability improved during the war, engine failure remained a serious problem. In the light of these mechanical problems, the RN showed commendable interest in aircraft at sea. The first trial of the ability of an aircraft to sight a submarine was carried out by the French in 1911. The gallant aviator flew three miles out to sea and had little difficulty in detecting a surfaced submarine while flying at 500-1000ft. He then sighted a submerged submarine, probably showing its periscope.

Similar trials were carried out by the RN off the east coast in June and September 1912. English tidal waters were 'opaque' and fully submerged submarines invisible, but in clear weather and a calm sea the wash of a periscope could be spotted at a considerable distance. It was thought that there was a good chance of a successful bomb attack on a submarine caught surfaced in poor visibility.

Just prior to these trials an influential paper had been submitted to the Admiralty by Lt Hugh Williamson, at that time commanding officer of the submarine B3. Williamson had learnt to fly at his own expense (Licence No 160) and could write with experience of both flying and submarine operation, a true three-dimensional traveller.[97] His paper recognised the major problem of 1912 as engine reliability and proposed coupled engines. He preferred a monoplane for better visibility, carrying an observer, wireless, 300lb of bombs and fuel for five hours, a capability beyond that of aircraft of 1912 but soon exceeded under wartime pressure. Using his submarine experience he also recognised the potential of the air-

Particulars of Major Airship Classes

Class	Capacity, cu ft	Length, ft'in	Disposable lift, tons	Endurance, ½ power, hrs	Speed, mph
Early SS*	60,000	143' 5	0.64	14-16	50
Coastal	170,000	195' 6	1.6	22	52
C Star	210,000	207-217	1.8	20	57
North Sea	360,000	260	3.8	24	57

Disposable lift includes crew, fuel, armament, ballast etc
* BE 2c fuselage

Shore Based ASW Aircraft

Type	Span, ft'in	Speed, mph	Endurance, hrs	Loaded weight, lbs
H.4	72	n/a	6	4983
H.12	92 8½	85	6	10,670
F.2A	95½ 7½	95½	6	10,978
F.3	102	91	6	12,235
Kangaroo	74 10½	98	6	8017

craft. He thought that an aircraft at 4,000ft could detect a surfaced submarine at about 10 miles.[98] The submarine could stay on the surface in which case the aircraft could use its wireless to call up a warship to sink the submarine. If the submarine dived, the aircraft could drop a bomb which Williamson said should have two fuses, one contact and the other a time fuse set to burst the bomb at 20ft below the surface.[99]

Williamson thought that a submarine sighting an aircraft would almost certainly dive, which would reduce its speed to about 4 knots and help to exhaust its battery. The range of visibility submerged is far less than from a surfaced submarine. The ability of aircraft to force submarines to dive was very important, particularly as it was difficult for a submarine to know when it was safe to surface. Within one month of the receipt of Williamson's paper, he received a formal letter expressing their Lordship's appreciation, a further indication that the Board of Admiralty was was ready to listen to new ideas.

The Royal Naval Air Service (RNAS) was set up on 1 July 1914 and by the outbreak of war its strength was 7 airships, 52 seaplanes and 39 landplanes, by far the largest naval air force in the world—though not all were serviceable. The new service was well represented at the 1914 Review of the Fleet with a fly-past of 3 airships and 17 seaplanes. An illuminated Sopwith 'Batboat' flew round the fleet after dark.

The first air attack on a submarine was probably that of the Zeppelin *L-5* on *E11* off Norderney on Christmas Day 1914 which was unsuccessful. On 15 May 1915, *L-9* attacked three British submarines in three hours, claiming one sunk. The 'victim' was *D4* which was severely shaken and had some rivets loosened in her conning tower. Even in 1915 submarines were hard to sink and aviators inclined to be optimistic.

Airships

The landplane's limitations of lifting power and endurance, even worse in seaplanes, directed operational thoughts to the airship. The navy's pre-war airship activ-ities had not been very successful; the only rigid airship, unofficially known as 'Mayfly', was broken in half by inept handling before it flew.[100] In 1912 the Admiralty bought a civilian non-rigid which became HMA No.2, but was too small for operational use and was relegated to training. In 1913, two more airships were added to the Naval Wing of the Royal Flying Corps, an Astra Torres non-rigid (Naval Airship No.3) ordered from France, and a design based on the German Parseval semi-rigid type (Naval Airship No.4). No. 3, on trial, attained 51.1 knots, a world speed record for airship. On 1 January 1914 the army handed over its four serviceable airships to the navy together with some personnel. Nos 3 and 4 carried out a number of patrols protecting the transports taking the army to France.

On 28 February 1915 Fisher called a meeting of senior RNAS officers and representatives of Airships Ltd and Armstrong Whitworth. He wanted a new class of airship with a speed of 40-50 mph, a crew of two, 160lbs of bombs, wireless and fuel for 8 hours. They should have a ceiling of 5,000ft and be ready in weeks which meant they had to be simple to build and simple to operate. Airship Ltd produced a ship designed by Willows which was completed as S.S.2 but it was expensive and unsatisfactory. The Armstrong ship entered service as S.S.27 and some repeats were ordered. The real success came from some young officers who met in the mess at Farnborough on the evening of Fisher's meeting. They devised a ship which used the spare envelope of the original Willows ship and hung the fuselage and engine of a B.E.2c aeroplane underneath.

This lash-up was completed on March 18 as S.S.1 and after a few teething troubles had been cured a slightly modified version was ordered in some numbers. (S.S.1-26 ex 2,3) The Airship company built S.S.28-39 with a Maurice Farman fuselage and Armstrong S.S.39A-47. Fifty-nine airships designated S.S. were built.[101] In most cases their life was short, many were unserviceable after a year, few lasted over two. (See Table.)

In addition there were a number of similar but improved ships. There were six S.S.P. with pusher propellers and 77 S.S.Z. (Sea Scout Zero) based on a free-

An S.S.Z. airship, an wartime improvement on the original S.S. airships used by the Royal Naval Air Service.

lance design by officers at the Capel station, the main difference being in the car. They normally carried two 100lb or one 250lb bomb and also mounted a Lewis gun. The first production model entered service in June 1917. There were also a total of 16 S.S.E. and S.S.T. with twin engines. Of 134 variants of the S.S. design, 27 were wrecked, lost at sea or caught fire.

Soon after the outbreak of war the Admiralty ordered two Astra-Torres ships. One (No.8) had a short but uneventful life; the other (No.10) was dismantled and rebuilt as Coastal Airship No.1 becoming the first of a class of 35. They were much larger than the SS ships with greater load and endurance. The usually had four 100-112lb or two 250lb bombs and two Lewis guns. They do not seem to have been altogether successful and of the 30 operated by the RNAS 12 were lost. A much improved derivative was built as the C* class of which ten were completed. It was even planned to equip them with torpedoes which would run in circles at periscope depth.

The ultimate non-rigid was the North Sea class, 252 ft long. The original design had a complicated and unreliable transmission which led to two losses and a bad reputation for the rest. However, the modified design was very successful and 14 were built.[102] N.S.11 set up an endurance record of 100 hours 50 minutes in 1919. Armament was 2 or 3 Lewis guns and up to six 250lb bombs.[103] Several rigid airships were built but none became operational.

Kite balloons had a 'scarecrow' role, for which airships were too sluggish.

The first five bases were set up in mid-1915 and by the

Armistice there were 41 either operating or building. Airships needed a fair amount of maintenance but less than an aeroplane—1.62 man/hours for one hour's operating compared with 3.52. By the end the airship service had 7,114 men, few of whom ever flew. The statistics are impressive:

Numbers: 7 ships in 1914, 225 delivered (1 not accepted, 24 sold to Allies) during the war, in Nov 1918 100 scrapped or lost, 107 in service.
Flying hours: 1914-15 3000; 1916 7,000; 1917 22,000; 1918 56,000. Some 2 million miles were flown in the war.
Losses: 48 killed
From June 1917-Oct 1918: 56 ships on duty each month; 9059 patrols, averaging 6hr 17min; 59703 hours; 2210 escorts; sighted 134 mines (destroyed 73), 49 U-boats (attacking 6 alone and 21 with surface ships).

Seaplanes and Flying Boats

The development of machines which could take off and land on the water had been hastened by the Schneider Trophy race first contested in 1913 when it was won by a Deperdussin at 45.75mph.[104] The following year's race was won by a Sopwith Tabloid on floats at 86.75 mph. Engine reliability was still the main problem in flying over the sea and it seemed natural to use aircraft which could land on water, fix the engine and take-off again. There was even a plan to fly across the Atlantic in a US

Curtiss H.4 flying boat named *America*, piloted by an Englishman, John Porte, a plan frustrated by the war.[105]

On the outbreak of war Porte joined the RNAS and persuaded the Admiralty to buy the *America* and her sister aircraft. They were the best large flying boats in the world and 62 production aircraft entered service,[106] later known as the 'Small America'. The best was not good enough and Porte tried a number of major modifications to improve their performance, particularly waterborne. They did make clear the potential of such aircraft and three remained in service until mid-1918.

The Curtiss H.12 'Large America' was a bigger and more powerful aircraft incorporating some of Porte's improvements. It was originally powered by two 160hp Curtiss engines but these were replaced by Rolls Royce, first of 275hp and later of 345-375hp.[107] A total of 71 entered service and it proved valuable not only in ASW but also as a 'fighter' against Zeppelins, shooting down two. The hull was weak and some were modified by Porte giving them a very similar appearance to the Porte-designed Felixstowe F.2A. The H.12 carried four 100lb or two 230lb bombs and up to four Lewis guns.

In mid-April 1917 a series of patrols were instituted, centred on the North Hinder lightship and covering an area some sixty miles in diameter over the submarines' main transit route.[108] Known as the Spider's Web, H.12s carried out the majority of them. The only sinking was that of *UB-32* as she was diving on 22 September 1917 by a Large America with two 230lb bombs. However, numerous submarines were forced to dive.

Porte began to develop his own designs of flying boat, known as Felixtowes. The F.1 was an experimental boat which led to the F.2 and then to the first produced in numbers, the F.2A. By the Armistice just under 100 F.2As had entered service out of 160 ordered. The F.2A combined the Porte Mk I hull with the wings and tail of the H.12, while it was of simple construction enabling a large number of firms to take part in building. It proved rugged and manoeuvrable which, together with its heavy armament of up to seven Lewis guns and two 230lb bombs, enabled it to hold its own against enemy fighters. It was the most expensive aircraft of the day costing £9983 without armament or instruments and only the most skilled pilots were selected to fly them.[109]

The next Porte design, the F.3, was also built in large numbers about 100 entering service (263 ordered). It had a longer endurance than the F.2A and carried more bombs but was less manoeuvrable and, for that reason, many preferred the earlier machine. It carried four 230lb bombs and four Lewis guns.

The first large landplane used in ASW was the Blackburn Kangaroo. It was only half the weight of the flying boats but carried double the bomb load, was slightly faster (98 mph) and had a little more endurance.[110] It also won praise for an excellent view. Only one squadron of eight aircraft became operational in May 1918 but they sighted 12 U-boats, attacked 4 and shared in the sinking of *UC-70* in a total of 600 hours flying. There was a lesson here, ignored by the post-war RAF, that the carrying capacity of the landplane made them the preferred vehicle for ASW. Post-war it was thought that aeroplanes could take off and land in bad weather, unlike flying

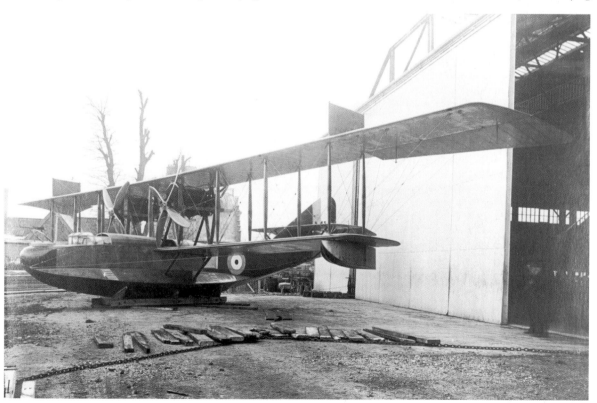

A Felixstowe F.2A was John Porte's fuselage with the wings and tail design of a Curtiss H.12. (Philip Jarrett)

A British seaplane escorting a convoy.

boats on rough water.[111] They had better payload but the then current flotation gear created a lot of drag and 'did not instil confidence'.

Most of the bombs used were 100 or 230lb though trials of a 520lb were carried out from a Kangaroo. The 'Wimperis sight' made a considerable improvement. The fuse was set at 2½-second delay corresponding to a burst at 80 feet; too deep for periscope depth and too shallow for deep diving boats. A dual fuse which could be set just before release for shallow or deep was proposed, or two 200lb would be dropped, one set shallow, one deep.

During the last quarter of 1917 the U-boats had moved inshore again and it was suggested by Captain R Groves (Air Ministry) that protected routes be established down the east coast with the aim of an aircraft passing any given point every 20 minutes. The only aircraft available were some 300 de Havilland 6s which had just been superseded in the training role. They were Cinderellas with poor crews[112] and poor maintenance. In fact, Price says their only virtue was that they floated well when their single, unreliable engine failed. They usually operated as single seaters but when working with a convoy they needed an observer and the wireless and bombs had to be left behind. These 'Scarecrow' patrols sighted submarines sixteen times and, at least, simulated attack on eleven. They probably forced many more to submerge.

Late in the war, some flying boats were fitted with a small hydrophone which could be used from a boat on the water with its engines switched off. Since the engines did not always re-start, this was not popular and the hydrophones were rarely used. During trials in late 1917 it was found that hydrophones could be used from a blimp drifting at up to 8 knots. It was still necessary to switch off the engines but since these could be reached in flight there was a better chance of re-starting. Hydrophones were on order for all blimps when the war ended.

By late 1915, it was established that four-fifths of submarine sightings from aircraft were on the surface and the rest at periscope depth. Three-quarters of the surfaced sightings were able to submerge before the aircraft could attack. On average, a surfaced submarine could be seen at five miles but an alert submarine lookout could see an aeroplane at a rather greater distance and an airship at about ten miles. The U-boat could usually dive unseen.

The last U-boats designed before the war could dive in two minutes and later ones in half that time.[113] Smaller boats could dive in 25 seconds. In two-minutes' diving time an aircraft at 60 mph could cover 2 miles, an airship at 45 mph would move 1½ miles so the odds favoured the U-boat unless visibility was less than 3 miles.

Lessons

Any air cover is better than none, but large numbers were needed.

Only in very calm seas and perfect weather could submerged submarines be seen from the air. The feather
from a periscope could be seen.

Once sighted, it was a race between the diving submarine
and the aircraft—speed matters.

Heavy bombs were needed with suitable fuses

Long endurance was needed—time on station versus
transit.

Convoy escort was more effective than patrols. In the last
eighteen months of the war, 257 ships in convoy were
sunk out of 84,000 sailings; but of these only two were
sunk under air cover. Co-operation with surface ships
was valuable.

Early in 1918 an air operations group was set up for each
area in direct contact with the area Senior Naval
Officer. It was becoming recognised that aircraft, too,
were more effective as convoy escorts than in
patrolling—'hunting'—though each area should have
a 'mobile' squadron to pursue sightings.

Aircrews needed training in ship recognition. Kite balloons and airships could be used for convoy escort with
aeroplanes (de Havilland 6s) up to 15-20 miles offshore and seaplanes further out. It was concluded that
twin engines were less reliable than one.[114]

	Seaplane	Aeroplane	Total
Requirement for 1918	525	66	591
Revised Mar 18	459	726	1180
Operational 1 Jan 18	291	23	314
Operational 9 Nov 18	285	272	557

The Dover and Other Barrages: The Early Years

The policy of distant blockade called for both the Straits
of Dover and the northern exits from the North Sea to be
closed to all enemy ships. Closing the Straits would seem
easy; only just over twenty miles across, partially
obstructed by shoals and quite shallow. However, strong
currents up to 2½ knots and a tidal range of some twenty feet caused numerous problems, many of which were
not recognised in Whitehall.

The overwhelming priority for the Dover Patrol was
the safety of troop ships and supplies crossing the
Channel and in this they were totally successful. During
the whole war there were some 16 million troop crossings
of the Channel and there were no losses. There were
about four sailings a day, each of three troop ships. In
addition, there was heavy traffic passing through the
Straits—150 vessels a day in 1915 and 1916, 100 in 1917.

During the winter of 1914-15 over 7000 mines were
laid off Ostend. While they may have accounted for two
U-boats, their effect was short-lived as the mine sinkers
were too light for the strong current and these early
mines were prone to detonate prematurely. In April 1915
Admiral Reginald H Bacon took over the Dover command. Having commanded the early RN submarine force
and with experience in technical matters he seemed the
right man for the job.

In early 1915 considerable use was made of indicator
nets laid by drifters which could lay up to ten nets, each
1,000 feet long. Later, small contact mines were fitted to
the nets. Soon after Bacon took command the Admiralty
proposed and Bacon accepted a plan to lay a net barrage
from Folkestone to Cap Griz Nez with heavy wooden
floats anchored to the bottom. There were many problems, mostly in mooring, and this barrage was abandoned
in May 1915. It had some effect on morale as Bauer for-
bade the larger U-boats based on Heligoland from using
the Straits. This ban remained in force until December
1916, an undeserved success for a barrier which had been
removed—adding 1,400 miles to a round trip to the
southwest approaches.

In April 1916 Bacon laid a barrier some ten miles in
length and ten miles off the Belgium coast. Mines and
13½ miles of nets were laid on 24 April scoring a kill the
same day. A similar operation in July 1917 sank two more
U-boats.[115]

Bacon tried another cross-channel barrage in
September 1916 using light nets supported from buoys.
They extended down only to 60 feet so that the nets were
backed up by two rows of mines. The barrage was
removed in May 1917 but the nets were re-laid in July,
without mines. By September 1916 the UB-boats from
Flanders were regularly using the Straits and in December
Bauer lifted his ban, making use of the Straits compulsory in January 1917. This rule was soon changed to
optional but in November his successor, Michelsen,
made use of the Straits compulsory—just as the Straits
defences became truly effective.

Success at Last: November 1917-November 1918

The H II mine had been ordered in late 1916 but it took
some time to produce in numbers, probably due to shortage of TNT. By December 1917 12,450 had been produced. The 6320 older mines laid in the Bight during
1915-16 had been almost entirely ineffective, sinking
only six trawlers.

From 1 February to the end of May 1917 122 UB and
UC boats passed the Straits. By the Admiralty's own estimates there were about 30 transits per month. Early in
1918 the net barrage was abandoned.

A new minefield with H II mines was laid from 21
November 1917 to February 1918. By the war's end 9573
mines had been laid. A considerable amount of care went
into the arrangement of the mines within the field.
Mines had to be sufficiently far apart to prevent counter
mining (about 150ft). This distance was much greater
than the beam of a submarine (20ft) and hence there was
a real chance of a U-boat passing through a single line.
To be sure of sinking a submarine seven rows of mines
would be needed and this was all at one depth. Repeating
the staggered rows of mines at each of five depths would
mean thirty-five rows of mines extending over eighteen
miles needing 26-28,000 mines. However, it was recog-
nized that the barrage would be effective against U-boats
if there was a one in six chance sinking a German sub-

Aftermath of the raids on Ostend (top) and Zeebrugge (bottom) in April 1918. These were undoubtedly the most spectacular anti U-boat operatons of the war, but though they were meticulously planned and carried out with immense courage, their success was limited. At Ostend ill luck and resourceful German defence combined to thwart the attempted blocking of the port, while Zeebrugge only remained closed for a few weeks.

marine on a single passage. This implied two rows at each depth with a total of 4,000 mines though it was hoped to increase coverage to four rows in due course.

To protect the patrol vessels and also to force submarines to dive, a double row of mines at 8ft below low tide level was planned from near Folkestone to Cap Griz Nez. Bacon planned illumination by night but intended to defer its introduction for one month after the mines were laid since the illuminations would disclose both the existence and position of the field while surprise might win a few victims in the first month.

Bacon was opposed to the use of flares as this would disclose the position of the patrol vessels and render them liable to attack by surface vessels.[116] Instead he proposed the use of searchlights mounted on three moored vessels based on light vessels.[117] Each ship would have four searchlights, two with fixed beams meeting those from its neighbour and two sweeping sectors. These vessels would be armed giving protection against submarine guns and even able to offer some defence against destroyers. They would be bulged to protect against torpedoes.

In the meantime Sir Eric Geddes (First Lord from July 1917 to early 1918) set up the Dover Barrage Committee under Sir Roger Keyes within the Admiralty. The committee included 3 captains and a civil engineer. When this committee was initiated, U-boats were passing the Straits frequently, with few losses. It was not unreasonable for Geddes to demand action. On the other hand, it is always wrong to set up a committee at headquarters to second guess an operational commander. Under Keyes' energetic leadership the committee even proposed that there should be an officer in London in command of the barrage, independent of the Admiral at Dover. (This proposal was dropped when Keyes went to Dover!)

Keyes accused Bacon of belonging to the material school dedicated to preserving his ship while he, Keyes, saw attacking the enemy as the prime objective. Keyes seems to be wrong on two counts. There seems no evidence that Bacon attached undue importance to preserving his ships but, more importantly, the Dover barrage was a material problem.

By October 1917 there were 20 parallel lines of mines over a depth of 6 miles. Successes soon began; UB-56 was sunk on the night of 19 December, U-109 on 26 January 1918 and UB-38 on 8 February and nine more would be sunk before the Armistice.

The risk of passing the minefield was of great concern to U-boat commanders. In January 1918 there were only five attempts and the next month Commodore Andreas Michelsen, the operational chief, accepted that any attempt at passage should be optional. The last fleet boat to transit the Straits was U-55 which left Heligoland on 18 February. The Flanders flotilla continued to transit but in small numbers: 26 in January, 29 in February, only five in June and 9 in July—the last was UB-103 on 14 August. Four were mined off Flanders. Note that the Zeebrugge and Ostend raids are not discussed as they had virtually no effect on ASW—but were good for British morale.

The Straits were finally closed but Bacon had gone. He was dismissed in January failing at that date Fisher's requirement to sink U-boats. His 'failure' was almost entirely due to the lack of a satisfactory mine, but that was not his fault—the reason was a lack of understanding of the local problems in Whitehall.

The Nab Tower[118]

One interesting proposal from Keyes' committee was the use of mines controlled from magnetic indicator loops being developed at Aberdour. The control would be in ten fixed towers spaced across the Channel. This was designed by G Menzies under Sir Alexander Gibbs, Civil Engineer-in-Chief. Two, started in spring 1918, were built for the RN at Shoreham by Royal Engineers. There was an abundance of shingle with a single track rail to the eastern end of the harbour. The bases were built on land, behind a dam, then removed and the superstructure added afloat. On the base there were three hexagonal tiers with ledges about 12ft wide. Above this was a 50ft tower of steel, timber covered. Davits, crane, and an AA gun crew of 90 were installed. Each tower was about 190ft tall and 170ft across base and cost about £1.5 million. Unfinished at the Armistice, one was towed out to act as a lighthouse on Nab Rock on 12 September 1920 and may be seen off the Isle of Wight. The other was demolished during the 1920s.

The Fast 'R' Class Submarine

In March 1917 DNC proposed a submarine design with a very high underwater speed. This was rejected initially but later in the year Commodore (S) suggested that the design should be completed and 12 were ordered as the 'R' class in October.[119] The final design had a single British built 'H' class diesel giving a surface speed of 9.5 knots. Submerged, there was a 1200 hp motor driving a single propeller with a trial speed of 15 knots.[120] This could be sustained for one hour using maximum discharge rate on the battery. Later it was suggested that 12½ knots was a practical maximum which could be held for an hour and three-quarters. They had four large hydrophones in the bow which it was hoped would enable them to attack fully submerged with six bow tubes. Experience after the Second World War showed that an attack using only passive sonar was difficult. No records have been found of the 'R' class attacking in this way.

Only two 'R' class submarines were operational when the war ended and they were deployed in the Irish Sea, which was not a good hunting ground for anti-submarine operations. R8 carried out an attack on a U-boat in which there was a torpedo failure.[121] R7 made a contact and used high speed to get within 2500 yards, 3 points off the enemy bow and then used slow speed.[122] Most were sold in 1923 but two were retained for antisubmarine training until the early 1930s.

Particulars

Displacement tons	503 (Submerged)
Dimensions ft	163·9 x 15·3 x
Armament	6-18in tubes (Design shows 6 spare)

1-4in gun may have been mounted at first in some.

Shipbuilding

During the early years of the war the output of merchant ships from UK shipyards fell below pre-war levels due to concentration on warships and to the loss of skilled men to the army.

UK Losses and Output in 1,000 gross tons

Date	Losses	Output	World output
1914	497	675	1013
1915	1103	651	1202
1916	1498	542	1688
1917	4010	1163	2938
1918	1924	1310 (10 Months)	4008

In December 1916 an Act was passed which appointed a Shipping Controller responsible for 'providing and maintaining an efficient supply of shipping.' The first meeting of the Merchant Shipping Advisory Committee took place five days before Christmas. It was decided to start an extensive shipbuilding programme with ships of simple design and, as far as possible, with standard hulls and machinery.

These measures began to take effect late in 1917 as did an enormous building programme in the USA. The last months of the war will be examined in more detail.

Losses and World (Allied) Output in 1,000 gross tons

Year	Quarter	Losses World	Output UK	World
1917	3rd	1494	249	675
	4th	1273	420	991
1918	1st	1143	320	870
	2nd	962	443	1243
	3rd	916	411	1384
	Oct	178	136	511

By the second quarter of 1918 world output was comfortably exceeding losses, indeed output exceeded all but losses in the worst quarter of the war. By the third quarter, UK output was close to UK Losses. (512 lost, 411 built) These figures form part of the evidence that the U-boat war was won in 1918 and that there could not have been a successful new offensive in 1919.

Standard Ships[123]

The first order for standard ships was placed by the Shipping Controller for 100 ships which were to have priority over the 500 private merchant ships already on order. Orders were also placed in the USA. In early 1917 that country was still neutral, so the orders were placed through the Cunard company. Several other companies were also involved, in the management. By March 1917 some 700,000 tons were on order in the USA. Soon after the USA declared war (4 April 1917) all ships building in that country were requisitioned (3 August).[124] Others were ordered in Canada and Japan. All these ships were allocated names beginning with 'War' (except the later, small concrete ships).

Excluding US production, 821 ships were ordered. Of these 416 were completed to government order and 279 were sold to private owners at the end of the war, before completion, while the remaining 126 were cancelled. Of the 416 government ships, 23 were lost, 15 became Admiralty oilers and the remainder were sold. The USA built 3,500 cargo ships.

Within the UK ships were built of a few different lengths so that every building slip could be used to full advantage. Designs for cargo ships were obtained from builders experienced in that type of ship with a maximum of cargo capacity whilst requiring the minimum of materials and labour. Some builders had problems with the first ship of unfamiliar design but later ships would show savings. Altogether, 61 shipbuilders and 34 engine builders were involved.

Some features reflected wartime experience: the crew were accommodated in the poop rather than the forecastle (presumably as protection against mines), masts and derrick posts were designed to hinge down, the single wireless mast was telescopic and the funnel was short. These later changes not only helped to reduce the dis-

Particulars of major British Built Standard Ships

Type	A	B	C	D	E	F	G	Z	N
Length, pp	400	400	331	285	376	411'6	450	400	411'6
Drft, load	25	25'1	21'8	19	23'9	28'7½	29	25'1	28
Gross tons	5030	5030	3000	4750[1]	4400	6440	6000	5800	6500
Dwt tons	8175	8075	5050		7020	10795	10800	8000	10500
ihp	2500	2500	2200	1900	2500	3650	5500	2500	2300
Speed, kts	11	11	11½	11½	11½	12	12	11	11
Lead yard	Henderson	do.	Tyne SB	Austin	Duncan	Thompson	W, Clark	Swan Hunter	Harland & Wolff

1 Displacement

tance at which a ship could be seen but made it more difficult to estimate their course also helped by the introduction of 'dazzle' painting, later made compulsory.[125] The A and B designs (See Table) were the most numerous; A with a single deck and B with two decks. The designs were adapted to form the AO and BO oilers.

War Shamrock, A type, was the first 'Standard' to go to sea, completed by Harland and Wolff in August 1917. This company was the biggest builder of standard ships, completing 26 in 1918. Before the war they employed 13,735 workers at Belfast which rose to 21, 550 by August 1918 (Over 40,000 counting Clyde, Mersey and Southampton sites).

Some of the building times were remarkable; one Harland and Wolff ship in August 1918 was launched twenty-three weeks after being laid down and completed five days later. Records did not last long and in September Workman Clark completed *War Beetle* (B type) in 3½ days from launch while in November the North Eastern Marine Engineering Co installed the machinery of *War Citadel* (F1) in 63 hours after launch.

The C type was smaller and designed for coal or iron ore using shorter building slips and the D type was even shorter. The two-deck E type was intermediate between the C and the 400ft A and B. These five ship designs needed only two basic sets of machinery, 2,500 ihp for A, B and E and less for the smaller ships. (The Ds were 1,900 ihp while the same engine developed 2,200 ihp for the Cs with watertube boilers).

These were followed by the shelter deck F and F1 and by the big and fast Gs, designed as refrigerated ships.[129]

The provisional payment agreed when the contract was placed came under four headings, two fixed and two variable. The 'fixed' costs were the establishment charges (overheads) and profit whilst materials and labour were seen as 'variable' and estimated as an average when the contract was placed. On completion, the estimated price was paid in full but if the variable cost was less than the estimate the builder had to refund the difference. If he could show that his variable costs were greater than the estimate, the difference was paid to him. No increase in the fixed costs was allowed.

National Shipyards

In the summer of 1916 a yard was set up on the Wye by a group of major shipowners. This incorporated a small yard belonging to Edward Finch. The first problem was skilled labour and Deputy Controller of Auxiliary Shipbuilding suggested the use of prisoners of war as unskilled labour. It was difficult to use prisoners in a private yard and skilled labour was very difficult–and expensive–in the area. The government decided to set up three new yards with a total of 38 slips costing £3,887,000.[130] Much of the work was to be placed with structural steel companies who would fabricate units to be brought by rail to the yards for assembly on the slip. It was hoped to build 78 ships of 10,500 tons dwt each year.

By April 1918 two berths were complete at Chepstow, now incorporating the private yard, and six were building. The first ship was laid down in October 1918 but the war ended without a single completion. Six ships were completed after the war. This project appears as an

A convoy at sea escorted by American destroyers. (CPL)

expensive failure but had the war continued into 1919 it might, possibly, have been viewed differently. To start up new yards using an unfamiliar prefabrication process takes time and good management.

Conclusions

The Admiralty and the Royal Navy made two principal mistakes before the war. The first of these, that ethical considerations would rule out a submarine attack on trade, was entirely excusable in terms of peacetime thinking but it had unfortunate consequences in that ASW was given low priority. Ryan developed a usable hydrophone with about three years from start in 1914; what a pity he did not start in 1910.

The second mistake was in neglecting and opposing convoy. As discussed earlier, this was a long-standing error and was not corrected until nearly too late. To some extent this was due to the lack of a co-ordinated ASW staff and, perhaps, a C-in-C. Similarly, research may have suffered from lack of co-ordination, though too much direction from the centre can be harmful.

Looking at the achievements, it is remarkable that aircraft like the Large America (and variants) and the Kangaroo were brought into service so quickly. Hydrophones, depth charges and other devices were in service in under three years despite shortcomings in scientific knowledge and industrial production. ASDIC was almost ready. Despite some problems the old Admiralty machine did well.

On any criterion—monthly sinkings, sinkings per U-boat at sea or losses of U-boats—the unrestricted attack on trade which came so close to success in early 1917 had failed by the Armistice in 1918. Any attempt to extend the war into 1919 would have met ASDIC, more depth charges, better aircraft used more effectively and a variety of advanced mines. The vast building programme in the USA was proving successful whilst the increased orders for U-boats were already looking unrealistic, particularly in the supply of essential components. Training of crews and, most important, training of commanding officers was already a serious problem with the 1918 force and might have been impossible if the intended 1919 figures were achieved.

The U-boats were defeated.

Notes

1. V E Tarrant, *The U-Boat Offensive 1914-1945* (London, 1989); J Terraine, *Business in Great Waters*, (London, 1989). Two excellent books.
2. *Nottingham* and *Falmouth* 19 Aug, 1916. (*Hampshire*, whose sinking was notorious for bringing about the death of Kitchener, was not acting with the Grand Fleet when sunk.)
3. I have leant heavily on Nicholas Lambert's book—*Sir John Fisher's Naval Revolution* (University of South Carolina, 1999)—in this section though it is reasonably consistent with my own *The Grand Fleet, design and construction*, (London, 1999).
4. Brown, *Grand Fleet.*
5. Lambert, p 46

6. The lack of bow hydroplanes meant that they were virtually unstable at speeds less than full.
7. ADM1/7515 quoted at length by Lambert
8. Peter Padfield, *Aim Straight*, (London, 1966).
9. Ignored in the US Civil War.
10. Terraine gives an excellent account of the legal complications.
11. In the United Kingdom the Liberal government said it would abide by the declaration.
12. Sources vary on the fuel used by these engines. Roessler is probably the most reliable saying paraffin (kerosene).
13. This first satisfactory design entered service in 1912 demonstrating that it would not have been possible to build a large U-boat force prior to the war as is sometimes suggested.
14. Before the war the German command only envisaged North Sea operations and it is unclear why their U-boats had this endurance.
15. C Ritchie, *Q-ships*, (Lavenham, 1985). An accurate and comprehensive work
16. Stowed externally meant that depth settings and hence location of the field had to be selected before leaving harbour.
17. Mines now carried internally.
18. Known as the Children of Sorrow; they carried 34 mines
19. There should have been two but *U-22* had to return with defects.
20. It will be suggested that repairs to the High Seas Fleet caused considerable delays to the U-boat building programme.
21. Early middle sized U-boats carried 6 torpedoes whilst later developments had up to 16 torpedoes.
22. Much of France's coal mining area was occupied by the Germans.
23. After the Second World War it was assumed that 25-30 mines would be needed to sink one ship.
24. This conference also approved a programme for a considerable number of U-cruisers which was to disrupt the building of standard U-boats.
25. Peter Kelly, 'War against the Wounded', *Warship 2000-2001*.
26. It is often said that there were only sox weeks food supplies left. This may have been true but it was not an unusual figure as the new harvest approached. The winter of 1918-19 would have been the danger point if losses continued at the April rate.
27. Many of these were a new, simple class—UF—discussed later.
28. Said to be about one quarter for ships in convoy.
29. Some of the key papers are summarised in D K Brown, *Warrior to Dreadnought*, (London, 1997). pp 19, 87, 106, 109, 121: Spencer Robinson—evidence to 1871 Committee on Designs; also E J Reed evidence. Sir Nathaniel Barnaby. 'On the Fighting Power of the Merchant Ship in Naval Warfare'. *Trans INA 1877* Also his book *Naval Developments of the Century*, London, 1904. Capt P Colomb. 'Convoys: Are they any longer possible?' RUSI ,March 1887. Carnavon Committee 1879. 'Defence of British Possessions and Commerce Abroad'. (Parliamentary Papers).
30. A Price, *Aircraft versus Submarine*, (London, 1973).
31. Stephen Roskill, *Hankey Man of Secrets*, (London, 1970). Vol 1. p335
32. Rear Admiral (Sir) Alexander Ludovic Duff had been second in command to Admiral Sir Doveton Sturdee, the victor of the Battle of the Falklands in 1914. He was no 'Yes

Man' though Roskill quotes Leslie Norman as having no confidence in him. He was put in charge of the Anti-Submarine Department created by Jellicoe in December 1916.

33 W S Churchill, *Thoughts and Adventures*, (London 1932). p97

34 This is disputed by Lloyd George who maintained that there were only crack liner captains present. See John Winton, *Convoy*, (London 1983). p51.

35 No one noticed that this would correspond with imports of 200 million tons per year, six times the pre-war figure!

36 One may guess that Henderson had a hand in drafting it.

37 The various accounts do not agree on key dates.

38 None of this was in his book.

39 When a squadron of US battleships joined the Grand Fleet, the USN was asked to send only coal burners because of the oil shortage.

40 I was confused for years as a result of the poor education I received in statistics. My two children seem to have been taught as badly.

41 Admiral Spindler. 'The Value of the Submarine in Naval Warfare'. *USNI Proceedings*, May 1926, p841. Quoted in R H Gibson and M Prendergast, *The German Submarine War 1914-1918*, (London, 1931), p333

42 The figure of deaths among aces is unclear. It was at least six and may have been higher.

43 Second World War experience showed that the strain of commanding an operational submarine was too great and in some cases their nerve would fail.

44 Barley & Waters Papers. Naval Historical Branch.

45 D K Brown. 'Atlantic Escorts', *The Battle of the Atlantic (Conference) papers*, (London, 1994).

46 It is said that only five ships were sunk while under aircraft escort.

47 As with the 'milch cows' of the Second World War.

48 In the context of this article there can only be a short section on 'intelligence'. For a fuller account see: P Beesley, *Room 40*, (London, 1982) and R Grant, *U Boat Intelligence 1914-1918*, (Hamden, CT, 1969).

49 This might well have changed with the introduction of Asdic.

50 The author qualified in such a suit ca 1950.

51 Merz was Director of Experiment and Research from late in 1917. (See below under 'Board of Invention and Research'.)

52 More advanced structural theory, better steels and welding gave the Second World War boats a much increased diving depth.

53 This had been recognised before the war and the G class were intended to try alternative designs of engine.

54 Diesel advised on the design.

55 This was developed by Scott's with the help of McTaggart Scott for HMS *Swordfish* and further developed for the 'K's whose size made power operation essential.

56 The exact number varies slightly from one source to another due mainly to uncertainty concerning boats under construction when the war ended. A W Johns, 'German Submarines', *Transactions of the Institution of Naval Architects* 120, Vol. 62, p. 19, gives 378 which excludes those broken up at the end of the war. The table is based on Gibson and Prendergast.

57 Vulkan Hamburg, Blohm & Voss Hamburg, A G Weser Bremen, Bremer-Vulkan Vegesack. These major yards accounted for all those completed but forty-one of boats built or building. The smaller yards were mainly brought in for the UF programme of which none were finished.

58 In late 1916 (post Pless; see footnote 24) orders were placed for 2 medium, 9 cruisers and 16 UB.

59 Detection of these minute currents with First World War technology would be very difficult. J A Craig 'The First Ten Years', written for the *Journal of Naval Science* but, I think, not published suggests that something similar was tried in the war and worked at close range. I am grateful to the last editor R A D Heward for letting me see this paper.

60 Note that McEvoy's work was two years earlier than H B Jackson's pioneering work on wireless at the Torpedo School, then a very effective research establishment.

61 For a fuller account see W Hackmann, *Seek and Strike*,(London, 1984).

62 He was described as a 'Forceful character' and soon upset the scientific staff.

63 Ryan's secretary was Lt Cdr A Ashley Froude RNVR, son of the historian J A Froude and cousin of Edmund Froude, Superintendent of the Admiralty Experiment Works (AEW), Haslar. I am amazed that AEW was not brought into ASW work.

64 Sir J J Thompson, Sir Charles Parsons and Dr George Beilby.

65 It was frequently known as the Board for Intrigue and Revenge, Fisher's vehicle to re-establish himself and punish those who had led to his resignation.

66 *Journal of Naval Science*, July 1965.

67 A B Wood was to dominate underwater research for the navy for the next half century. His career is described in The A B Wood Memorial Number, *Journal of Naval Science* (July 1965), effectively Wood's autobiography. I am grateful to the last editor R A D Heward for letting me see this.

68 *Nyker* was used for experiments in radio control and it is said that it was an acronym for 'No Yachting Knowledge Required.

69 Wood is described by all who knew him including Second World War naval officers as modest and very easy to get on with.

70 Sir Sothern Holland, Sir Ross Skinner and Sir Alfred Egerton (MID)—known as the Holland-Skinner report.

71 It is worth noting that NPL's hydrodynamic work was under an ex-AEW naval constructor!

72 One suspect he was another maverick. He demanded that his work be kept secret from the BIR with whom he had quarrelled over an earlier invention and, correctly, ignored Admiralty advice on the hydrophone system.

73 In December 1916 the ASD was set up with some 15 officers and relieved Operations of control of ships and aircraft in ASW and sweeping. The Director came under the First Sea Lord but close was to the Chief of Naval Staff. This was a big step forward in bringing together aspects of ASW though it may be argued that a C-in-C Western Approaches was also needed (as in the Second World War). But the primitive radios of the day may have made central command too difficult.

74 A much more detailed account is given in Hackmann.

75 *Journal of Naval Science*, July 1965, p39. The word Asdephone was also used in the very early days.

76 Hackmann has found no trace of an Investigation

Committee, the usually quoted interpretation of -ic.

77 He was a Russian who had escaped when under supervision by tsarist police for his socialist activities.

78 French amplifiers became available in Parkestone Quay.

79 Much later Chief Scientist ASWE.

80 Built 1908, requisitioned 1915; 78 tons.

81 Built 1898, hired 1915; 193 tons.

82 See illustrations in Hackmann: 4.6 & 4.7.

83 It was later found that the draught of the P boats was too small for Asdic to function well.

84 'Taffrail', *Endless Story* (London 1931): 265.

85 This size of charge would not be certain to open the pressure hull of a double hull submarine.

86 Technical History series of the Naval Historical Branch: TH 40.

87 Only 1000 were ordered in August 1915.

88 The figure of 14ft seems to have originated with Jellicoe. There is no supporting evidence. D R Messemer, *Find and Destroy*, (Annapolis 2001), p77, claims 70ft to sink and 140ft serious damage, very unlikely figures.

89 Trials were carried out in January 1917 with various guns against a replica U-boat hull. Repeat trials in June confirmed that nothing less that 4.7 was effective. Improved shells and fuses were issued in 1918. I have been told that there were more trials against surrendered U-boats after the war confirming that a 4.7 was needed but I have been unable to trace any record.

90 See *Find and Destroy*.

91 By May there were 2056 on order of eight designs.

92 TH7.

93 Viscount Jellicoe, *The Crisis of the Naval War*, (London 1920) says that on 23 March 1917 an incoming torpedo was hit by a howitzer at 600 yards!

94 They have been discussed in detail in D K Brown, 'Some thoughts on British mines in World War I', *Warship 2001-2002*: 99-102.

95 See the subsequent parts of Iain McCallum's 'The Riddle of the Shells', the first instalment of which appears in this edition of *Warship*.

96 The air contribution to the ASW war is not well covered in either the RN or RAF official histories—each left it to the other. The best published account is in: Price, *op. cit.* and TH4 is a valuable source.

97 Williamson was to concentrate on the 'air' side and had a major input into early aircraft carriers (Grand Fleet). He was probably the originator of the 'island' superstructure. In his 1912 paper he suggested converting a *Monmouth* class cruiser to a carrier. This probably influence the conversion of HMS *Hermes*, but no ASW operations were tested during the 1913 trials with *Hermes*.

98 Note that it would take 15 minutes to cover 10 miles at the airship speed of 40 mph.

99 Even during the Second World War it took some time to develop reliable fuses.

100 Patrick Abbott, *The British Airship at War, 1914-1918*, (Lavenham 1989). An excellent book.

101 Re-numbering and rebuilding complicate the issue. See Abbott.

102 Three more were completed but not accepted when the war ended.

103 One Lewis could be mounted above the envelope but was rarely fitted.

104 The pilot had given up but finding no one else was flying he restarted and completed the race. His flying average was about 61 mph.

105 Judging by the subsequent performance of the H4 Porte was lucky the trans Atlantic flight did not take place.

106 Including eight built in the UK.

107 O Thetford, *British Naval Aircraft since 1912*, (London, 1962).

108 T D Hallam, *The Spider Web*, (London, 1919). (Reprinted by Arms and Armour Press, 1979.)

109 G E Livock, *To the Ends of the Air*, (London, 1973).

110 The extra weight of a flying boat hull means that wings have to generate more lift by increasing their angle of attack which, in turn, means more drag.

111 TH4.

112 TH4 says the observers were former trawlermen of poor physique. There was a great shortage of armourers.

113 The design differences were small, I suspect better procedures were used.

114 A familiar problem in reliability studies. The chance of one engine failing in a twin-engined plane is greater but, more important, the chance of a twin-engined plane being forced to land is less.

115 There were a considerable number of U-boats lost from unknown causes and it may well be that some of these fell victim to mines or barrages.

116 This happened.

117 Admiral Bacon (*The Concise Story of the Dover Patrol*, London 1932) points out, p159, that the Official History, Vol V, p180 is 'utterly untrue'.

118 J Stafford, *The Mystery Towers*, Marlpins Museum Publication No 1, (Shoreham, undated).

119 Two cancelled at the end of the war.

120 Speed was measured using the log which would not be very reliable. Raising the periscope slowed the boat by 1 knot.

121 Why did she not fire a salvo?

122 TH1.

123 W H Mitchell and L A Sawyer, *British Standard Ships of World War I*, Liverpool, 1968.

124 A few of these finally entered British service during Second World War with 'Empire' names.

125 It is often claimed that losses fell after the introduction of dazzle painting in the spring of 1917. This is unlikely and any reduction was due to convoy. There was no great reduction in losses of unescorted ships though dazzle may have helped.

126 Many shelter decks ran with special freeboard certificates enabling them to operate at deeper draught with the shelter deck openings closed.

127 Chepstow, Mon, Beachley, Glos and Portbury, Som.

WARSHIP NOTES

This section comprises a number of short articles and notes, generally highlighting little known aspects of warship history.

BRITISH MILITARY POWERBOAT TRUST

Stuart Robertson describes the activities of an organisation preserving the heritage of some unusual British service craft.

Developed from the record-breaking speedboats of the inter-war years, the British military powerboats of the 1930s and 1940s were the finest in the world, so far ahead of their time that their design has never been surpassed. Operated by the Royal Navy, RAF and Army, they performed in various roles including rescuing downed airmen, tending seaplanes, and as powerful gunboats. Most of them are now long gone. However, the British Military Powerboat Trust has been established to save and restore important examples, for operational and static display to the public.

The BMPT, set up in 1998, is based in the former Husbands Shipyard Estate on the waterside at Marchwood in Hampshire, England, itself a site of historic interest. Nearby is the Royal Navy Ordnance Depot where the famous Mulberry Harbours used after D-Day were constructed.

The first vessel restored by the Trust was RAF *ST 206*, a 37ft seaplane tender (re-launched in 1993 after 3 years' work), built in 1931 and sea-trialled by Lawrence of Arabia. Pride of the collection is the 30kt, 64ft *HSL 102* (an RAF Air-Sea rescue launch) built in 1936 and active in the Battle of Britain and the Dunkirk evacuations.

An ambitious project was recently completed with the re-launch of the

72ft, 40kt *MGB 81* in September 2002. *MGB 81* (renamed *MTB 416* in September 1943) served with the famous 8th MGB Flotilla (later the 1st MTB Flotilla) as part of the Plymouth Command (Dartmouth) and Nore Command (Felixstowe), and was in fierce, high-speed action with German forces on nine occasions during the war.

Another notable project included bringing Schnellboot *S-130* over from Wilhelmshaven in February 2003 for restoration. *S-130* took part in the attack on US Navy LSTs practising for Operation Overlord, the invasion of Occupied France in 1944. In the evening of 27 April 1944, S-130 left Cherbourg, one of nine boats from the 5th and 9th S-boot flotillas sent to attack eight American LST landing craft on invasion training in Lyme Bay and escorted by a single British corvette, HMS *Azalea*. The ensuing action left 638 American sailors and soldiers dead.

Work has also begun on the Trust's first project to be funded by the Heritage Lottery Fund, the restoration of the fleet tender *FMB 43597*. This vessel saw action with HMS

Diadem from 1943 to 1950 and served HMS *Ark Royal* from 1954 to 1969. The HLF is also considering supporting a large project for the renovation of the 40kt torpedo-boat *CMB 331*, an obsolescent 55ft vessel based on First World War designs, ordered by the Philippine government in 1940 and requisitioned by the RN upon completion in 1941.

Several other boats have already been assembled in the sheds to form the basis of the exhibition centre. These include a 44ft Rivers class Army launch, 41ft seaplane tender *ST 1502*, 23ft German river defence vessel, and a 21kt 12ft target launch *Queen Gull*.

As well as static craft undergoing restoration, there is an extensive collection of models, photographs and drawings of craft. Engines permanently on display include the ubiquitous Perkins S6M diesel, Packard 2500M, two Rolls-Royce Sea Griffons, and a huge 3700hp Napier Deltic on loan from the Napier Heritage Trust. BMPT archives may be accessed; they also have an honorary Trust historian who will conduct research by agreement. The BMPT welcomes visitors, and *Warship* readers may like to know that RAF *ST 206* and *HSL 102* are available for charter.

For further information contact:

British Military Powerboat Trust,
Husbands Shipyard Estate,
Cracknore Hard,
Marchwood,
Hampshire,
SO40 4ZD
Tel: 02380 428 443.
web: www.bmpt.org.uk;
email: bmpt@supanet.com

HMS GANNET SAVED
Steve Dent and Martin Robson report on the latest news in the campaign to restore the last Victorian gunboat

The future of HMS *Gannet*, one of Britain's very few surviving Victorian warships, has been secured with the announcement in 2002 of a £1.4 million grant by the Heritage Lottery Fund. This award, together with previous sums set aside for the vessel by both the Heritage Lottery Fund and Medway Council, takes the total grant package to over £3 million and means that after several years of uncertainty, work on the ship, now berthed at Chatham Historic Dockyard, can at last be resumed.

Built at Sheerness and launched in in 1878, the 1130-ton, 170-foot long *Gannet* was built of teak with an iron frame, and was powered by both sail and steam. Confusingly described at various times as a sloop, gunboat or corvette, she and her sister ships were among the workhorses of the Royal Navy in the later years of the nineteenth century, policing the waters of the Empire and protecting British interests worldwide.

After years as a training hulk near Gosport, the *Gannet* arrived at Chatham in 1987 with her masts and guns, many of her fittings, and even parts of her deck removed. While the hull has since been conserved at considerable expense, little other work has been carried out while funding was sought for the remainder of the restoration. The ship received a major boost in 2000 when her significance was recognised by the National Historic Ships Committee who listed her among the Core Collection of Britain's heritage fleet.

The planned restoration, the result of detailed consulatation between the Heritage Lottery Fund, Medway Council and the Chatham Historic Dockyard Trust, will include further work to the hull, together with the decks, masts, spars and rigging. This phase of work is expected to last until 2004 when it is planned to open the vessel to the public. The aim is for her to be returned to her 1886 appearance, when she saw action defending of the port of Suakin in the Sudan.

HMS Gannet;
(above) in her present location in dry dock at Chatham Historic Dockyard, and (left) photographed while in service, at Malta.
(Courtesy of Chatham Historic Dockyard)

Commenting on the grant, Bill Ferris, Chief Executive of Chatham Historic Dockyard Trust, said "We have been waiting to resume work on HMS *Gannet* for some time. This project will be fascinating for our visitors to watch. A range of traditional dockyard crafts and skills will be used to return this unique ship of the Victorian Navy to her former glory. When completed *Gannet* will change the dockyard skyline, her masts will be almost 100ft tall and the ship will become a stunning attraction".

HMS *Gannet* can be seen at:
The Historic Dockyard,
Chatham, Kent ME4 4TZ
Info Line +44 (0)1634 823807
Fax +44 (0)1634 823801
E-mail: info@chdt.org.uk
http://www.chdt.org.uk/

NAVAL HISTORICAL COLLECTORS AND RESEARCH ASSOCIATION
The Association has changed its contact address

The NHRCA was formed in 1988 by a group of naval enthusiasts, many of whom were retired naval officers and ratings, who did not feel that any existing organisation catered for their interests. The Association covers a wide range of subjects including war-ships, merchant vessels, memorabilia, medals and naval genealogy. The Association also has its own research service which will search service records for officers and ratings, honours and awards, action reports and chronologies of ships' service.

The NHRCA's quarterly journal, *The Review*, contains a wide range of articles on naval history from the eighteenth century to the present day. *The Review* also includes medal rolls, casualty lists, news from museums and the Public Records Office, plus book reviews. There is also a free facility to place notes and appeals for information.

For more details please contact:

Membership Secretary, NHRCA,
30 Compit Hills, Roughton Road,
Cromer, Norfolk. NR27 9LJ
United Kingdom.

BISMARCK: CONTROVERSY
Stuart Robertson reports on a celebrity entering an old debate concerning one of the world's more famous warships.

Traditional British accounts of the demise of the *Bismarck* took a salvo recently as new evidence gathered from submarine expeditions to the wreck by a Hollywood film-maker and US teams argues that it was not British gunfire and torpedoes but German scuttling charges that sent the *Bismarck* to the floor of the Atlantic on 27 May 1941.

American investigators and the Canadian director of *Titanic*, James Cameron, claim that their new underwater photography, taken for a US documentary on the ship, shows the hull in surprisingly good shape, and that no damage from British fire is visible along the sides. Thus, while the *Bismarck* was disabled by British action, the battleship sank only because the Nazis scuttled it. 'There isn't any evidence of shells or torpedoes near the water line, much less below it. We conclusively proved there was no way the British sank that ship,' said Alfred McLaren, a submarine expert who studied the wreck on two expeditions. The case for a scuttling rests further on the claims of a number of German veterans' testimonies that charges were set, and similar evidence from previous US dives in 1989 and 2001.

The *Bismarck* sank after an epic eight-day chase through the North Sea and Atlantic; a hit by Swordfish torpedo bombers damaged its rudder before it could reach the safety of occupied France. During the last stages of battle, Royal Navy battleships and cruisers fired nearly 3,000 shells and torpedoes at the *Bismarck* until she finally sank.

Despite the US claims, British naval experts have continued to dis-

AUTUMN 2002   VOLUME 15.2

The Review, *quarterly journal of the NHCRA.*

Bismarck *photographed from* Prinz Eugen *in Grimstadfjord, Norway in May 1941. Views like this, giving a vivid impression of her size and her majestic, powerful appearance, help explain how the myth of her being 'unsinkable' grew up, especially under a regime such as the Nazis' where image played such a central role.*

miss the idea that *Bismarck* was scuttled. David Mearns, a British explorer and author who has independently examined the wreck, disagrees with the recent findings: 'It is only when you start getting closer and closer,' he says, 'that you see that this beautiful hull is actually peppered with torpedo holes and large-calibre shell holes, that she was actually sort of beaten to death by all this British gunnery.' Historian Antony Preston, who argues that the *Bismarck* embodied inherently flawed technology, blames the 'widespread reverential attitude' to any example of Nazi German technology for perpetuating the myth that the *Bismarck* was 'unsinkable', and points out that 'these rather dubious claims ignore the testimony of survivors to the effect that the ship was an inferno between decks, and nobody from below survived. Enemy gunfire had shredded everything except the main machinery. That would explain why no guns were firing after 20 minutes.' Furthermore, in response to American claims that not a single shell penetrated the 12.6-inch thick armour, Preston draws attention to British underwater photographs, which show around 400 holes in the hull: 'eyewitnesses say that the *Bismarck* was a waterlogged hulk. Something made those 400 holes, many of them heavy-calibre hits which penetrated the armour. The salvo of four 21in torpedoes fired by HMS *Dorsetshire* undoubtedly hastened her end, but she had already been flooded by thousands of tons of seawater.'

Dr. Holger Herwig of Calgary University appeared to scupper Cameron's controversial claims when, after acting as historical adviser to Cameron's expedition in spring 2002, he admitted the wreck showed signs of massive damage from British guns. 'The port side...looks like Swiss cheese. I would say I'm now 99% certain that the *Bismarck* was sunk, not scuttled,' he said.

Sources:

A Preston, *The World's Worst Warships* (Conway, 2002)

William J Broad, 'New cry? "Scuttle the *Bismarck*!"', *The New York Times*, 5 December 2002

Ned Potter, 'Who Really Sank the

Bismarck?', ABCNews, 6 December 2002

The Centre for Military and Strategic Studies (University of Calgary) website, November 2002.

James Cameron's Expedition: Bismarck: Q & A, Discovery Channel website, 23 January 2003

USS MASSACHUSETTS

R. P. Largess provides a series of photographs of the USS Massachusetts *entering dry dock in Boston in November 1998*

The battleship *Massachusetts*, built at the Fore River Shipyard in the state after which she was named, was launched in September 1941 and commissioned in May 1942. In November of that year, on her first operation, she had the distinction of taking part in one of the last battleship versus battleship actions, when she engaged the incomplete French *Jean Bart*, moored in Casablanca harbour, during the landings of Operation Torch (see *Warship 2000-2001*). During this engagement she hit the French ship six times, inflicting considerable damage to her, as well as to other vessels and harbour installations. In return *Massachusetts* was hit by one of the French shore batteries, and narrowly missed by a salvo of torpedoes. One unexploded shell from *Massachusetts* was subsequently put on display in Casablanca.

'Big Mamie', as she was nicknamed, spent the remainder of her war career in the Pacific, participating in the Solomon, Gilbert, Okinawa, Iwo Jima and Marshall Islands invasions, as well as raids on Truk and elsewhere, and finally the bombardments of the Japanese islands themselves. By the end of the war she had acquired eleven battle stars.

With peace the ship was deactivated in 1947 and spent the next decade and a half mothballed as part of the Atlantic Reserve Fleet at Norfolk, Virginia, with her guns cocooned and machinery spaces dehumidified. She was then sold for scrap in 1962. However by vigorous lobbying and fund raising her wartime crew, who had held annual reunions since 1945, and citizens of the State of Massachusetts managed to raise the $100,000 necessary to buy the ship.

A view showing how much drydock was left to spare. (R P Largess)

The port 5in dual purpose mountings. (R P Largess)

A good view of Mk 38 fire director on Spot Two. (R P Largess)

A view astern. (R P Largess)

During the preservation campaign seven deadlines for her scrapping were survived, and she had been just 48 hours from an eighth when she was transferred to her new owners from the US Navy. On 12 June 1965 she arrived in her new home at 'Battleship Cove', Fall River, where she was opened to the public as part of the rejuvenation of the waterfront area.

For over thirty years she resided there as a visitor attraction, being gradually joined by an assortment of other preserved vessels, until on 4 November 1998 she began a four-day, 300-mile journey under tow to Boston, to go into dry dock for survey, repairs and renovation. Over the next four months her bottom was scraped, cleaned and repainted; leaks were repaired using epoxy; and reinforcement plates were fitted along most of her waterline where corrosion had been most serious. In addition both outboard propellers were removed prior to being cleaned and polished ready to go on separate public display.

On March 13 1999 she returned home to Battleship Cove, firing a 21-gun salute from her secondary battery as acknowledgement of the enthusiastic welcome she received.

Contact Details:
Battleship *Massachusetts*,
Battleship Cove,
Fall River, MA 02721
Telephone: 001 (508) 678 -1100
Fax: 001 (508) 674-5597
e-mail:
    battleship@battleshipcove.org
Web site:
    http://www.battleshipcove.org/

THE NAVAL AND MARITIME LIBRARIES AND ARCHIVES GROUP
News of an initiative to promote the use of Britian's extensive resources for naval and maritime history

The Naval and Maritime Libraries and Archives Group is a new initiative aimed at increasing the awareness and use of sources of primary and secondary material relating to naval and maritime history in the United Kingdom. The Group was established in May 1999, and initially consisted of a number of libraries, museums, record offices and naval establishments in the area round Portsmouth. Since then it has steadily grown and now includes collections from as far apart as Liverpool, Plymouth, Southampton, Medway, Winchester, Yeovilton, London, Dartmouth, Taunton and Newcastle upon Tyne, as well as several more in the Portsmouth area.

The stated main aim of the Group is to 'improve access to information through a better understanding and knowledge of the various collections', and to achieve this by acting collectively in providing a service to users. To further this, in 2000 a guide book was published listing all the member organisations and giving full

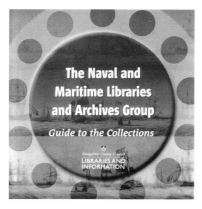

details of their collections and associated facilities, together with contact details, location and travel information, and opening hours. With the continued growth of the group a new, updated guide book is in preparation, and a web site is planned to follow.

Copies of the current guide book are available from:

Julie Denyer,
Naval Collection Librarian,
Hampshire County Library Service,
High Street,
Gosport,
Hampshire. PO12 1BT
Telephone: 023 9252 3431.

SAS SOMERSET
Ian R Hancock provides photographs of the SAS Somerset, preserved by the South African Maritime Museum in Cape Town.

One of the most unusual preserved naval vessels anywhere in the world has to be SAS *Somerset*, a 960 ton, 173 foot boom defence ship originally built in 1941-2 in Blyth as HMS *Barcross*.

She was one of seventy-six vessels

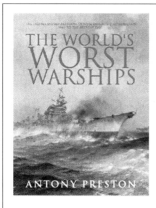

THE WORLD'S WORST WARSHIPS

To mark the publication of the latest book by Antony Preston, the editor of Warship, *we invite readers to join in a debate on the topic.*

The book provides a history of steel navy mistakes, beginning in in the 1860s when steam propulsion, turret mechanisms and armoured hulls were all in their infancy, and the 'cheesebox on a raft', the USS *Monitor*, fabled for participating in the first battle between ironclad warships, was built. Constructing its story through a succession of thirty case studies, it reaches the 21st century with a demolition of the concept of the fast attack craft, en route taking apart the reputations of such icons as the *Yamato* and the *Bismarck*.

The complete list of Antony Preston's worst warships is as follows:

Civil War monitors
Turret Ship HMS *Captain*
Vitse-Admiral Popov and *Novgorod* Coast Defence Ships
Armoured rams HMS *Polyphemus* and USS *Katahdin*
Armoured cruiser *Rurik*
Dynamite cruiser USS *Vesuvius*
Powerful class protected cruisers
Borodino class battleships
Destroyer HMS *Swift*
Viribus Unitis class dreadnoughts
Normandie class dreadnoughts
AA class fleet submarines
'Flush-decker' destroyers
K class submarines
HM Ships *Courageous*, *Glorious*, *Furious*, light battlecruisers

Fast battleship HMS *Hood*
Omaha class scout cruisers
HMSwS *Gotland* hybrid cruiser
Duquesne class heavy cruisers
Deutschland class 'pocket battleships'
'Condottieri' class light cruisers
IJNS *Ryujo* aircraft carrier
Mogami class cruisers
Yamato class super battleships
Bismarck class battleships
Implacable class fleet aircraft carriers
Hydrogen-Peroxide Submarines
'Alpha' class nuclear attack submarines
Type 21 anti-submarine frigates
La Combattante type fast attack craft

Warship would welcome contributions from readers offering lists of worst warships, or appeals on behalf of some of those vessels standing before the court martial. Submissions should reach us before 1 August 2003, and those published in the next *Warship* annual will win a voucher worth £25, for the purchase of Conway Maritime Press books.
Write to: 'Worst Warships', Warship 2003, Conway Maritime Press, 64 Brewery Road, London N7 9NT.

of the successful 'Bar' class built during the Second World War for the laying and maintenance of boom defence equipment. Originally coal-fired, her triple-expansion reciprocating engines could develop 850 horse power, giving her a maximum speed of 11.75 knots. She carried a crew of one officer and 37 men, and had one 3-inch AA gun for her defensive armament.

After completion she sailed to South Africa, where in 1943 she was renamed HMSAS *Barcross*. She continued to serve under that name until 1947 when she was laid up at Durban. In 1955 she was re-commissioned and renamed SAS *Somerset*, not after the English county, but after the horse which Lt. Dick King rode on his famous journey from Durban to Grahamstown in 1842 to alert the British authorities to the fact that the Boers were besieging the fort there. In the course of a long and varied career SAS *Somerset* took part in a number of major salvage operations, as well as oil pipeline laying, telephone cable repairs, laying and recovering buoys and moorings, diving training and support, and torpedo recovery work. She was decommissioned in 1986 and two years later, repainted and refurbished, she was handed over to the South African Maritime Museum to become a museum ship.

Today she is moored in the shadow of Table Mountain at the Victoria and Alfred Waterfront, a prestigious redevelopment of part of the old nineteenth century harbour area with hotels, restaurants, a brewery, berthing for cruise ships and the ferry terminus for Robben Island.

Contact details:
South African Maritime Museum,
Victoria & Alfred Waterfront,
PO Box 645,
Cape Town 8000,
South Africa.
Telephone: +27(21) 419 2505/6
Fax: +27(21) 405 2888
E-mail:
  museum@maritimemuseum.ac.za
Web site:
  http://maritimemuseum.ac.za/

SAS Somerset, *moored in the shadow of Table Mountain.* (Ian R Hancock)

Amidships detail of SAS Somerset. (Ian R Hancock)

SOVIET SUBMARINE PROGRAMMES 1945-90
Antony Preston makes notes on the Red Navy's submarine fleet during the Cold War.

The Russian defence industry periodical *Military Parade* has published some remarkable details of submarines built for the former Soviet Navy. The figures contradict some of NATO's more hallowed myths, but also help to explain the Soviets' submarine strategy. By checking against other sources *Warship* has arrived at the following summary:

Project No.	No. built/ converted	Notes
601	1	'Golf III' *K-118*, lengthened test-bed for underwater launch of D-9 (SS-N-8)
605	2	'Golf IV' *K-102* converted to six D-5 (SS-N-6) tubes, while *K-418* tested SS-N-23
V-611	1	'Zulu' *B-67* converted to launch single R-11FM missile
AV-611	5	'Zulu V' converted to launch two 11FMs
P-611	1	'Zulu' experimental oiler
PV-611	1	'Zulu' test-bed
611RA	1	'Zulu' missile test-bed
611RU	1	'Zulu' converted for 'special training'
611RE	1	'Zulu' test-bed
AV611D	1	'Zulu' experimental 'penetrating' minelayer
AV611E	1	'Zulu' test-bed for engines (?)
AV611K	1	'Zulu' experimental flotilla leader
AV611S	1	'Zulu' salvage conversion
AV611Ts	1	'Zulu' test-bed
611	10	Unconverted 'Zulus'; all later upgraded to 611M, minus deck gun and snort mast added
613V	35	'Whiskey' with extended range
V613	1	'Whiskey' test-bed
P613	1	'Whiskey' missile test-bed, presumably 'Single Cylinder' variant
613M	1	'Whiskey' upgrade prototype, without deck guns, streamlined fin
613A	1	'Whiskey' weapons test-bed
613D-4	1	'Whiskey' *S-229* test-bed for SS-N-5 ballistic missile
613D-5	1	'Whiskey' test-bed
613D-7	1	'Whiskey' test-bed
613AD	1	'Whiskey' minelayer
613E	1	prototype export variant of 'Whiskey'
613S	1	'Whiskey' *S-43* salvage/rescue conversion
613RV	1	'Whiskey' *S-65* torpedo test-bed
613Kh	1	'Whiskey' missile test-bed
613Ts	1	'Whiskey' *S-384* torpedo-target
613Sh	1	'Whiskey' test-bed
619	1	'Golf V' *K-153* tested D-19
615	1	'Quebec' *M-362*1/2 AIP test-bed, conversion stopped
A615	30	'Quebec' production model
617	1	'Whale' Walther AIP test-bed S-99; scrapped after major accident May 1959
627	1	'November' (*Kit*) SSN prototype
627A	12	'November' SSN production model
629A	22	'Golf' SSGs armed with 3 SS-N-4s; *K-102* achieved first underwater launch of SS-N-5 (R-21) in February 1962. *K-129* lost in Pacific in April 1968 and recovered by US *Glomar Explorer*
629B	1	Improved 'Golf'
629M	13	Improved 'Golf II'
629V	1	Improved 'Golf' *K-142* armed with two missiles; test-bed for underwater launch of D-5
629R	3	'Golfs' converted to SSQs; *K-83, K-96* and *K-105* mid-1970s
629I	1	'Golf' *K-113* converted to minelayer 1974
633	20	'Romeo' production model
633A	1	'Romeo' missile conversion, cancelled October 1955
633L	1	'Romeo' test-bed
633RV	2	'Romeo' weapons test-beds; *SS-128* and another converted to test SS-N-16 missile and 65cm torpedo
636	2?	Improved 'Kilo' for export; 2 sold to China
637	1	AIP design test-bed; *M-361's* trials programme halted in 1960

Project No.	No. built/ converted	Notes
640	4	'Whiskey Canvas Bag' radar pickets *S-62, S-73, S-144, S-151*; one reverted to attack rôle, others scrapped
640Ts	1	'Whiskey', possibly radar picket conversion, may be confused with 640V
641	58	'Foxtrot' production model
641B	18	
I641	4	'Tango' 'emergency' design
I641K	13	'Tango' command variant
644	6	'Whiskey Twin Cylinder' with two SS-N-3 launchers: *S-44, S-46, S-69, S-80, S-158, S-162*. *S-80* lost (with all 68 crew) in Barents Sea on 27 January 1961; the wreck was found at 196m on 23 June 1968 by rescue ship *Altai* and raised on 24 July 1969
644-7	1	'Whiskey' conversion, possibly replacement for *S-80*
645	1	*K-27*, redesigned 'November' with new lead-bismuth powerplant; decommissioned 1968 after machinery breakdown, and hull was later scuttled in White Sea
651	16	'Juliett' SSGs armed with four SS-N-3
651E	1	'Juliett' rearmed with SS-N-12 *Bazalt*
652	-	Project for 651 successor, with six short-range ballistic missiles
658	8	'Hotel' SSBNs. *K-19* nicknamed 'Hiroshima' after July 1961 major radiation leak, followed by two more serious accidents. Developed from 627 design
658M	7	658 modified to launch SS-N-5
658Ts	1	Modified 658
658U	2	*KS-1* (ex-*K-1*) and *KS-2* (ex-*K-2*) converted to SSQs
	5	'Echo I' SSGN; *K-154* lengthened by 5m to allow two more SS-N-3 launchers to be added (suffered nuclear accident in June 1989)
661	1	'Papa' *Anchar* ultra-high speed SSGN with titanium hull, but proved too noisy, expensive and unreliable to be put into series production
665	6	'Whiskey Long Bin' converted 1961-63 to launch four SS-N-3 missiles: *S-61, S-64, S-142, S-152, S-155, S-164*
666	1	'Whiskey' *S-64* experimental salvage/rescue conversion based on 613S
667A	34	'Yankee' SSBNs armed with 16 SS-N-6;
667AU	9	'Yankee' class, *K-219, K-228, K-241, K-245, K-430, K-436, K-444, K-446* and *K-451* rearmed with SS-N-6 Mod 21 (R-27U)
667M	1	Unidentified variant of 'Yankee'
667AK	1	Unidentified variant of 'Yankee'
667AT	3	'Yankee Notch' *Grusha, K-236, K-399*, and *K-408* or *K-415*, rearmed with SS-N-21 and lengthened by 3m
667AN	1	Possibly modified 667A
667B	18	'Delta I' (*Murena*) SSBNs armed with 12 SS-N-8s
667BD	4	'Delta II' (*Murena-M*) SSBNs armed with 16 SS-N-8s
667BDR	14	'Delta III' (*Kalmar*) SSBNs armed with 16 SS-N-18s
667BDRM	5	'Delta IV' (*Delfin*) SSBNs armed with 16 SS-N-23s
	11	'Charlie I' (*Skat*) SSGNs armed with 8 SS-N-9s; *K-43* leased to India
670M	6	'Charlie II' (*Skat-M*) SSGNs armed with 8 SS-N-9s
671	15	'Victor I' (*Ersh*) SSN production model
671RT	7	'Victor II' SSN design, armed with 65cm SS-N-16 ASW missile
671RTM	26	'Victor III' (*Shchuka*), fitted with new sonar suite, four 65cm TT and new combat system
671RTMK	5	'Victor IIIs' upgraded with new *Viking* combat system, allegedly based on Norwegian MSI-90U
675	29	'Echo II' SSGNs; suffered numerous accidents.
675T	5	'Echo IIs' converted to fire SS-N-12 *Bazalt*
675MK	14	'Echo IIs' converted to modified to fire SS-N-12 *Bazalt* with *Kasatka-B* satellite targeting downlink in fin
675MU	1	'Echo II' test-bed
675K	1	'Echo II' test-bed
675MKV	4	'Echo IIs' *K-1, K-22, K-35* and one other modified to launch P-1000 *Vulkan*
685	1	'Mike' (*Plavnik*) SSN prototype *Komsomolets*; lost 7 April 1989 after internal fire
	4	'Bravo' *Kefal* class rescue boats, *SS-256, SS-310, SS-368* and *SS-356*
701	1	*K-145*, 'Hotel III' SSBN used as trials boat for SS-N-5

➤

Project No.	No. built/ converted	Notes
705	4	'Alfa' (*Lira*) high-speed SSN; *K-377* scrapped in 1974
705K	3	Improved 'Alfa'; *K-123* suffered reactor meltdown 8 April 1982, and took nine years to repair
	2	*Piranya/Losos* type midgets *MS-520* and *MS-521*
877	16	'Kilo' (*Granay*) class SSKs
877E	2	'Kilo' export variant
877EKM	9	'Kilo' variant for India
940	2	'India' type rescue submarines *BS-203* and *BS-486*
941	6	'Typhoon' (*Akula*) class SSBNs armed with 20 SS-N-20s
945A	2	'Sierra I' (*Barrakuda*) SSN; follow-on to 'Victor III'
945	2	'Sierra II'
949	2	'Oscar I' Antey class SSGNs, armed with 24 SS-N-19s
949A	6	'Oscar II' SSGNs; *Kursk* (*K-141*) lost by torpedo explosion August 2000
06709	1	Indian *Chakra* (ex-*K-43*); second lease did not proceed
	1	'Uniform' small experimental nuclear boat *AS-15* or *AS-16*
	1	'Lima' experimental SSK *BS-555*
09774	1	'Yankee Pod' *K-403* lengthened by 4m as a sensor test-bed in 1984
09780	1	'Yankee Stretch' *K-411* lengthened by 160m, possibly to support midget or research submarines

Of course this list has gaps, if for no other reason that Russian records are incomplete and Western intelligence could only report what it saw or learned through intercepted traffic (SIGINT). There were a number of abortive projects as well, such as 630, 631 and possibly an earlier SSK Project 636, which never left the drawing board

Glossary: SSN = nuclear-powered attack submarine; SSB = diesel-electric strategic submarine; SSGN = nuclear-powered cruise missile-armed submarine; SSBN = nuclear-powered strategic submarine; SSQ = communications relay submarine; B = armament change; U = enlarged; K = new command system; I = 'emergency' design; M = modernised; RT = homing torpedo-armed weapon.

Sources: *Military Parade*; *Conway's All the World's Fighting Ships 1947-1995*; *Warships of the USSR and Russia 1945-1995* (A S Pavlov, translated by Gregory Tokar)

WOLVERENE AND WOLVERINE
Colin Jones reviews how two navies spell gulo luscus

Despite computer spell-checks, the Oxford English Dictionary allows two spellings of the name for *gulo luscus*, a carnivorous North American mammal, and the resulting variation in many reference books of the several warships of the name has added to the confusion, the most recent being in *Warship 2001-2002*. The Royal Navy started with one and finished with the other, while the US Navy was consistent. The table (right) shows how the ships of the name are properly spelled.

Royal Navy

Wolverene	1798–1804	gun brig, ex-mercantile *Rattler*
Wolverene	1805–1816	brig sloop, Cruiser class
Wolverene	1836–1855	brig sloop, Racer class
Wolverene	1864–1892	screw corvette, Jason class
Wolverine	1910–1917	destroyer, 'G' class
Wolverine	1919–1946	destroyer, 'W' class

United States' Navy

Wolverine	1905–1927	paddle gunboat, ex-*Michigan* of 1844
Wolverine	1942–1947	training aircraft carrier, ex-mercantile *Seeandbee*

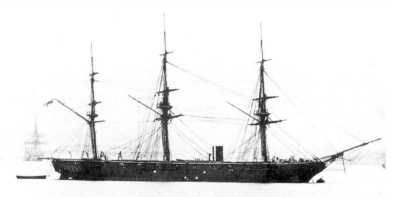

The USS *Wolverine* (left) and HMS *Wolverene* (above) took different approaches to the same name.

NAVAL BOOKS OF THE YEAR

Jürgen Rohwer and Mikhail S. Monakov, Stalin's Ocean-Going Fleet: Soviet Naval Strategy and Shipbuilding Programs 1935-1953.
London: Frank Cass, 2001.
334 pages, 24 drawings, 32 photographs, footnotes, index.
Price £39.50/ $57.50
ISBN 0-7146-4895-7.

One of the unexpected side-effects of glasnost has been the publication in Russia of hundreds of books and articles on naval history. Unfortunately, this wealth of information has remained inaccessible to most western readers due to the difficulties of the language. This book, the result of a collaboration between one of the west's most renowned naval historians and the chief of the Historical Branch of the Russian navy, goes a long way toward remedying this situation. Based on the authors' own researches and a comprehensive use of recent Russian-language publications, it describes in great detail Stalin's attempts to make the Soviet Union a major naval power.

The book begins with a discussion of Soviet naval policy and construction programs in the 1920s, before Stalin had gained undisputed control of the nation. In addition to outlining the Old School/Young School debate, familiar to many western readers thanks to the works of Robert Waring Herrick, the authors cover some less familiar ground, describing Soviet war plans and construction programmes, putting the more famous debate into its proper context.

The events of the 1930s then take centre stage. Stalin's push for a huge fleet based on battleships and 'heavy' cruisers (battlecruisers) is described

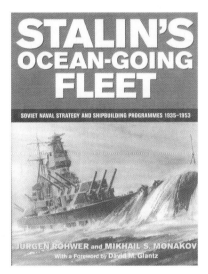

in detail. Key factors in this new naval policy were the growing threat from Japan in the Far East and the rise of Hitler in Germany. But Stalin's fascination with big-gun warships played the decisive role in shaping the construction programmes in the second half of the 1930s. Ironically, the shipbuilding programmes was to a large extent sabotaged by the dictator's own paranoiac obsessions, which led to the purges of 1936-1937. This bloodbath had an even greater effect on the navy than on the army, and many experienced naval officers and constructors were imprisoned or shot. In an environment where any deviation from Stalin's views was likely to have fatal consequences, it was impossible to formulate a realistic naval policy. Stalin underestimated the value of aircraft carriers, and so tactical and strategic doctrine were distorted in order to harmonize with his views, even as evidence from the first years of the European war showed the increasing importance of naval aviation. Seen against this background, Navy Commissar N G Kuznetsov's

constant arguments in favour of building carriers take on an almost heroic character.

One of the most interesting parts of the book is the description of the reasons behind Stalin's sudden shift to an accommodation with Hitler in August 1939 and the effects of subsequent German victories on Soviet policies. As for the 'Great Patriotic War' itself, wisely the authors do not attempt to provide an operational history of the war, focusing instead on how it affected policy, building programmes and the nation's industrial and technological resources.

The lessons of the war did not shake Stalin's faith in big-gun warships, and the effects of this prejudice on naval policy can be clearly seen in the post-war building programme. Kuznetsov used American experience in the Pacific war in support of carrier construction, but Stalin once again rejected these proposals. As a result of the dictator's flawed understanding of naval realities, the post-war programme was virtually a repeat of the outdated pre-war capital-ship construction policy.

Despite the date limits set in the title, the authors continue their story for some years after the death of Stalin, describing Admiral Kuznetsov's last attempts to create a balanced navy before Khrushchev's decision to radically restructure the Soviet armed forces brought an end to the admiral's hopes.

Although the book is not intended to be a technical history of Soviet warship design, there are brief descriptions of the tortuous process that led to the *Sovetskii Soyuz* class battleships (Project 23) and the *Kronshtadt* class battlecruisers (Project 69). Design work on other classes is outlined as well, from cruisers to submarines to river monitors, and many of these are illustrated by sketches taken from the journals *Sudostroenie* or *Gangut*. There are also useful appendices on ships laid down and completed, warship losses during World War II, and lend-lease vessels supplied to the Soviets by Britain and the United States.

It should be noted that, despite its many strengths, the book also has a few flaws. The translation is often too literal, and some passages that would make perfect sense in Russian hover on the brink of unintelligibility in English. The transliteration of Russian words and names is somewhat misleading, being based on German rather than English pronunciation. The details of the various construction programs are enumerated in the main body of the text, and the many dates, project numbers and ship characteristics can have a quite dizzying effect. This sort of information would have been easier to digest in tabular form. The photo sections are somewhat disappointing. But ultimately these are minor matters; this is without question an extremely valuable book, and deserves widespread attention by all western students of Soviet naval history.

Stephen McLaughlin

John English, Afridi to Nizam, British Fleet Destroyers 1937–43.
World Ship Society, Gravesend, 2001. 152 pages, 117 photos. (Soft cover) £22 + £3 p&p (£15 to members of the Society) ISBN 0 905617 95 0.

The style is the same as that of the author's earlier books on RN (Royal Navy) destroyers; there is a brief design history for each class followed by the operational history of the individual ships. Though brief, the design histories cover the main points and seem accurate.

These big, modern destroyers were in the forefront of the fighting, particularly in the difficult early years, and losses were heavy—only four of the sixteen Tribals built for the RN survived the war and those four were worn out. There are a considerable number of photos showing the last

moments of sinking ships. The numerous photos are well selected and well reproduced. (Inevitably, some of the action shots are less perfect.)

The Tribals were much bigger than earlier ships with double the number of main guns. In consequence, three Tribals cost as much as four of the older destroyers and the author might have discussed this point.

Certainly, if you enjoyed John English's earlier books you will like this one.

Eur Ing David K Brown, RCNC

Hans-Joachim Krug, Yōichi Hirama, Berthold J. Sander-Nagashima, Axel Neistlé. Reluctant Allies: German-Japanese Naval Relations in World War II.
Naval Institute Press, 2001. 416 pages, 15 photographs, Price £25.00 ISBN 1 86176 195 3

The principal obstacle to co-operation between the armed forces of Germany and Japan during the Second World War was one of basic geography. However, as *Reluctant Allies* shows, there were, especially concerning naval operations, many other problems. Some were just as fundamental as the geographical one, indeed many at least in part resulted from it. But others were totally self-inflicted and could, had the respective parties so wished, been resolved, with potentially serious bearings on the course of the conflict.

The two navies had completely different underlying strategies, with the IJN (Imperial Japanese Navy) being wedded to the concept of the 'decisive battle' between main fleets while the Kriegsmarine emphasised a war on trade, owing to their inability to challenge the Royal Navy's overall command of the seas. The clearest manifestation of these differences appears in submarine operations, where Japan's policy of targeting American fleet units was notably unsuccessful. On the occasions when the Japanese did use their submarines against merchant shipping they did

considerably better, yet they never pursued this strategy wholesale. Indeed, once their initial surge of victories had ended, Japanese plans became characterised by confusion and paralysis and their ever dwindling naval forces were frequently used in an ineffectual and impractical manner.

The very different command structures of the two navies also hindered co-operation, as did their positions within their countries' political/military hierarchies, with the Kriegsmarine being markedly less influential than the IJN. That said, there was endless rivalry between the Japanese army and navy for influence over policy and the allocation of resources. The army usually won these battles, with the navy then forced to go along with aggressive policies. This caused dreadful problems, for the army's greater influence meant it also received more resources, while the navy, the force that would bear the brunt of the inevitable fighting, got less than it needed. It was almost a 'Catch 22' situation, and in it one can see the seeds of Japan's eventual defeat.

The two naval commands also had completely different war aims, which were always selfish, with each simply wanting to utilise the other's successes to their own ends. Hardly, it must be said, the ideal basis for an alliance. The IJN had in fact opposed the Tripartite Pact (Germany, Japan, Italy) precisely because the Kriegsmarine was too weak to challenge the Royal Navy seriously. The Germans for their part regarded the IJN as 'unimaginably backward' in many areas, though not in naval aviation where they pumped them for as much help as possible.

Mutual distrust existed in the circles of government too, strikingly exemplified in the spring of 1941 when the Japanese Foreign Minister Matsuoka Yosuke, on a visit to Berlin, was not told of Germany's impending attack on the Soviet Union, while he in turn did not inform Hitler of his intention to sign a non-aggression pact with the Soviets on his way home!

Behind all this was basic, simple racism. The Japanese regarded themselves as 'pure' compared to westerners, many of whom at the same time quite genuinely believed the Japanese to be short-sighted, unable to see properly after dark. (In naval terms this was particularly ironic considering the proficiency they then proceeded to show in night fighting.) Hitler referred to the 'Yellow Peril', and was unenthusiastic about British influence in the East being replaced by Japanese. In fact in 1940 Germany was already looking at plans for war with Japan after victory over Britain was complete.

Further problems existed within the individual navies themselves. In the Kriegsmarine, especially towards the end of the war, there were individuals who cooperated with the IJN very fully indeed, but frequently this was in direct contravention of superiors' orders. While many senior Japanese officers had some residual affection for Britain—a consequence of a twenty-year alliance from 1902 to 1922—the junior ones were as enthusiastic as their army counterparts in carrying out atrocities against Westerners, such as the murder of sixty-five British sailors on board the *Tone* in January 1943. *Reluctant Allies* tends to gloss over such acts, and while they are not central to the book's subject, this is still noticeable, especially since other less relevant areas get considerable coverage. At the same time the book doesn't go into detail on Britain's break with Japan, although this was one of the underlying causes of the whole situation.

Indeed it is this lack of comprehensiveness that is one of the major criticisms of *Reluctant Allies*. The fact that there are four authors probably helps explains this, as well as the book's tendency towards repetition. These could have been sorted out by tighter editing, and likewise the many proofreading errors.

Another area that could have been dealt with better is the choice of illustrations; several of the photographs bear little or no relation to what is covered in the text. Pictures of some of the major characters in the story, such as German naval attache Wenneker and his Japanese counterpart Maeda, although possibly quite hard to find, would have been preferable to photographs of

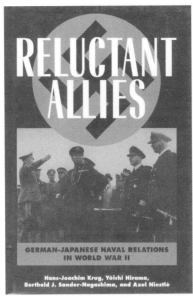

barely mentioned events. Conversely, the eighty pages of chapter notes (a fifth of the book) provide page references to what the notes cover, and are easy to use.

It is difficult to recommend wholeheartedly this book to *Warship* readers, for it is less about the technology of ships and the impact of that upon operations than about strategy, politics and diplomacy.

Stephen Dent

David Williams, Naval Camouflage 1914 - 1945, A Complete Visual Reference. *Chatham Publishing, Rochester, 2001. 256 pages, about 350 illustrations. £40. ISBN 1 86176 154 6.*

This book describes the work of camouflaging warships in two World Wars and also the related but opposite scheme of dazzle painting. While the author concentrates on the RN and USN there are substantial sections on schemes used by other major navies. Dazzle painting (Devised by the artist (Lt) Norman Wilkinson) did not make the ship less visible but made it difficult to determine the course and, sometimes, where the ship ended. False bow waves helped to make it difficult to estimate speed.

The first two parts of the book describe approved schemes by country of origin, numerical order and, generally, chronological order. The

third part contains essays on camouflage research and trials, the specification of paint schemes and colours, and on implementation. Model makers will be pleased that most Second World War paints are identified in terms of 'Humbrol' paint numbers.

The RN is known to have made early attempts at camouflage in 1915—though one may see the adoption of grey paint (black for destroyers) in 1906 as an early attempt at reducing visibility. The 1915 schemes were freelance ideas by individual captains. By about 1917 there was more formal guidance on both camouflage and dazzle. The USN had a more scientific approach but their schemes seem to have ended up very similar to the more intuitive approach of the RN.

The Second World War followed a somewhat similar pattern with initial designs by freelances before official schemes came in later. The Western Approaches scheme was devised by Peter Scott in 1940 and later became official for all North Atlantic ships. (This scheme was identical on both sides of the vessel). It was particularly intended to reduce visibility at night, the designer realising that light colours were needed.

The general conclusion seems to have been that actual operational value was slight but it could do no harm and might have a beneficial effect on morale.

The numerous photographs are absolutely splendid. Wartime colour photos are nonexistent for the First World War and rare for the Second, but the author has used postwar preserved ships to help towards a total of 14 colour photos. (Including the unfortunately anachronistic *Belfast*). The black and white pictures are clear and well chosen while the large page size has helped to do them justice. A little more on the effect of film type (panchromatic or ortho) and exposure on the rendering of colour into black and white would be welcome.

This book is an essential reference for model makers (beware—the schemes for the two sides of a ship were usually different), and for photograph collectors of the World War periods. The book stops at 1945 and hence there is no mention of the two peacetime navies which camouflaged their ships (Sweden & Chile). During the Falklands war your reviewer was asked by the staff to advise on the value of camouflage but passed the question to Sir Peter Scott, sailor and bird painter, who had devised the most effective schemes of the Second World War. Central to this subject, however, is the fact that seen from above, the wake of a ship is far more conspicuous than the ship itself, much reducing the value of camouflage.

Eur Ing David K Brown, RCNC

John Campbell, Naval Weapons of World War II.
Conway Maritime Press, London, 2002. 413 pages, innumerable photos and plans.
Price £45.00
ISBN 0 85177 924 7

This book was first published in 1985 and has been reprinted to satisfy continuing demand. It describes in great detail the naval weapons (including aerial anti-ship weapons) of the seven major naval powers with brief notes for eleven smaller navies. For a gun and its mounting one is told bore, weight of gun, shell and charge, length, rifling details, muzzle velocity, rate of fire, life and range and much else. The text lists the principal classes of ship which carried the

gun and comments on, among others, reliability. Other weapons are described in similar detail. For most there are drawings and there are many photographs.

There is a lengthy introduction to each of the major powers covering gun and mounting design, propellants, shells, fire control including high angle and close range weapon control. For the Royal Navy the introduction runs to twenty pages, guns take another forty-seven, followed by nineteen on underwater weapons and two on bombs etc. Numerous artists have contributed to the splendid drawings and even more individuals have helped the text and tables.

The value of a reference book such as this depends entirely on its accuracy—it has been one of my principal references since it appeared in 1985 and I have never had reason to doubt it. Before his death, the author gave me a short list of corrections which were all quite trivial, mainly additions to the list of ships carrying a particular weapon. (This is a reprint of the original, without changes.) He also completed a companion volume on weapons of the First World War which we hope will be published one day.

It should be clear by now that this book is strongly recommended to anyone interested in the subject.

Eur Ing David K Brown, RCNC

David Ramsay, Lusitania Saga & Myth
Chatham Publishing, 2001. 319 pages, 18 illustrations. Price £20.00
ISBN 1 86176 170 8.

In the opening months of the First World War the Admiralty seriously underestimated the U-boat threat to merchant shipping in the Western Approaches, and consequently failed to protect this vital life-line adequately. The loss of the Cunarder RMS *Lusitania* off the coast of Ireland in May 1915, was one of the most horrifying sea tragedies of the war. With a single torpedo, Kapitan-Leutnant Schweiger's U-boat *U-20*

shocked neutral America, embarrassed Britain and Germany, and added fuel to the flame of anti-German sentiment developing in the free world. The German naval staff attempted to justify the sinking with unsubstantiated allegations that *Lusitania* variously carried troops, explosives, or was an Armed Merchant Cruiser. Churchill and the Admiralty attempted unsuccessfully to side-step the inevitable claims of naval culpability, by launching a dubious campaign in the ensuing Mersey Enquiry to blame *Lusitania's* hapless captain for her loss. In the wake of the disaster, there remains a groundswell of controversy that has never completely subsided. The most flagrant propaganda of both sides was quickly dispelled, but the seeds of falsehood had fallen on fertile ground, from which legendary tales inevitably grew. Within a surprisingly short time, the more plausible fabrications became accepted as facts, which effectively nurtured the growing seedlings of myth.

Lusitania Saga and Myth is set against the background of commercial and political intrigue that spanned the Atlantic in the period prior to May 1915. Unfortunately the author's account of the great ship's final Atlantic crossing and subsequent sinking off the Old Head of Kinsale is bland and lifeless. He fails to portray the vitality of shipboard life, or the sickening fear and urgency a disaster of this magnitude must have generated on that fateful afternoon. Coverage of the ensuing Mersey Enquiry and the Mayer Liability Trial that followed in America is rather cursory, but adequate to establish the origins of most of the myths that have obscured the facts for nearly a century. The author challenges the official misinformation and imaginative anecdotes that beset the story, using a resourceful blend of modern science, incisive argument and factual evidence. He attempts to systematically explode each myth, but meets with only mixed success. Some of his analytical examination appears to be the product of sound technical advice from authoritative sources, notably his explanation of a secondary explosion which immediately followed the torpedo strike. Refutations of other allegations are less convincing, in particular the claim that the *Lusitania* carried a contingent of Canadian troops on her final crossing. The work is plagued throughout with spelling and grammatical errors that detract immeasurably from the theme.

Despite its shortcomings, *Lusitania Saga and Myth* offers rational alternative views of the subject, devoid of the sensationalism that characterises many former accounts. Although it is difficult to disprove the legacy of falsehoods that inevitably flourish in the wake of a high profile disaster, especially when it occurs in wartime, the book manages to fulfil most of the promise its title suggests.

Peter Kelly

Dwight R Messemer, Find and Destroy: Antisubmarine Warfare in World War I. *Naval Institute Press, Annapolis. (Distributed by Chatham Publishing, Rochester), 2001. 315 pages, 25 photographs, 19 maps and diagrams. £25. ISBN 1 86176 188 0*

This book is very welcome as well researched accounts of Anti Submarine Warfare (ASW) in World War I are hard to find. The early years of the war were dominated by the Declaration of London of 1909 which attempted to set regulations for maritime war. It was never ratified but Britain, Germany and most other powers said they would abide by it; indeed, the German 'Prize Regulations' were based on the Declaration. The early years of the war were dominated by attempts on both sides to stretch the rules without annoying the USA to the point of war. The author, an American, covers this aspect well. It was practically impossible for a submarine to carry war against trade under these rules and hence the RN had made virtually no preparation for such action.

The earlier German attacks on shipping were limited in scope and ended when US protests strengthened. They caused grievous losses but fell short of a decisive blow. At the

beginning of 1917 the U-boats launched unrestricted attacks on merchant ships and by April losses were so severe that the Admiralty was warning that defeat was possible in the near future. Victory was snatched from the jaws of defeat by the introduction of convoy against the long-standing opposition of almost all naval officers. The author covers all these topics in narrative style but the U-boat war was a war of numbers. Tables or graphs are needed showing sinking of merchant ships per month both in absolute tonnage and in tons per U-boat at sea. Parallel figures for U-boat sinkings are also required.

This is the only criticism of the book. There are many threads to the story and the author has done a fine job in melding accounts of weapon and sensor development with tactics and other procedural changes. By 1917 many of these developments were becoming effective, and co-ordination was much improved.

While the main story rests in the Atlantic and English Channel, there is full treatment of the important operations in the Mediterranean, while little-known ASW work in the Baltic and Black Sea are mentioned. German ASW also gets a brief mention. The author has made use of his ability to read German accounts. It is an interesting and readable book.

Eur Ing David K Brown, RCNC

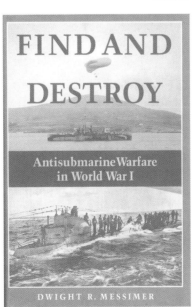

John de S Winser, British Invasion Fleets – The Mediterranean and Beyond 1942 – 1945. *World Ship Society, PO Box 706, Gravesend, 2002 (Softback). 152 pages (A4), 157 photos and illustrations. £25 (£17 to WSS members) + £5 post. ISBN 0 9543310 0 1.*

This is a companion volume to the author's *D-Day Ships* published in 1994. Part A tells the story of 10 landings from Madagascar through North Africa, Italy, the South of France to Burma and Malaya and the ships which took part in them. The operations occupy 36 pages which are followed by 80 pages listing the ships, naval and civilian, which took part in each. There is a detailed list of sources and a key to the code names used. The Foreword is by Captain Chris Page, Head of Naval Historical Branch.

The operational accounts in Part A are brief but clear and there is a map of each area. They concentrate on British and British-controlled ships; US-led Task Forces are given credit but not described in detail and land operations are not covered. These invasions are far less well known than that of Normandy and this book is welcome for that reason. Plans for the invasion of Malaya are covered and there is brief mention of the British Commonwealth contribution to the invasion of Japan. The organisation of the invasion fleets is made clear and the significance of the convoy designation letters is explained.

Section B outlines the adventures of individual ships divided into merchant or naval and then into main categories. Tonnage and date of build are given. Photographs in Part A are contemporary, including some sad views of sinking ships. The author is to be congratulated on identifying ships in the background. In Part B many of the photographs are peacetime shots but there are a few 'before and after' illustrations showing wartime changes. The identification numbers of photos from major collections are given so that prints may be ordered. Overall, the numerous photographs are well chosen and clearly reproduced—indeed, I suspect many customers will buy the book for the photographs.

The index shows how a few ships were used time and time again; one may single out the converted LSTs (*Bachaquero*) and the Mk Is (*Thruster*). Deployment distances were far greater than for Normandy so there are many large liners too.

A fascinating book.

Eur Ing David K Brown, RCNC

Peter Truscott, Kursk, Russia's Lost Pride.
Simon & Schuster, 2002.
221pp, 22 photographs, 1 map,
£16.99
ISBN 0 7432 3072 8

Warships seldom make the news headlines in peacetime except when they are involved in accidents, something that was tragically borne out in August 2000 when the Russian submarine *Kursk* sank while on exercise in the Barents Sea. Since then one or two books have been published in Russia, but Peter Truscott's is one of the first to appear in the English language. The jacket proclaims it to be 'The gripping true story of the Russian navy's worst submarine disaster', which is stretching things somewhat. It is certainly a gripping read, but as for 'true', that is more debatable for the author makes it clear that the horrifying account of the *Kursk*'s last moments, with which the book begins, is to a considerable extent speculation, albeit speculation based on all the evidence available.

After this, however, the book reverts to a more straightforward narrative, recounting the shambolic efforts to rescue members of the submarine's crew and the simultaneous attempts to cover up what had happened and to apportion blame (both of which served to further hinder the rescue efforts), and the subsequent wide-ranging political fallout in Russia. In addition Truscott also examines the background to the continuing allegations of an underwater collision with a NATO submarine, in the process painting a depressing pic-

ture of continued mistrust between former Cold War rivals. The tone is gloomy throughout; the account of the raising of the wreck is just about the only part of the story from which anyone emerges with much credit at all.

The author is a former Labour MEP and has a Russian wife, so not only has he been able to access an unusually wide variety of sources, but he has also produced a book that is less inclined to NATO/Western prejudices. Britain, the United States, Norway and even France (for the sabotage of the *Rainbow Warrior*) all come in for criticism, even though the lion's share is reserved for Russia, and in particular for the Russian Navy. Truscott has in effect used the *Kursk* tragedy to shed light upon the state of a country in a painful process of transition. Both this breadth of scope and the author's somewhat bipartisan attitude may make the book unusual fare for many *Warship* readers, but it is a pacy read, and never dull.

Where it does fall down somewhat is in the editing. It can only be described as 'bitty', with far too much repetition (new characters in the story are introduced more than once, the same asides crop up in several places), and this sloppiness is something that really should have been corrected by the publisher.

If there is a genuinely 'true' account of the loss of the *Kursk* any-

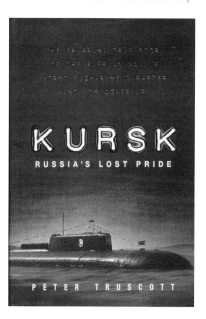

where, then it is most unlikely to emerge for a substantial length of time considering the innate sensitivity of the subject. For, as this thought-provoking book demonstrates, there is still a long way to go to erase the legacy of half a century of ideological conflict.

Stephen Dent

Ruari MacLean, Half Seas Under: Seaman, submariner, canoeist.
Thomas Reed Publications, 2001.
216 pages, illustrated with photographs and drawings, £14.95
ISBN 0 901281 27 1

This entertaining book is an account of the author's varied naval service during the Second World War, beginning with a spell as an Ordinary Seaman on the destroyer *Windsor*, before joining the Free French submarine *Rubis* as British Naval Liaison Officer. It is his time on board this famous boat that forms the main part of the story, and fascinating stuff it is too, taking in action in the North Sea, Biscay and off the coast of Norway, the latter including a hairraising trip home on the surface after the submarine had been damaged by depth charges.

After he left *Rubis*, MacLean joined the Inter Service Topographical Department, before moving on to something much more dangerous, the Combined Operations Pilotage Parties (COPPs): canoeists carrying out night time surveys of possible landing beaches in enemy held territory. Further adventures ensued in the Far East, involving a lot more submarine work, before the war ended and he was able to return to his civilian life as a typographer.

Unsurprisingly, given this choice of vocation, the book is beautifully produced. As well as a number of photographs it is illustrated with many of MacLean's drawings, and these help give it a very different feel from most naval memoirs, rendering it a much more personal and human story. Add to this the fact that *Rubis*' crew, perhaps because of their unusually stressful situation, always seem to have been determined to enjoy themselves whenever possible; and MacLean's self-deprecating sense of humour, and you get a much cheerier read than many such wartime accounts. As a vivid description of life aboard one of France's most successful warships, as well as of one man's distinctly unusual naval career, it is highly recommended.

Stephen Dent

H W Fawcett and G W W Hooper (with foreword by John Roberts) The Fighting at Jutland.
*Chatham Publishing, Rochester, 2001. 448 pages, 17 charts, 29 illustrations and 45 photographs. £25.
ISBN 1 86176 179 1.*

In 1920, on their own initiative, Lieutenants Fawcett and Hooper, who themselves saw action at Jutland, collected and arranged for the publication of some sixty personal accounts of the battle. Their book has now been republished by Chatham, with a reset text and the original drawings and photographs (though the last, which are printed with the text, have lost some of their original definition). John Roberts' foreword introduces what he rightly calls 'a unique record' that has become 'a major source of reference'.

The book has four parts. In the first three, the editors have constructed, from the individual accounts linked by their own short explanatory passages, a remarkably coherent narrative of the three major phases of the Battle of Jutland: the battlecruiser action, the encounter of the battlefleets and the fighting during the night. The final part provides additional complete accounts, some by specialist officers. In their introduction, Fawcett and Hooper declare: 'This book is not a criticism; it is a record of personal experience'. Thus, unsurprisingly, it does not comment on Beatty's initial failure to concentrate his squadrons; on the other hand, it shows that most of his battlecruisers opened fire with both excessive ranges and underestimates of the range-rate. In contrast, *Tiger*

was straddled by the second of *Moltke's* salvoes; a number of contributors agree with the midshipman in *Malaya* who soon realised that 'the Germans were rather good shots'. *The Fighting at Jutland* is an essential source for the sinkings of *Indefatigable* and *Queen Mary*, as well as for *Tiger's* two lucky escapes and for the hit on *Lion's* Q turret: though the accounts from *Southampton* and *Nicator* place the subsequent cordite fire much later than those from the flagship.

Shortly before the meeting with the High Seas Fleet, a series of hectic encounters began between the destroyer flotillas; of the several graphic descriptions, the most moving are of the stoical courage of the crews of the crippled *Nestor* and *Nomad* as they waited to be overwhelmed by the oncoming German battle line. During the subsequent run northwards, the main weight of the German fire fell on the 5th Battle Squadron. The chaos between decks in *Warspite* is memorably described by her Executive Officer, even if, as Andrew Gordon has shown, his list of hits does not match John Campbell's. A number of contributors from Beatty's force recall their relief on sighting the advanced units of the Grand Fleet. However, when the battlecruisers hauled across the heads of the deploying columns, the confusion among the smaller craft seemed 'like Picaddilly Circus with the policemen on strike'; if not for the ships concerned, it was fortunate that the German fire was attracted by '*Warspite* doing her famous stunt at "Windy Corner"' and by Sir Robert Arbuthnot's fatal determination to finish off the already damaged *Wiesbaden*. Yet, after the sinkings of *Defence* and *Invincible* and the successful formation of the British line, for the remainder of the day little could be seen of the enemy 'enveloped in mist and smoke, appearing out of it at short intervals like rabbits running from one hole to another in a burrow'.

After dark, the heavy ships lost touch, with the tragic exception of *Black Prince*; after being lost to both sides for some six hours, she blundered into the German line and, as glimpsed from the destroyer *Spitfire* just before her final explosion, was

reduced to 'a mass of fire from foremast to mainmast'; no one survived to tell her story. *Spitfire* belonged to the 4th Flotilla, whose costly attacks, at almost point-blank range, are vividly recounted. Yet, despite the efforts of the British destroyers, the German line remained unbroken and successfully crossed astern of Jellicoe's battle squadrons, leaving only 'the bitter disappointment of that dawn of June the 1st, 1916, when the German fleet was found to have escaped to its harbours'.

In an appendix, the editors (who must have recognised the historical importance of their work) gave their assessment of the reliability of each narrative. Only eight, at most, were not written by officers. Nonetheless, the fortitude in action of the lower deck is well recorded, though not, one suspects, its speech; on picking up a recently arrived unexploded shell, an RNR seaman in *Galatea* probably did not exclaim: 'Crikey, the blighter's hot'. Other more authentic details are fascinating; the hatch into the top was still, as in the days of sail, called the lubber's hole: one of the first aid party in *Princess Royal* had been present at the bombardment of Alexandria: in *Indomitable's* fore turret, two gramophones were played, with different records, during every lull in the action: many smoked furiously—one of *Maenad's* officers 'got through 100 cigarettes and a $1/2$-lb. of [pipe] tobacco in just over 12 hours'. However, contributors were reluctant to dwell on the terrible injuries which they saw, though two refer to the extraordinarily arbitrary effects of high explosive, which could leave a single man almost unhurt while all around him were wiped out. Some could mention the dismembering effects of flying splinters or the smell of burnt flesh, but no more; none contradicted Stephen King-Hall: 'The most dreadful cases were the "burns"—but this subject cannot be written about'. Despite the reticence of the time, 'the accounts...confirm what other experiences of 1914-18 have taught, that the horrors of war go hand-in-hand with the glory of war—such as there is of glory' (the editors).

Historians must be grateful to Fawcett and Hooper for collecting these essential accounts of Jutland; and now also to Chatham Publishing for making them readily available, at a reasonable price, to every student of the dreadnought era.

John Brooks

Mark R Peattie, Sunburst. The Rise of Japanese Naval Air Power, *1909-1941.*
Naval Institute Press, Annapolis, and Chatham Publishing, Rochester.
392 pages, black-and-white illustrations, hardback, £25.00
ISBN 1 867176 194 5

This book is a companion piece to *Kaigun*, by Peattie and the late David Evans. It has its origins in the same broad subject, the Imperial Japanese Navy in the Second World War, but in this case exclusively covering the navy's air arm.

The book began life as three chapters of *Kaigun*: 'our original manuscript included four long chapters on the Japanese naval air service…Such extensive attention to the rise of Japanese naval aviation made for too bulky a manuscript, and…in any event the story deserved to stand on its own.' At certain times, the join between the material excised from *Kaigun* for reasons of space, and the text originated by this volume, is faintly apparent. However, this is by no means a criticism, because Peattie is quite right to say the story deserves to stand on its own.

The book begins with the origins of Japanese naval aviation itself, with reports from officers resident in Europe about the developments in military and naval aviation following the visit of Orville Wright to France in 1908. The Japanese embraced the technology with the enthusiasm for which they have become well known, initially by copycat methods, and then developing their own particular approach. The first use by Japan of naval aviation in war, during the campaign against the German leased territory of Tsingtao, is briefly described.

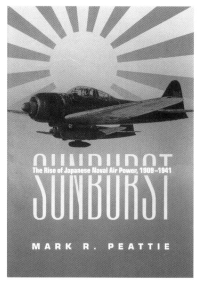

We are then taken on a journey through the interwar experience of developing a doctrine, the creation of an aviation industry, and the shaping of an infrastructure for training pilots.

The core of the book is the description of the Japanese Naval Air arm during the Second World War. This is not a narrative history, but rather a thematic one. It explains how the fighter and bomber squadrons, whether land or carrier based, operated. How many aircraft would fly a combat air patrol? How were torpedo and dive bombing attacks co-ordinated? Where were aircraft rearmed and refuelled between missions? Where were fuel and munitions stored on a carrier? What was the main emphasis in Japanese aircraft design? These questions and many others are answered in these pages.

In addition to this narrative of rise and fall, the book also includes nine appendices. There is one of potted biographies of important personalities in the story. Two long ones cover the major naval aviation vessels of the navy and the principal aircraft from biplanes to Betty bombers. Others supply a glossary of naval aviation terms, the organization of the naval air arm, a list of air bases and air groups, the superficially complex system of designations. The nine are rounded out by a description of

engines and of the turning-in manoeuvre that made fighter pilots flying Zeroes so deadly in the early stages of the war.

The book illustrates some useful lessons for strategic and operational thinking. While there are plenty of 'what-if' histories showing how Operation Barbarossa could have succeeded, the possibility of a Japanese triumph against the United States has attracted less enthusiasm, even though both Japan and Germany relied on the same principle of war, one that has been successfully applied in several post-1945 conflicts: that a small, focused force can defeat a larger, unwieldy one.

First, the Japanese record of successful wars against bigger nations before 1937, such as China and Russia, perhaps made it difficult for them to perceive how their advantages in those particular conflicts would not pertain in every such attack.

Second, the main Japanese advantage, a superbly trained fighting force closely wedded to one another and its equipment, is as short-lived as any cherry blossom in spring. It was a craft industry confronting an assembly line, and it would inevitably be overwhelmed by the competition.

If there is a fault with the book, it is an understandable one. Throughout the story, Peattie makes his comparisons between the Japanese naval air service and their eventual opponents, US naval aviation. However, the Japanese Navy had traditionally looked to the Royal Navy for its model; and in spite of Britain's choice in 1921, under pressure from the United States, to end its alliance with Japan, it would be a comparison still worth making. There were only three navies in the interwar world whose strategic policy required substantial investment in carrier air power. Peattie could usefully have incorporated some information from the Royal Navy's experiences.

All in all, a 'must have' volume for any enthusiast of the Pacific theatre in the Second World War.

Paul M. Brewer

WORLD NAVIES IN REVIEW 2002-2003

Antony Preston looks at recent naval developments around the world.

Naval events in the past year have been profoundly affected by the destruction of the World Trade Center and its aftermath. We have witnessed increased naval activity by the United States and her allies, including land-attacks from submarines and a renewed vigour in the pursuit of intelligence and 'network-centric' warfare. The war on terrorism also exposed the weaknesses in the US Navy caused by short-term decisions made by the Clinton Administration. The Royal Navy has benefited, with Prime Minister Tony

Blair showing no sign of weakening in pursuit of his 'imperial' ambitions.

Western Europe, however, continues to treat defence as a theoretical exercise, and little has been done to turn the nightmare of a European Union Navy into reality (so the news is not all bad). To create a European counterweight to the armed might of the United States would cost money that France, Germany and Italy are unable or unwilling to spend. The notion current a few years back, that the French Navy is more powerful than the RN, is now laughable.

Western European Navies

Belgium The three *Wielingen* class light frigates are in the middle of a rolling programme of upgrades planned to be completed in 2005. These include an updated main radar, and new diesel engines. Their replacements, three 4000-5000-tonne Multi-Purpose Escort Vessels (MPEVs) are planned to be delivered in 2010-2012. Six of the seven *Aster* class Tripartite minehunters are to be equipped with the German *Seefuchs* (Seafox) mine-disposal remotely

The Belgian frigate Weilingen. *(L& L van Ginderen)*

operated vehicle (ROV), and the French Sterne shallow-draught sweeping system (the French sonar and command system are also likely to be upgraded).

The KMV minesweeper project has vanished into limbo. A joint Belgian-Luxembourg Transport Ship (BLTS) was approved in June 2001. A displacement of about 19,000 tonnes is envisaged, with a floodable welldeck to accommodate utility landing craft (LCUs) and mexe-flotes.

The Baltic Republics The Latvian Coast Guard's second and third ex-Norwegian patrol vessels *Lode* (P-02) and *Linea* (P-03) were commissioned in June 2001. They are partially disarmed *Storm* class fast attack craft (FACs). Another pair, the *Selis* (P-32) and *Skalvis* (P-33), were commissioned into the Lithuanian Navy.

Denmark The Royal Danish Navy (RDN) acquired the submarine *Nåcken* on 17 August 2001, renaming her *Kronborg* under a five-year lease, partly as a 'sweetener' to help

keep the RDN in the 'Viking' Nordic Submarine Project. As the *Nåcken* she was the first submarine in the world to adopt the Stirling engine for air-independent propulsion (AIP). One of the *Narhvalen* class vessels is likely to be taken out of service to ease the strain on manpower. The *Saelen* has been given air-conditioning and other minor modifications to help her operate in the Mediterranean on international peacekeeping operations.

Contracts were awarded in October 2001 for detailed design of the new Stanflex Patrol Ships and the slightly larger Stanflex Support Ships. The latter have since been ordered from Odense Shipyard, but the armament of the former has not yet been finalised as their keels are not be laid until 2006. They will replace the *Nils Juel* class corvettes

Delivery of the last batch (six units) of the *Aldebaran* class MHV 800 type coastal patrol craft was completed by the *Sabatoren* (MHV-818) in October 2001. Eight more MSF Mk 1 class mine countermeasures (MCM) drones are planned.

Finland The second *Hamina* class fast attack craft (FAC) is to be delivered in 2003. The first T2000 Griffon hovercraft was commissioned in September 2001, and if successful will be followed by three more.

France The *Marine Nationale* has allocated funding for Project Barracuda, the construction of six nuclear attack submarines (SSNs) to replace the *Rubis* class. All that has been revealed is a vessel length of about 895 metres, an armament of torpedoes and ten Scalp Naval land-attack cruise missiles, and a building-rate of two a year, starting in 2004. The strategic submarine (SSBN) force will be reduced to three boats when *l'Indomptable* is withdrawn in 2004, but shortly thereafter *le Vigilant* will join the fleet. *Le Terrible* will replace *l'Inflexible* after 2008.

The nuclear-powered aircraft carrier (CVN) *Charles de Gaulle* became fully operational on 1 December 2001, but until she receives a new propeller in 2003 speed is limited to 23 knots. In theory another carrier is planned, but no funding is allocated.

Belgian minesweeper Myosotis. (Hanny & Leo van Ginderen)

Strategic submarine L'indomptable. (Leo van Ginderen)

French corvette Second Maître le Bihan. (L & L van Ginderen)

If the Thales design for the Royal Navy's CVF wins the competition, it might be adopted as the basis for the Charles de Gaulle's running-mate.

The first of two new Horizon-type anti-air warfare (AAW) frigates was laid down at DCN Lorient late in 2001, with first steel cut on 8 April 2002. They are to be completed in December 2006 and April 2008 respectively, and two more are planned, to replace the *Cassard* and *Jean Bart* in 2013-2015.

A class of 17 multi-role frigates is planned, using a common hull with a variety of armaments and sensors to carry out a broad range of missions. The first eight have been authorised and combat systems and radars for two have been ordered for delivery in 2005-2006.

Only nine of the original seventeen *d'Estienne d'Orves* class coastal corvettes remain. It is hoped to run them until 2009-2010 unless buyers are found. Modernisation of the thirteen *Eridan* class minehunters started, in 2001, including upgrading the hull sonar to DUBM-21D, adding a TSM 2022 Mk 3 propelled variable-depth hull sonar based on the Swedish Double Eagle, and a new tactical data system.

Germany The first Type 212A submarine, *U.31*, was launched in October 2001 at Kiel, and will be commissioned in March 2004. Her sister vessels will enter service between May 2005 and September 2006, a long time after authorisation of the work in 1994. Two Type 205 boats retained for trials, *U.11* and *U.12*, will be out of service in 2003 and 2006 respectively. The first Type 206 boat, *U.28*, will be paid off in 2003.

Work on the Type 124 *Sachsen* class AAW frigate progresses, with the *Sachsen* running trials in 2001-2002. She is to be handed over in November 2002 for Navy first-of-class trials and then formally commissioned in December 2003. She will be followed by the *Hamburg* in December 2004 and the *Hessen* in December 2005. The *Hessen* was launched on 31 July 2002.

Five Type 130 corvettes were ordered on 14 December 2001, for delivery in 2006-2008, but it seems unlikely that the remaining ten planned will be built.

Great Britain At the end of January 2003, the MoD announced a bizarre decision on the Royal Navy Future Aircraft Carrier (CVF) project. BAE systems was appointed prime contractor, but the design selected was the vastly superior Thales two-island one. In a dirty campaign BAE Systems peddled figures of alleged UK job losses, and did nothing to contradict media claims that the Thales design would be built in France. The fact that this was never going to happen, as the MoD stipulated from the outset that boths hips would be UK-built. The ships will be built in 'megablocks'—large blocks fabricated elsewhere, and not necessarily by a single sub-contractor—and assembled on the Clyde.

A rumour of a possible sale of HMS *Invincible* to India was given prominence by the media in the spring of 2002, but it seemed unlikely as the Indians have their hands full getting the ex-Soviet *Admiral Gorshkov* into

USS Wainwright, *photographed in 1980.* (L&L van Ginderen)

working order, and building the new CV (see below). Officially, *Invincible* will not be given the planned major refit, and will be laid up until the end of the decade, but the in the current international climate the Ministry of Defence (MoD) may be forced to run her on. In April 2002 HMS *Ark Royal* became Fleet Flagship and embarked the first operational HM.1 Merlin helicopter squadron. The media was understandably critical of the decision to phase out the FA.2 Sea Harrier and to replace it with the hybrid GR.9, a reworked AV-8B airframe that is the RAF GR.7 ground-attack aircraft. But the economics of a 'stretch' of the Sea Harrier to accommodate a new gas turbine and new avionics in its small airframe would involve too high a technical risk. The GR.9s will function as an interim joint RAF/RN aircraft until the F-35 Joint Strike Fighter appears.

In June 2002 the nuclear attack submarine HMS *Tireless* scored a notable 'first' at the end of a series of trials and exercises in the Atlantic Underwater Test and Evaluation Centre in the Bahamas. Ships and aircraft had fired missiles and shells at the old US Navy missile cruiser *Wainwright*, whose stiffened bulkheads and welded watertight doors kept her

afloat. In one of the rare live firings of a Spearfish torpedo, *Tireless* scored a hit under the *Wainwright's* bridge at a range of two miles, breaking her back and splitting her hull in two.

The commissioning date of the *Astute* has been moved on to 2006, but her two sisters are still on schedule for 2007 and 2009. There is now talk of a second batch of two or three. The retrofit of the Type 2076 integrated sonar suite to the *Trafalgar* class is well advanced, and the last three will be completed by 2006. At the moment all SSNs are armed with the Tomahawk Block III cruise missile, but a future purchase of a tube-launched variant of the cheaper and lighter Tactical Tomahawk Block V is under consideration.

Although the MoD has placed firm orders for only six *Daring* class Type 45 AAW destroyers, the costings are based on the full order of twelve. Vosper Thornycroft (UK) Ltd will build and pre-outfit the forward section, the masts and the funnel, and BAE Systems' Scotstoun yard will build the rest of the ship. Final assembly of the hull of *Daring* is planned to start at Scotstoun towards the end of 2004.

The ranks of the old Type 42 AAW destroyers have been temporarily

depleted by the serious damage inflicted on HMS *Nottingham*, when she made a 'heavy landing' on Wolfe Rock off the east coast of Australia on 7 July 2002. At first it was feared that she would sink, but with the help of Royal Australian Navy (RAN) divers and support from other ships, she was pumped out and towed to Newcastle, NSW on 6 August. After repairs she began the long haul home on a heavy-lift ship; doubts were expressed about the cost-effectiveness of repairing her, but the MoD has decided to put her back into service.

The 16th 'Duke' class anti-submarine warfare (ASW) frigate, HMS *St Albans*, was handed over to the RN in the spring of 2002. The new Type 2087 low-frequency active sonar (LFAS) will no be ready until 2004, when it will replace the Type 2051 in the rest of the class, HMS *Coventry* and HMS *London* have been sold to Romania and will be refitted locally, probably with a medium-calibre gun added. Chile is also showing interest in buying a pair of RN frigates, but the only Type 22 Batch 2 ships left are the paid-off *London* and HMS *Sheffield*. The only other option is the sale of a pair of the oldest 'Duke' class; the four *Cornwall* class ships

Type 22 frigate HMS London. (Hanny & Leo van Ginderen)

have command facilities which make them too valuable to be got rid of prematurely.

Five of the eight *Hunt* class mine-hunters are about to begin their upgrade, which involves installing the new Type 2193 sonar and upgrading their Nautis control systems to Mk 3 standard. The last three are to completed by 2005, but the upgrade will not be given to the *Brecon*, *Cottesmore* and *Dulverton*, which serve as Northern Ireland patrol ships. HMS *Cromer* was paid off in October 2001 and now serves as a static training ship at Dartmouth.

The expansion of the amphibious forces is going well. HMS *Fearless* was sold to Brazil in the summer of 2002 but her replacement, *Albion*, started sea trials at the end of 2002; her sister ship *Bulwark* will follow a year later.

The new ramped troop transport RFA *Hurst Point* entered service in August 2002, followed by RFA *Hartland Point* and RFA *Eddystone* in October and November. RFA *Largs Bay*, first of the four 'Bay' class Landing Platform, Dock (LPDs), is to be launched in 2003 and delivered in

2004. The new replenishment ship RFA *Wave Knight* was running trials in the Clyde in June 2002. HMS *Tyne*, first of the new 'River' class off-shore patrol vessels (OPVs), was commissioned in December 2002, to be followed by HMS *Severn* and HMS *Mersey*.

Greece The Hellenic Navy has allocated traditional names to its new Type 214 submarines: *Katsonis*, *Papanikolis*, *Pipinos* and *Matrozos*. The *Katsonis* is to be launched by HDW at Kiel in December 2003 and commissioned in 2005. The class will join the elite ranks of submarines with air-independent propulsion (AIP) systems, in this case the German fuel-cell system. In addition three of the existing *Glavkos* class Type 209 boats will have a hull 'plug' inserted, adding the same AIP capability.

Two of the former *Charles F Adams* class AAW destroyers, the *Formion* and *Themistocles*, as well as the *Epirus*, last of the ex-Knox class frigates, were taken out of service in 2002.

On 14 December 2001 a seventh

ex-Royal Netherlands Navy *Kortenaer* class frigate was recommissioned. The former *Pieter Florisz* is now HS *Bouboulina* (F-463). An eighth, HS *Kanaris* (F-464), will be delivered in November 2002 (she is the former *Jan van Brakel*). The major refit for the class is planned to be completed by the end of 2006. The first Vosper Thornycroft 62-metre fast attack craft (FAC) is HS *Roussen*, and she will be delivered by the Elefsis yard at the end of 2003. She will be followed by HS *Danilos* and HS *Kristallides* in May and November 2004 respectively.

The Hellenic Navy took delivery of the former RN minehunter *Berkeley* at Portsmouth on 28 February 2001 and renamed HS *Kallisto*. There are now four Russian/Ukrainian Project 1232 *Zubr* type hovercraft in service, the *Kefalini* (L-180), *Ithaki* (L-181), *Kerkyra* (L-182) and *Zakynthos* (L-83). Two of the *Mahitis* class (Batch 2 *Pyrpolitis* class) 56-metre patrol craft were delivered in 2002, the *Mahitis* (P-78) and *Nikiporos* (P-79). The *Aititos* (P-80) and *Krateos* (P-81) will follow in 2003-2004.

HMS Fearless, *photographed in Spithead during the D-Day commemorations in June 1994*. (Leo van Ginderen)

The Hunt class minehunter HMS Berkeley. (Hanny & Leo van Ginderen)

Frigate Pieter Florisz *in 1994. She now serves in the Greek navy.* (Hanny & Leo van Ginderen)

Ireland Appledore Shipbuilders in the UK delivered the offshore patrol vessel *Niamh* on 10 September 2001. She replaced the *Deirdre*, which was sold for conversion to a yacht.

Italy The *nuova unitá maggiore* (NUM) ordered from Fincantieri at the end of 2000 will be named *Andrea Doria*. She will be launched at Riva Trigoso in 2005 and delivered in 2007. Work on the first Type 212A submarine *Salvatore Todaro* is proceeding at Fincantieri's Muggiano yard, outside La Spezia. She was laid down in January 2001 and will be launched in May 2003, but will not be completed until June 2005. The second was laid down in April 2002.

The first 'Horizon' type AAW frigate was laid down in 2001 at Riva Trigoso and will be launched in 2005. Only one *Lupo* class, the *Perseo*, remains in service, and the three laid up vessels may be offered to Peru or another export customer. On 9 April 2002 the Defence Committee of the Chamber of Deputies approved a $5 (US) billion programme to build ten new 500-tonne frigates in 2004-2018. They will be armed with the PAAMS AAW missile system and the Otomat anti-ship missile; the first is to be delivered in 2008. The first of a new class of 1520-tonne corvettes, the *Commandante Borsini*, was commissioned in January 2002, and was followed by the *Commandante Cigala Fulgosi* in September.

A *Gaeta* plus minehunter design is under consideration, equipped for hunting, sweeping and clearance diving.

The Netherlands The four *Walrus* class submarines now have a prominent exhaust at the after end of the fin, intended to diffuse diesel exhaust fumes when the boat is snorting.

The AAW frigate *de Zeven Provincien* was commissioned in Mach 2002, and her sister *Tromp* will follow in Mach 2003. The *de Ruyter* will follow a year later, and the *Evertsen* will follow in March 2004. The two Jacob van Heemskerck-class AAW frigates will have new fire-control trackers. Only one Kortenaer-class frigate, the *Bloys van Trelong*, remains in service, and will run on until January 2005.

Norway The Norwegian Defence Ministry has decided to withdraw from the 'Viking' submarine project as the hull-life of the *Ula* class turns out to be longer than predicted. They will serve until 2020. Five of the paid-off Kobben class have been sold to Poland (see below).

The first of the new Aegis AAW frigates being built by the Spanish builders IZAR (formerly Empresa Nacional Bazán), the *Frithjof Nansen* (F-310), is to be launched in 2003 and delivered in 2005. The *Roald Amundsen* (F-311) was laid down in 2002, and the *Otto Sverdrup* (F-312), *Helge Ingstad* (F-313) and *Thor Heyerdahl* (F-314) will follow in 2003-2005.

The modernisation of the Hauk-class FACs will be completed towards the end of 2003. It is hoped to replace the Penguin missiles with the new *Nytt Sjomalsmissil* (New Sea Target Missile or NSM) after 2004. The new surface-effect FAC *Skjold* has been evaluated in the United States by the Navy and Coastguard, but the contract for five more has not yet been awarded.

Poland Five *Kobben* class Type 207 submarines were bought from Norway in May and June 2002. They are to be renamed: *Sokol* (ex-*Stord*), *Jastrzab* (ex-*Kobben*), *Sep* (ex-*Skolpen*), *Bielik* (ex-*Svenner*) and *Kondor* (ex-*Kunna*). The fifth boat was originally intended to be 'cannibalised' for spares for the rest, but she is now intended to be used solely for training. The Project 641 Foxtrots, *Wilk* and *Dzik*, are likely to be paid-off.

Work has started at Gdynia on the first of six Project 621 2100-tonne missile-armed corvettes. They are built to the Blohm+Voss MEKO A100 design, and will be armed with eight Swedish RBS 15 Mk 3 anti-ship missiles, vertically-launched evolved Sea Sparrow surface-to-air missiles and an Otobreda 76mm gun.

At the end of June 2001 a contract was awarded to Thales Naval Nederland to modernise the three former East German *Orkan* class corvettes. They will receive RBS 15 missiles, the Tacticos combat management system, Sea Giraffe surveillance radar and other equipment.

Portugal The submarine force is down to two boats, the 34-year old *Barracuda* and *Delfim*; they will be withdrawn in 2005, making a decision on replacements urgent. Bids are on the table from DCN and the German Submarine Consortium.

Romania The purchase of two modern frigates from the Royal Navy, HMS *Coventry* and HMS *London*, has been completed, and the ships are to be refitted in a Romanian shipyard, probably with a medium-calibre gun added.

Spain The order for three or four Scorpène-type submarines is expected to be placed before the end of 2002. They will be fitted with the French MESMA type AIP powerplant, according to *Jane's Fighting Ships*.

The AAW frigate *Alvaro de Bazán* (F-101) was commissioned on 30 September 2002, and her sisters *Roger de Lauria* (F-102), *Blas de Lezo* (F-103) and *Mendez Nuñez* (F-104) will follow at yearly intervals. With their SPY-1D Aegis weapon-direction system and armament of thirty-two Standard SM-2 Block IIIA surface-to-air missiles, they are among the best AAW ships in European navies.

The fifth *Segura* class minehunter, being built at IZAR's Cartagena shipyard is to be delivered in 2003, followed by the last of the class in 2004. The planned order for four more *Segura* class vessels has not materialised.

Sweden The *Visby* class corvette programme has been cut to five ships and the lead-ship did not get her new CETRIS combat system until late 2002. Full trials will not start until late in 2003, and she will not be fully operational with the Royal Swedish Navy until 2004, and the remaining ships, *Helsingborg*, *Härnösand*, *Nyköping* and *Karlstad*, will follow in 2005-2007.

The 'Viking' submarine project has reached project-definition stage, but the only partner left is Denmark. It is hoped to fund six submarines, four for Denmark and two for Sweden, to be ordered not later than 2005 and to be in service by 2010. The Swedish submarine force is down to seven boats.

Turkey A seventh *Oliver Hazard Perry* class frigate, the former *Samuel Eliot Morison* (FFG-13), was transferred in 2002 and renamed TCG *Gökova* (F-496). The construction of six TF-2000-type frigates has been deferred because of funding problems, and no design has been selected so far.

Four IKL Type 209/1400 *Preveze* class submarines are in service, and the *Gür* was launched in May 2002. In the light of the Greek order for four Type 214 boats with AIP it seems unlikely that the Turks will be content with the older and less capable design. As Gölcük Shipyard is already experienced in building IKL/HDW designs, a switch to the Type 214 design seems likely.

The last of six ex-French A69-type *d'Estienne d'Orves* class coastal corvettes, the ex-*Second Maitre le Bihan*, was handed over at Toulon in June 2002 and renamed TCG *Bafra*. The fourth Kiliç-class fast attack craft, the *Tufan*, is fitting out at the Taskizak yard and will be delivered in 2003. The fifth, to be named *Meltem*, will be launched in 2004.

The Americas

United States The operations against Afghanistan in 2001-2002 put the aircraft-carriers under great pressure, not least because the air groups were under strength after the 'drawdown' of the Clinton years and the cutting of the number of carrier battle groups from fifteen to twelve. At the end of 2002 the *John F Kennedy* (CV-67) was found to be unfit for operational duties and capable of only 20 knots. The *Kitty Hawk* (CV-63) was converted to a 'special operations support' carrier operating only helicopters, but the reason was that her air group had to be distributed among the other carriers in the Indian Ocean to bring their air groups to full strength.

The next new carrier, the USS *Ronald Reagan* (CVN-76), will not be ready until April 2003, followed by CVN-77 at the end of 2008, when the *Kitty Hawk* goes out of service. CVN-77 will have the basic hull and powerplant of the *Nimitz* class, but will embody a number of detailed improvements.

Despite predictions to the contrary, all 27 *Ticonderoga* class Aegis cruisers remain in service as they are too useful to stand down. On 25 January 2002 the USS *Lake Erie* (CG-70) successfully tested an SM-3 missile armed with an Exo Atmospheric Projectile (LEAP) warhead against an Aries missile target. The *Hue City* (CG-66), Anzio (CG–68) *Vicksburg* (CG-69) and *Cape St George* (CG-71) took part in operational evaluation (OPEVAL) of Co-operative Engagement Capability (CEC) in 2001.

Ten of the Flight IIA improved *Arleigh Burke* class Aegis destroyers were in service by November 2002, with 26 more building, fitting out or planned. The USS *Cole* (DDG-67), badly damaged by a suicide boat in Aden in 2000, returned to service in the summer of 2002. Only nineteen *Spruance* class destroyers remained in service in 2002, and the last is to go in Fiscal Year 2006 (FY '06), which lends even more urgency to the DD(X) replacement.

The cancellation of the *Zumwalt* (DD-21) project in November 2001 took nobody by surprise, with the exception of the major contractors. The programme fell foul of a very predictable escalation of cost and complexity. Giving a team of engi-

USS John F Kennedy, *CV-67.* (Hanny & Leo van Ginderen)

The Canadian frigate Vancouver *at Sydney in 1995.* (Hanny & Leo van Ginderen)

USS Lake Erie, CG-70. (Hanny & Leo van Ginderen)

Above: The USS Vella Gulf *underway.*
Right: The USS Lake Erie *in the lead.*
Far right: View astern of a Towanda *class replenishment ship of the Japanese fleet.*

neers and designers *carte blanche* to use only the most advanced technology is like buying a casino for one's teenage sons. Much of the technology in DD-21 was either unproven or involved a dangerously high level of technological risk. In its place the Pentagon has chosen to build a smaller and cheaper DD(X), using the good bits of DD-21 development. Instead of a single hull it will have modular variants, including a cruiser, CG(X), an AAW destroyer, DDG(X) and a Littoral Combat Ship, LCS(X). Development contracts were awarded to Northrop Grumman and General Dynamics in April 2002

Four *San Antonio* class amphibious dock transports are under construction: the lead-ship (LPD-17), the *New Orleans* (LPD-18), *Mesa Verde* (LPD-19) and *Green Bay* (LPD-20) They will enter service in 2005-2006. Two more were funded in FY '01, with six more planned to come into service by 2012. The eighth *Wasp* class amphibious assault ship, the as-yet unnamed LHD-8, will be started in 2003, and she will be the first of the class to be driven by gas rather than steam turbines. The plant will comprise a pair of 35,000shp LM 2500+ gas turbines, and a unique hybrid electric drive for 'loitering' at low speed. This will make the *Iwo Jima* (LHD-7) the last large oil-fired steam turbine ship in the US Navy.

Canada All twelve *Halifax* class frigates will have their Sea Sparrow missiles replaced by the Evolved Sea Sparrow Missile Systems (ESSM) from 2004, the first phase of a major upgrade programme. In addition, an Integrated Towed Active/Passive Sonar System (IPTASS) may be

installed from 2006. Three of the *Iroquois* class AAW destroyers will have their STIR 1.8 tracker radars upgraded by Thales Nederland. A refit to incorporate the Thales Nederland APAR 3-D radar as part of an upgrading of their AAW capability does not seem to be urgent.

The work of getting the four *ex-Upholder* class into service has thrown up a number of minor problems, mostly caused by deterioration during their laid-up period. HMCS *Windsor* (ex-HMS *Unicorn*) was handed over in October 2001, followed by HMS *Cornerbrook* (ex-HMS *Ursula*) in August 2002 and HMCS *Chicoutimi* (ex-HMS *Upholder*) in December 2002. The Department of National Defence intends to retrofit a Ballard fuel cell AIP system in due course, and a successor to the Mk 48 Mod 4 torpedo and an air defence missile system will be procured.

Argentina The submarine force is down to three boats, the IKL Type 209/1200 *Salta* and the TR1700 type *Santa Cruz* and *San Juan*. Argentina had sent ships to the Gulf in 1990-1991 to support the Coalition, but at the time of writing had not sent any to the Persian Gulf in support of America's build-up against Iraq. The continuing economic crisis has imposed financial restraints.

Brazil The submarine *Tikuna*, first of a class developed from the IKL Type 209/1400 *Tupi* class, will be launched in March 2005, *nine* years since her keel was laid. The modernisation of the Mk 10 frigates *Defensora* and *Independência* was completed in 2002, with *Constituição* and *Niteroi* to follow

in 2003 and *União* in 2004. Apart from new electronics the visible changes are the replacement of the AWS-9 radar with the RAN-3L, the RTN-10X trackers by RTN-30X type, and Seacat missiles by an eight-cell Aspide launcher on the quarterdeck.

The old amphibious dock transport (LPD) *Fearless* was bought from the Royal Navy in the summer of 2002. Since 1989 three major amphibious ships have been acquired from the US Navy.

Chile The over-ambitious *Proyecto Tridente* was postponed indefinitely in January 2002, leaving the question of frigate replacements wide open. Rumours suggest that a pair of second-hand frigates from the RN are on the 'shopping list'. Only three ex-RN 'County' class destroyers remain in service and three Leander-class frigates.

The first Scorpène-type submarine, the *O'Higgins*, will be launched by DCN Cherbourg in 2003, while the *Carrera* will follow at IZAR's Cartagena yard in 2004. They will be armed with the new Italian Black-Shark torpedo. The old *Oberon* type *O'Brien* will be retained until the *O'Higgins* joins the fleet.

Venezuela The frigates *Mariscal Sucre* and *Almirante Brion* completed their modernization by Ingalls late in 2001, but *General Urdaneta* and *General Soublette* will receive a much less extensive overhaul from 2002 onward.

Russia

The final disposal of the remains of

the salvaged submarine *Kursk* was officially expected to be achieved in October 2002. The cause of the tragedy was finally admitted to be the explosion of a kerosene/hydrogen peroxide fuel tank in a torpedo, which started a fire and detonated all the torpedoes.

Despite its economic problems, the Russian Navy is trying to rebuild a force of effective submarines although not on the prodigal scale of the Soviet years. The Project 941 *Typhoon* type SSBN *TK.208* emerged in 2002 from a ten-year conversion to a missile trials boat, with the traditional name *Dimitri Donskoi*. She is now testing the new submarine-launched version of the *Topol*-M Bulava (SS-N-27) missile, and may be the boat which launched a 'mini' space shuttle on 12 July 2002. Work is also in hand on the prototype Project 995 SSBN Borey-class *Severodvinsk*, to be armed with the Bulava. The first Project 885 Yasen-type SSN, *Yuri Dolgoruki*, is to be launched in 2003. The first Project 677 Lada-type conventional boat, *St Petersburg*, was launched in August 2002 and is to be completed in 2003.

Middle East and Indian Ocean Navies

Egypt No contract has yet been signed for the construction of two Moray 1400 conventional submarines, but if it is they will be delivered by Ingalls at Pascagoula, MS around 2008, using Foreign Military Sales (FMS) funding. Details of the AIP plant have not been released.

The four 'Ambassador Mk III' 61-metre FACs ordered in January 2001 were cancelled because of Halter Marine filing for Chapter II bankruptcy three months later. They would have had have a Lockheed combat system and Harpoon anti-ship missiles. The modernisation of the combat systems of the six *Ramadan* class FACs is to be carried out in 2002-2007. They will have Nautis 3 combat systems and the Otomat missiles will be upgraded to Mk 2 standard.

India The agreement for the purchase of the Project 1143.4 hybrid cruiser-carrier *Admiral Gorshkov* was hoped to be finalised before the end

of 2002. Latest details released show that she is to have a full-length flight deck with a long 14-degree 'ski-jump'. Work on the new 32,000-tonne 'Air-Defence Ship' is supposed to start at Kochi (Cochin) as soon as the *Gorshkov* agreement is finalised; a launch date of 2005 and commissioning in 2007 is the current target. She will be named *Vikrant* to commemorate the old ex-RN light fleet carrier that served in the Indian Navy for many years.

The *Mumbai*, last of three *Delhi* class AAW destroyers, was commissioned in January 2001 by Mazagon Dock at Mumbai (formerly Bombay). The third Project 1135.6 'Krivak III' type destroyer was launched on 25 May 2001 at the Baltiisky Zavod shipyard in St Petersburg and named *Tabar*. She will be commissioned in May 2003, and the keel of a fourth unit was laid at Mazagon Dock in August 2001.

Three Project 75 'Scorpène' type submarines were ordered from the DCN Cherbourg/IZAR consortium early in 2002. The first two would be built by DCN Cherbourg and IZAR, but at least four more will be built by

Venezuelan frigate Almirante Brion. (L & L van Ginderen)

Mazagon Dock at Mumbai after the yard is upgraded. Five of the early boats have been overhauled by the Russians at Severodvinsk and St Petersburg.

The Admiralteyskiye Verf shipyard announced on 23 April 2001 that it will probably deliver the prototype Project 677 *Amur* 1650 boat to India, but progress is slow. The leasing of a Project 971 'Schuka-B' ('Victor III') type nuclear attack submarine has been cancelled, although no reason has been given.

The fourth and last 'Kora' class corvette *Karmukh* was commissioned in February 2002. The *Pralaya*, first of a new class of improved *Veer* class missile-armed corvettes, was launched in 2002 and will be commissioned in 2003. A fourth *Samar* class offshore patrol vessel is being built at Goa for the Coast Guard.

Israel The Navy wishes to acquire five new submarines of similar size to the *Dolphin* class (1900 tonnes submerged). However, they may not be of German design or construction, which limits the choice to France, Russia, Sweden or to a foreign design built under licence in the US.

Up to five more improved *Sa'ar V* type *Eilat* class corvettes are projected. The older *Sa'ar 2* type FACs are no longer operational. A new *Sa'ar 4.5* FAC, the *Herev*, was delivered in the second quarter of 2002; details are hard to establish because of the Israeli habit of transferring old names to new construction.

Pakistan New frigates are required to replace the six *Tariq* class (ex-RN Type 21) and the two *Leander* class, but no choice of design has been announced.

The new submarine *Saad* is to be commissioned in December 2002, and is to be followed by the *Hanza* (ex-*Ghazi*) a year later. The *Hanza* will be the first of the class to have the MESMA AIP system, and if successful will be retrofitted to the *Khalid* and *Saad*.

Saudi Arabia The *Makkah*, second of three modified *La Fayette* class AAW frigates ordered under the Sawari II project, will be commissioned in April 2003. She will be followed by

the *Dammam* in January 2004. The *Riyadh* was handed over at Lorient in July 2002.

Sri Lanka The Sri Lankan Navy's bloody war against the separatist Liberation Tigers of Tamil Eelam (LTTE) is temporarily in abeyance. Since early 2002 an international commission has been monitoring the ceasefire, and negotiations have begun with the government about local autonomy for the north-eastern region.

United Arab Emirates The first six of an eventual total of twelve 60-metre FACs are due (2002) from Constructions Mécaniques de Normandie (CMN). The 'Al Baynuna' Project replaces Project 'Lewa'. The programme will be a partnership between CMN and the Abu Dhabi Shipbuilding (ADSB) yard, with ADSB acting as prime contractor.

Work is in hand at ADSB for a series of 64-metre 'heavy' landing craft. Tenders have being sought for three coastal minehunters but no contract has been announced.

Asia-Pacific Regional Navies

Australia HMAS *Stuart*, fourth of the *Anzac* class frigates, was commissioned in June 2002. Plans to build three 6000-tonne Future Surface Combatant vessels continue, to replace the *Adelaide* class ships when they reach the end of their service lives from 2013. To keep costs down a number of foreign off-the-shelf designs have been looked at. The Spanish F-100 design comes out best, with its Aegis weapon-direction system, SPY-1D or -1F radar and Standard SM-2 missiles.

Five of the *Collins* class submarines are in service, with HMAS *Rankin* to be commissioned in 2003. It now seems that not all six *Collins* class boats will receive the full upgrade to their combat system, the Replacement Combat System, scheduled for 2007. They will, however, have other improvements intended to improve reliability and silencing.

HMAS *Diamantina*, fifth of the *Huon* class coastal minehunters, was

handed over to the RAN in March 2002, and her sister *Yarra* is intended to be handed over six months afterwards.

Brunei KDB *Nakhoda Ragam*, first of the new 'offshore patrol vessels' (corvettes), was undergoing trials on the Clyde in June 2002, and the third, *Jerambak* was launched on 23 June 2002 at the BAE Systems Marine Scotstoun yard. The second ship, *Bendahara Sakam*, is fitting out, and is planned to be commissioned in 2003.

China The People's Liberation Army-Navy (PLAN) now has its second Project 956E *Sovremenny* class destroyer, the *Fuzhou* (137). A contract for two more was signed in January 2002 with the Northern Shipyard in St Petersburg, and they are likely to be delivered in 2006. The PLAN also has an option to buy two more.

Construction of the new Project 094 SSBN started at Huludao in 2001. The first Project 093 SSN is to be launched in 2003 at Huludao, with the second following in 2005. Three Project 039 'Song' type SSKs are in service, and two more are expected to join the fleet in 2003. They are building in parallel with the Russian Project 636 'Kilo' type.

Indonesia The fortunes of the Navy continue to be frustrated by a shortage of funding. Grandiose plans for modernisation and expansion bear no relation to the chaotic state of the economy.

Japan The Self-Defence Force commissioned the fifth 'Oyashio' class submarine *Isoshio* in March 2002. The *Asashio* has been converted to AIP, with a 9-metre 'plug' inserted in her hull containing four Stirling closed-cycle engines. Trials will be completed in March 2003, and the next class of submarines is likely to incorporate a similar AIP installation.

Two improved *Kongo* class Aegis destroyers have been approved, and completion is planned for 2009-2010. Another two are planned. Two *Takanami* class destroyers are to be delivered in March 2003, and three more are to be in service by 2006.

The *Akebono* and *Ariake*, last of nine *Murasame* class destroyers, were delivered in March 2002.

The amphibious forces have been strengthened by a second *Osumi* class through-deck LPD, the *Shimokita*, and the *Kunisaki* is to be commissioned in 2003. The fifth *Sugashima* class coastal minehunter, the *Tyoshima*, was delivered in March 2002, and five more are in various stages of construction. Two of the new fast attack craft, the *Hayabusa* and *Wakata*, were delivered in March 2002 and four more are being constructed by Mitsubishi at Shimonoseki.

Republic of Korea Pre-building work has started for the KSS II programme, to build three IKL Type 214 boats at Hyundai's Ulsan yard. They are to be delivered in 2007-2009.

The KDX-3 AAW destroyers will have the American Aegis weapon-direction system, and the first ship is intended to enter service in 2008.

An engagement between the RoK Navy and units of the Democratic People's Republic on 29 June 2002 wrecked diplomatic efforts to bring the two countries together. The action was serious, with nineteen RoK Navy sailors killed and some thirty North Koreans killed by return fire, and an unidentified RoK Navy 'frigate' sunk. No information has been released about the name of the ship or its class.

Malaysia The report of the purchase of two ex-Royal Netherlands Navy submarines turns out to be false, doubtless a reflection of aggressive marketing. In fact the Defence Ministry signed a Memorandum of Understanding on 5 June 2002 for the construction of two Scorpène-type boats at DCN Cherbourg in France and IZAR in Cartagena in Spain. In addition, a redundant *Agosta* class SSK will be leased for training.

New Zealand After years of neglect, the Royal New Zealand Navy has announced its plan to build an ocean-going support ship, at least two offshore patrol vessels and four or five inshore patrol craft. Negotiations with several foreign consortia are in progress.

Singapore Although widely reported, the fitting of the Israeli Barak point-defence missile system in the Victory-class 62-metre corvettes cannot be verified visually. The third and fourth Endurance-class LPDs, RSS *Persistence* and RSS *Endeavour*, were commissioned in April 2001.

Taiwan The eighth Cheng Kung-class frigate, *Tien Tan*, is to be placed with the China Shipbuilding Corporation and will be launched in 2003 and delivered in 2004. The purchase of four redundant Kidd-class AAW destroyers from the US Navy has been cancelled.

The search to acquire eight modern submarines continues, but no progress has been publicly announced.

Thailand The Royal Thai Navy is investigating the possibility of acquiring two second-hand frigates from the RN. The question remains, which frigates?

African Navies

South Africa: The South African Navy is virtually the only African force showing any signs of activity. SAS *Amatola* is the first of four MEKO A200-type corvettes, and was launched in June 2002; she started trials in December 2002. The *Tsandhlawana* was named in the same month at Hamburg. The first IKL Type 209/1400 submarine will be delivered in September 2005.

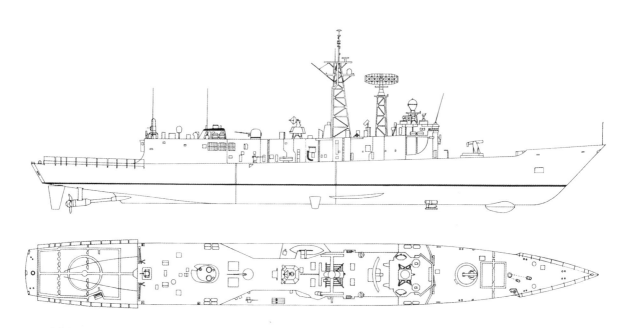

The 'Kwang Hua' class is an improved version of the US Navy's Oliver Hazard Perry class. (Antony Preston)

INDEX

Page references in *italics* refer to illustrations.